ANNALS OF THE IQSY

INTERNATIONAL YEARS OF THE QUIET SUN

VOLUMES IN THIS SERIES

1   **Geophysical Measurements:**
    Techniques, Observational Schedules, and Treatment of Data
    (Information and instruction for observation and treatment of data in all
    aspects of geophysical measurement such as meteorology, ionosphere,
    aurora, comets, solar emission, and information on World Days.)

2   **Solar and Geophysical Events 1960–1965**
    (Calendar Record)
    (300 pages of tables and comments, listing chronologically the occurrence
    of any solar or geophysical activity.)

3   **The Proton Flare Project**
    (The July 1966 Event)
    I Introduction
    II The Solar Active Region: birth and development — activity — the
        proton event — later development — summary of observations and
        conclusions
    III The Cosmic and Geophysical Event: high-energy particles — low-
         energy particles — summaries on high- and low-energy particles
    IV General Summary and Conclusions

4   **Solar–Terrestrial Physics: Solar Aspects**
    (Proceedings of Joint IQSY/COSPAR Symposium, London 1967, Part I)
    I The Activity of the Quiet Sun
    II Interplanetary Space
    III The Cosmic Radiation
    IV The Earth's Radiation Belts
    V Aurora and Airglow

5   **Solar–Terrestrial Physics: Terrestrial Aspects**
    (Proceedings of Joint IQSY/COSPAR Symposium, London 1967, Part II)
    I Meteorology
    II Ionospheric Measurements
    III Ionospheric Processes
    IV The Earth's Atmosphere
    V Geomagnetism

6   **Survey of Observations and Bibliography**
    I Historical Review of IQSY
    II Data Review Papers: a survey for each discipline of the main charac-
        teristics of the data collected and the basic conclusions drawn
    III Bibliography of IQSY Publications

7   **IQSY Data**
    I IQSY Stations: geographic and geomagnetic positions and schedule of
        observations
    II Satellites and Space Probes in Orbit in the IQSY Period
    III Catalogue of IQSY Data Available at World Data Centres
    IV Tables of Contents of Annals of the IQSY Series

ANNALS OF THE IQSY

INTERNATIONAL YEARS OF THE QUIET SUN

VOLUME 3

The Proton Flare Project
(The July 1966 Event)

General Editor
A. C. Stickland
IQSY Editorial Office
London, England

International Council of Scientific Unions
IQSY ANNALS EDITORIAL BOARD

The M.I.T. Press

Massachusetts Institute of Technology
Cambridge, Massachusetts, and London, England

Foreword

One of the scientific objectives of the International Years of the Quiet Sun (1964–1965) was the study of isolated solar events which would not then be complicated by the superposition in time of several different phenomena. One such event is the solar flare which produces high-energy particles — the so-called "proton flare".

The proposal for a "proton flare project" during, or immediately following, the 1964–1965 solar minimum period was first put forward by Commission 10 (Solar Activity) of the International Astronomical Union. The object of the project was to obtain, through organized international co-operation, the most detailed set possible of observations on a selected proton flare event. It was also planned to publish the collected results of this collective study in a single volume. The proposal was subsequently endorsed by the IQSY Committee as an appropriate contribution to the IQSY programme although it was recognized that a suitable proton flare was more likely to occur just after, rather than during, the solar minimum period. A full account of the preparation and planning of the Proton Flare Project (PFP) was published in Volume 1 of this series of *Annals of the IQSY*.

The results of this world-wide co-operative study in respect of the proton flare of 7 July 1966 are given in this present volume.

The IQSY Committee has been greatly indebted to Dr. Z. Švestka, Astronomical Institute, Ondřejov, Czechoslovakia, and to Dr. P. Simon, Observatoire de Paris, Meudon, France, for their generous assistance in organizing the project and in compiling this volume.

Aberystwyth,
April 1968

W. J. G. BEYNON, *President,*
Special Committee for the IQSY

v

Preface

Interest in proton flares has considerably increased in recent years, now that manned flights outside the earth's magnetosphere have left the field of science fiction and have become a serious scientific problem. Since proton flares inject into interplanetary space streams of atomic particles with energies often ranging up to hundreds, and at times even thousands, of MeV, they constitute one of the most serious hazards to man in space and may also be of concern to passengers aboard supersonic aircraft. On the other hand, intense proton flares are fairly rare phenomena that need a particular con-figuration of strong magnetic fields on the sun, and therefore it should be possible to try to forecast their occurrence and to create a warning service for this purpose. It is clear that any improvement in our knowledge of proton flares also adds a stone to the building of the theory of forecasts.

This, of course, is only one aspect of the problem, the practical one. We are also interested in proton flares from a purely scientific point of view. On the sun proton flares are the most powerful manifestation of solar activity, a peak of the fairly complex processes that occur in solar active regions. In interplanetary space the energetic particles released provide information on the magnetic field extending throughout the whole sun–earth region through which they travel. And at the earth the impinging particles form a natural means of sounding the earth's magnetosphere and polar iono-sphere.

When studying a proton flare we need reliable data on all the different aspects of the phenomenon: the evolution of the proton-flare active region, the proton flare itself, the coronal effects of the ejected particles, the particle propagation in space, and the associated phenomena at the earth. Unfortu-nately, however, it is not easy to get a complete set of all these data, and to get them in such a form that they can be clearly analysed. There are always gaps in data for some kinds of observation, and various active phenomena on the sun often overlap in such a way that it is quite difficult to draw definite conclusions from the complex material.

Therefore we have tried to make good use of the rising phase of the solar cycle when some, but not too many, proton flares appear, for a detailed study of one properly selected proton flare event. The fairly low activity and isolated bursts of activity during this period make both the forecasts of proton flares and the analysis of the flare-associated effects in space and at the earth easier.

The series of papers presented in this third volume of the *Annals of the IQSY* shows to what extent we have been successful in our aims. The 7 July 1966 proton flare discussed in this volume is now the first event for for which we know the complete development of its active region, from the birth on the eastern solar hemisphere through the date of the occurrence of the proton flare, up to its disappearance behind the western solar limb. We know all the changes in the active region and the sunspot group that preceded the proton flare, and extremely interesting phenomena were observed, in particular during the last twelve hours before the occurrence of the flare. Owing to the correct forecast of the proton flare, we also have very complete data on the magnetic field variations in the active region. A combination of space and ground-based observations has led to the discovery of interesting effects in space and at the earth which occurred when a magnetic field sector boundary crossed the earth 30 hours after the proton flare, before the arrival of a sudden-commencement shockwave at the earth. Many observations have raised new problems to be solved in the future.

With these results in mind, I think that the Proton Flare Project can be considered as successful. I should like to take this opportunity to express sincere thanks to all the co-operating scientists and to the chief co-ordinator of the Project, Dr. P. Simon, for all their contributions to this international enterprise. And on behalf of all of us, my thanks also are due to the IQSY Committee who have kindly made this publication of the PFP results possible and to the IAU and COSPAR for their interest in our activities and for giving us opportunities to hold special meetings on the PFP results in London and in Budapest.

Ondřejov,   Z. ŠVESTKA,
April 1968   *President,*
                                                                        IAU Commission 10

Contents

I

INTRODUCTORY

A

The Proton Event of 7 July 1966: Introductory

P. Simon

Co-ordinator of the Proton Flare Project, Meudon Observatory, Paris, France

Abstract

The purpose of the Proton Flare Project was to obtain detailed observations of at least one proton flare event from all possible aspects and to publish the results and conclusions from this co-operative study.

Observations were co-ordinated by means of the International Ursigram and World Days Service, and a system of "alerts" was introduced to warn observers of the incidence of special conditions. Over 100 workers from 54 institutions and 18 countries collaborated in the project.

The most impressive event of the solar activity is what we have called the Proton Event: bright flare, strong X-ray and radio emission, high-energy particles, many geophysical effects. With these numerous physical processes to be studied, it is a fascinating experiment for scientists. But its study is a difficult enterprise: so many different techniques have to be used in the observation and only a proportion of the ground-based observatories can carry out useful observations simultaneously. It is a typical subject for international co-operation.

The project, first suggested by Dr. de Feiter, has been under discussion by the members of the IAU Commission 10 (Solar Activity) ever since the Hamburg meeting. The president, Dr. Švestka, began to write systematically to most of his colleagues during the second half of 1965. Starting as a local project, it had moved slowly to become a broad international co-operative study by the beginning of 1966.

According to Dr. Švestka's first circular letter sent in March 1966 by the IQSY Secretariat to most of the institutions and observatories concerned, the Proton Flare Project was described as an appropriate addition to the IQSY Programme endorsed by the Bureau of the IQSY Committee and organized by the IAU Commission 10.

It had two main objectives:

1. To obtain detailed observations of at least one selected proton flare event (and possibly of more such events) from all possible aspects.

2. To publish all the results of this co-operative study in one series of co-ordinated papers.

The first phase (co-operation in the observations) would begin on 1 May 1966 and end on 30 September 1966. This enterprise would be co-ordinated by a team of experts at the Meudon Observatory with one leading scientist, myself, as the chief co-ordinator of the project.

The IQSY/COSPAR meeting in London in July 1967 and the IAU Symposium at Budapest in September 1967 would offer a good opportunity to discuss the papers. The publication of the first series as a volume of the *IQSY Annals* would begin during October 1967.

Many scientists kindly agreed to co-operate in this work, perhaps with a sceptical smile for this naïve schedule. The greatest disappointment would have been the prevention of the enterprise by the absence of any proton event in this period. The difficulty most feared was that full international co-operation might not be achieved. The most unexpected support has been the issue and the dissemination on time of valuable forecasts. And today the co-ordinator himself is still astounded that he is able to write so soon the story of this exciting and successful scientific co-operation.

The choice of the period for this PFP came from a statistical study by Dr. Švestka: according to this study (Švestka 1966) about four Proton Events (PE) might be expected during this period. Actually there were three PE during the PFP: 7 July, 28 August and 2 September: Dr. Švestka's first forecast was successful.

To co-ordinate the observing phase, we must have a network to disseminate the different kinds of messages from the co-ordinator to the observers and to facilitate the sending of information from any observer to the co-ordinator. The International Ursigram and World Day Service (IUWDS) network has been established for this general purpose and this was the first opportunity of using its world-wide structure to achieve easy communication with most of the observatories or institutions scattered around the world. Its Regional Warning Centres and their contributing observatories were accustomed to the business of fast transmission of data and alerts. The new point was only that the Meudon centre would issue the daily messages. The system of alerts was established according to the experience of SPARMO (Legrand and Simon 1966) with some minor improvements. I must emphasize this friendly contribution of the IUWDS: the problem of contacts and of tested message forms is one of some importance in this kind of co-operation in real time.

Another necessity is a normal daily message issued at the same hour each day: most of these messages would not report any alert, but they act as a check on connections, and with the arrival of such a message the observer knows that no further alert has to be expected that day.

For the alert itself, the experts of Meudon need daily information and scientific, impersonal criteria. For the forecast one or two days in advance, the most useful observations are the centimetric localization (Kundu 1959), the centimetric spectrum (Tanaka and Kakinuma 1964), the magnetic field measurement of the active centres (Severny 1964, Martres *et al.* 1966) and the classical chromospheric and photospheric observations (Caroubalos 1964): with the kind co-operation of the radio-astronomical group of the Nagoya University and of Dr. Kai, we have succeeded in receiving on time the centimetric spectral measurements and we have confirmed the radio localization from Nançay (France). The magnetic field data were obtained at Meudon and, with the co-operation of the observers, were made available immediately. This means that any of our experts, i.e. Mme. Martres, Mme. Pick, or myself, can most of the time issue the forecast based on good material.

Thus for the first time we feel we are in a position to give a daily probability of a proton event. Most of the material we use comes from the decreasing phase of the solar activity, and the criteria are related to the forecast of a proton event from an active centre but not to the time of this event. Finally we send the forecast to solar astronomers with wide experience of solar activity, describing the criteria fulfilled at the origin of any alert; this gives information to the astronomers, who may have other evidence or new observations which they can contribute, and who will have some means of evaluating the confidence that they can place in these alerts.

From 154 daily messages, only 21 were positive, with alerts. But actually there were just *three suspected proton centres* and on two of them three proton events have been observed.

For the July event the series of messages are reported here:
5 July at 0845 UT Suspected centre 21034 25W34N appropriate magnetic field stop very favourable spot configuration
5 July (normal message at about 1400 UT)
Centre 21034 27W34N very bright 3 cm centre stop appropriate magnetic field stop favourable spot configuration but small area stop low energy protonalert for 05/06
6 July
Centre 21034 40W34N
Definite increase of the 3 cm brightness protonalert for 06/07

7 July
Centre 21034 53W34N
Protonalert for 07/08
News: proton flare on centre 21034 observed today 0020 UT class two bright
stop exceptionally large type IV burst stop definite proton event at 0130 UT
observed in north auroral zone on balloons of SPARMO
8 July
Centre 21034 66W34N
Nearly same radio, magnetic and optical feature
Protonalert for 8/9 geomagnetic alert for 8/9
9/10 July
Centre 21034 79W34N
Protonalert for 9/10

This is an example of the scheme: an active centre has some of the criteria
of a proton centre and we send an alert each day. The messages report how
many criteria are fulfilled and the protonalerts precede and follow the event
itself. This active centre does not change so quickly; on the one hand this
means that we have time to issue a forecast and on the other hand the proton
centre aspect continues for a few days after the PE; sometimes a second PE
can occur as was the case for the September event.

At the end of July a circular letter was sent to the co-operating observatories urging them to specify the time and the quality of their data related to
this active centre and to the event itself. With these reports and the scheme
of the work we then began to co-ordinate this co-operative study.

The first difficulty was to decide who should be invited to study each aspect
of this material. In this field, material and experts are often not in the same
institution, so with Dr. Švestka we have developed a compromise in order to
give scientists the chance to study the material obtained in their own institution, with the co-operation of experts from other establishments. In fact
116 authors from 54 institutions and 18 countries are contributing. At the
beginning of November most of these invitations had been sent and the work
begun. The co-ordinator at this time only had to give assistance to the authors
in a few minor difficulties.

At the beginning of April 1967 we entered into the last part of this co-
operation: circulation of the draft reports summarizing the work and planning the London and Budapest meetings. Some unexpected papers came from
these two meetings and from some new proposals. These facts explain some
duplication. During these two meetings, many co-operating scientists had a
final opportunity of discussing their reports and of pointing out the most
striking results.

And now I must thank all the contributors to this enterprise. First of all,
Dr. Švestka for his initiative and his will to succeed, Dr. Friedman as Chair-

man of the Working Group II of COSPAR and as President of IUCSTP, Dr. Kiepenheuer as organizer of the Budapest meeting, Professor Beynon as President and Dr. Minnis as Secretary of the IQSY Committee, the hundreds of authors whose names appear in the reports, the personnel of the observatories contributing to the forecasting work (Nagoya, McMath–Hulbert, Sacramento Peak, Ondřejov, Meudon, Nançay, etc.), and particularly the following for their kind interest or their important contribution: Dr. Michard, Mme. Pick, Mme. Martres, Professor Severny, Professor Dieminger, Professor Krimigis, Dr. de Feiter, Mrs. Dodson Prince, Dr. Kai, Dr. Zhulin, Dr. Bruzek, Dr. Fokker, and Mr. De Mastus. I must also acknowledge the work of the IUWDS Regional Warning Centres and particularly of the staff at the Meudon centre: Mlle. Barse, Mme. Bertrand, and especially Mme. Petit for her conscientious secretarial work during the last part of the co-operative study.

References

CAROUBALOS, C., 1964, Contribution à l'étude de l'activité solaire en relation avec ses effets géophysiques, *Annls Astrophys.*, **27**, 333–388.

KUNDU, M. R., 1959, Structures et propriété des sources d'activité solaire sur ondes centimétriques, *Annls Astrophys.*, **22**, 1–100.

LEGRAND, J. P., and P. SIMON, 1966, Process of a Sparmo alert for the periods of solar activity, *SPARMO Bulletin*, No. 2, June 1966, pp. 1–6.

MARTRES, M. J., R. MICHARD, and I. SORU-ISCOVICI, 1966, Etude morphologique de la structure magnétique des régions actives solaires, *Annls Astrophys.*, **29**, 245–253.

SEVERNY, A. B., 1964, Observations of transverse and longitudinal magnetic fields connected with solar flares, *Izv. Krỹm. Astrofiz. Obs.*, **31**, 159.

ŠVESTKA, Z., 1966, Proton flares before 1956, *Bull. Astr. Insts Czech.*, **17**, 262–270.

TANAKA, H., and T. KAKINUMA, 1964, The relation between the spectrum of slowly varying component of solar radio emission and solar proton event, *Rep. Ionosph. Space Res. Japan*, **18**, 32–41.

II

THE SOLAR ACTIVE REGION

I

The Magnetic Fields and Proton Flare of 7 July 1966

A. Severny

Crimean Astrophysical Observatory, Crimea, USSR

Abstract

Longitudinal $H_\parallel$ and transverse $H_\perp$ components of magnetic fields inside the active region which produced the proton flare of 7 July 1966, recorded with the aid of the double magnetograph of the Crimean Astrophysical Observatory, are considered. The mean gradients of the longitudinal field $\Delta H_\parallel / \Delta S$ along the straight lines joining magnetic "hills" of the isogauss maps, the total magnetic flux over the active area $F_S + F_N$, and the difference of fluxes $F_S - F_N$ all behave similarly, showing small initial values (at 4 July), then increasing to peak values before the flare (at 6 July), and then dropping to small pre-flare values after the flare. The total magnetic energy $H_\parallel^2 / 8\pi$ shows a similar behaviour. These changes with time are more pronounced for lower levels (5250 Å) than for higher levels (6103 Å). The rotation of directions of the transverse field $H_\perp$ by 90° was found at the place where the flare appeared, if one compares these directions before and after the flare. The consideration of the behaviour of the total vector $|\mathbf{H}|$ and total energy $H^2 / 8\pi$ suggests the possibility that the bulk of magnetic tubes of force are pushed up from below, and then lowered.

The two brightest clouds of the flare appeared simultaneously in regions of opposite magnetic polarity; one of the clouds is very close to neutral line $H_\parallel = 0$ in the region of highest gradients $\Delta H_\parallel / \Delta S$ and of the crossing (or bifurcation) of directions of transverse field $H_\perp$ as was found in earlier results. The comparison of these brightest clouds with distribution of vertical electric currents j_z over the area shows that the clouds are just above the points where the electric currents are strongest.

I Introduction

27 maps including 17 of longitudinal, $H_\parallel$, and 10 of transverse, $H_\perp$, components of the magnetic field, were obtained for the sunspot group where the proton flare of 7 July 1966, 0030, appeared. By means of the double magnetograph of the Crimean Solar Tower (for description see Severny 1966) magnetic fields were recorded in different lines, mostly in $\lambda = 5250$ Å (14) and 6103 Å (9), and most of them simultaneously in the two lines. In most cases $H_\parallel$ and $H_\perp$ were also recorded simultaneously by the method described by Bruns *et al.* (1965). The distribution of the records according to date, wavelength, and magnetic field components is given in Table 1. All the records

Table I   Summary of Magnetic Field Maps

λ	Magnetic Field $H_\parallel$	$H_\perp$	Date July 1966	Number of Maps $H_\parallel$	$H_\perp$
5250	9	5	4	3	–
6103	6	3	5	3	3
4808	2	2	6	4	1
			7	7	6
	17	10		17	10

were analysed to give, for $H_\parallel$, the isogauss contour maps, and, for $H_\perp$, the vector field of the transverse vibration vector. (Fig. 1 gives an example of such maps.) A device for the automatic compensation of brightness fluctuations was used (Nikulin 1964) and maps were calibrated in gauss according to the following table (Severny 1964) which gives the values for full deflection of the recorder, which corresponds to the range from east to west borders of the disk:

λ (Å)	5250	6103	4808
E–W (gauss)	1600	2088	3936

These values were used for the calibration of the longitudinal fields $H_\parallel$ when recorded separately from $H_\perp$. For simultaneous records of $H_\parallel$ and $H_\perp$ the sensitivity of $H_\parallel$ records is theoretically reduced by a factor of 2, but by a factor of 3 according to measurements. The response of the magnetograph $\delta_\parallel$ when recording $H_\parallel$ is proportional to the actual $H_\parallel$ only for small values of $H_\parallel$ ($\lesssim 100$ G), and at values of $H_\parallel \simeq 300$ G the signal $\delta_\parallel$ is practically completely saturated. To get correct values of $H_\parallel$ in gauss an empirical calibration curve between magnetograph signal $\delta_\parallel$ and field strength $H_\parallel$ was used (Severny 1967). A similar empirical curve for the dependence of the transverse field signal $\delta_\perp$/E–W on the field strength $H_\perp$ can be applied to get the actual values of transverse field strength.

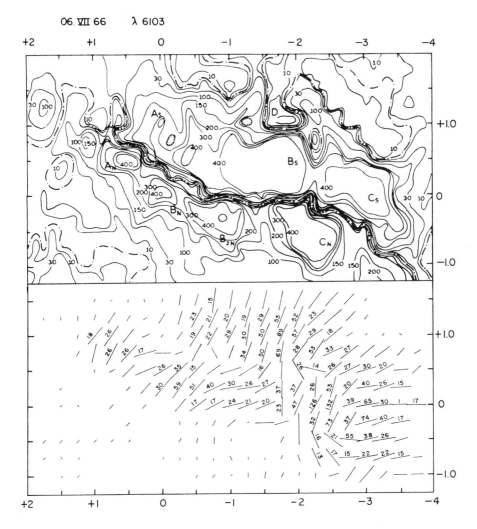

Fig. 1   Example of isogauss maps of longitudinal magnetic field (top) and transverse field (bottom) for the active region at 6 July 1966. Chain line is the line $H_\parallel = 0$. Scale: 1 unit = 25″ of arc (zero corresponds to position of guiding sunspot).

2 Longitudinal fields

The comparison of maps for different days shows that they are very *similar*; on each map we can identify the same three strong magnetic "hills" A_S, B_S, C_S of south polarity in the northern part of the map, and two or three A_N, B_N, C_N not-so-strong "hills" of north polarity located to the south just opposite to the former (see examples in Fig. 1). The distributions of field strength $H_\parallel$ along the straight lines joining these magnetic hills were examined

(Fig. 2) and the mean gradients $\Delta H_{\parallel}/\Delta S$ along the lines were plotted against time (Fig. 3).

For the three directions (A_S–A_N, B_S–B_N, C_S–C_N) we found some systematic variations: an increase from initial values ~ 0.1 G km^{-1} (at 4.4 July), before the proton flare, then a peak value ~ 1 G km^{-1} (at $\sim$ 6.2 July) and the final value ~ 0.2–0.1 G km^{-1}, the same at the initial value, after the proton flare

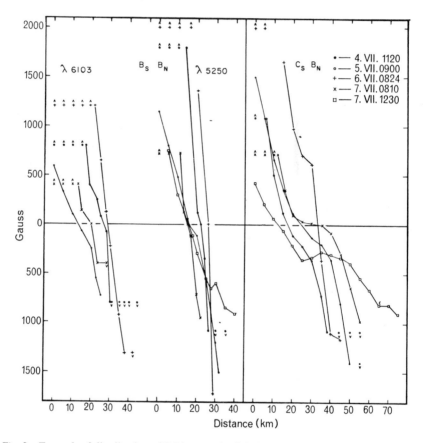

Fig. 2   Example of distribution of field strength of the longitudinal component $H_{\parallel}$ along straight lines joining magnetic "hills" for the days 4, 5, 6, and 7 July 1966. The steepest gradient is that for 6 July before the flare.

(at 7.2 July). There are no such appreciable variations of $\Delta H_{\parallel}/\Delta S$ for other directions (A_S–B_S, etc), and if present they are not so well defined.

The maps for two different levels, e.g. 5250 Å and 6103 Å (or 4808 Å) are also similar. For 6103 Å the changes of $\Delta H_{\parallel}/\Delta S$ for the same directions are smoother (see Fig. 3) than for 5250 Å, and the gradients $\Delta H_{\parallel}/\Delta S$ are about half the value.

The form of corresponding isogauss contours is similar for the maps for 5250 Å and 6103 Å, but the area inside a contour of given strength is some-what larger for 5250 Å than for 6103 Å in all cases, except 4 July. This means that the magnetic flux of the longitudinal field is larger for a deeper layer. The same conclusion follows from planimetry of isogauss maps of $H_{\parallel}$ for 5250 Å and 6103 Å (see Fig. 4). The sum of fluxes of both polarities $F_S + F_N$

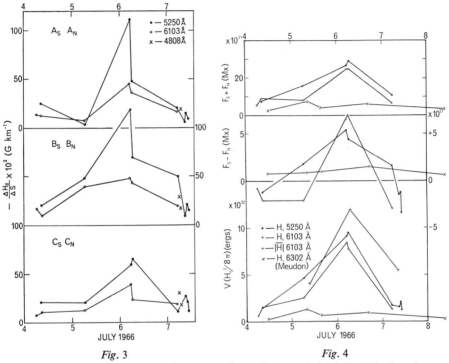

Fig. 3

Fig. 4

Fig. 3   Showing the variation of mean gradients of magnetic field $H_{\parallel}$ with time along several directions connecting magnetic "hills". The peak values are those before the flare.

Fig. 4   The variations with time of: the sum of fluxes $F_S + F_N$ (top), the net flux $F_S - F_N$ (middle), the magnetic energy determined by the total field strength $|H|$ and the magnetic energy determined by the longitudinal field $H_{\parallel}$ (bottom). The peak values are reached just before the flare.

(top of Fig. 4) behaves with time in the same manner as $\Delta H_{\parallel}/\Delta S$, i.e. it shows an increase up to a peak value (42 × 10²¹ Mx for 5250 Å and 25 × 10²¹ Mx for 6103 Å), and then, after the proton flare, the initial value is recovered. We see that the relative increase of flux in the deeper layer (5250 Å) is larger than in the upper layer (6103 Å). The imbalance of fluxes $F_S - F_N$ (S is the polarity of the leading spot) behaves in the same way, but the initial and final values here are negative and are about 0.1 of the peak value (∼ 10²² Mx). These results are in general agreement with those obtained by Michard and Tsap (1968) quite recently for nine flares observed during the QSAR (1966 flare) period. Here we have a relative increase of S-polarity flux as compared with N-polarity flux before the appearance of the flare.

Planimetry of isogauss maps of $H_\parallel$ permit us to evaluate the total magnetic energy of the active region, $V(H_\parallel^2/8\pi)$, where V is the volume occupied by different isogauss contours (calculated as 10^4 km × area occupied) (see Fig. 4). The energy increased from 1–2×10^{32} ergs up to 20×10^{32} ergs during the time interval 4.3–6.4 July, and decreased down to its initial value after the proton flare. The variation of the energy at 6103 Å is also similar to that at 5250 Å but the values for the upper layer (6103 Å) are 2–3 times smaller than for the deeper layer (5250 Å).

The only difference between the 5250 Å and 6103 Å maps is some small systematic shift of the 6103 Å magnetic "hills" to the east, as compared with those of 5250 Å. The effect is small, about 2.5″ (in the mean for all maps) for the eastward direction and 1.8″ for the northward direction, although in separate cases it can reach larger values, and in some cases we have shifts in the opposite direction. It can, probably, be explained as an eastward deflection of the upper part of tubes of force, an effect frequently observed in the case of magnetic elements of the general magnetic field. It can also be mentioned that after the proton flare the isogauss became of lenticular shape and elongated in the same direction as the flare filaments. The general character of the longitudinal magnetic field inside the sunspot group, the behaviour of the magnetic energy $H_\parallel^2/8\pi$, and of the gradients $\Delta H_\parallel/\Delta S$ are very similar to those observed in the group connected with the great proton flare of 16 July 1959 and described by Howard and Severny (1963).

Six observations of longitudinal magnetic field were obtained also at Meudon where they were measured with the aid of a lambda-meter (Michard and Rayrole 1965) to produce isogauss contour maps. The maps were available for our consideration through the kindness of Professor Michard. There is good qualitative correspondence between the Meudon and Crimean maps. The quantitative difference appears when, instead of magnetograph signal values (proportional to the calibrated signal of the magnetograph), we use the actual values, particularly for values of $H \geqslant 100$ G. If we used these uncorrected (for saturation effect) values the maximal field strength would be only 500 G, and the values for the energy of the active region, $V(H_\parallel^2/8\pi)$, should be ten times smaller than those presented in Fig. 4. Values of $V(H_\parallel^2/8\pi)$, $F_S - F_N$ and $F_S + F_N$ for the Meudon maps are plotted in Fig. 4 by crosses. If we adopted these values the total energy of the active region would not be enough to produce a flare with the loss of energy reaching 10^{31}–10^{32} ergs.

3 Transverse Fields

From the representative map of the transverse field given in Fig. 1 we see that the predominant direction of the $H_\perp$ vector is SE or NW. There are, as a rule, no appreciable differences between directions of $H_\perp$ on the maps for the two levels (5250 and 6103 Å) nor for different times during one day. Moreover, the map of $H_\perp$ on 6 July (6103 Å) corresponds well with the map for the same level for 5 July. Appreciable differences in directions of transverse fields first appear in the middle of the maps obtained after the proton flare on 7 July. If the directions before the flare form roughly a cross in the middle of a map, after the flare there are no traces of vertical straight line directions through the whole region (especially in the region between $y = -0.25$ and $y = +0.25$, Fig. 1), and instead we have a stream of purely horizontal directions (E–W orientation) of $H_\perp$ as if the proton flare forced the directions

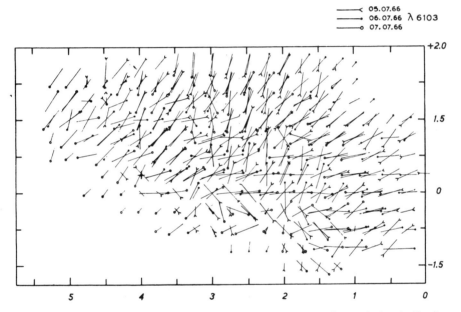

Fig. 5   The behaviour of the transverse component with time (before and after the flare): the directions of the vector $H_\perp$ for the days 5–7 July. The rotation through 90° is probably connected with the flare. Scale: 1 unit = 25″ of arc (zero corresponds to position of guiding sunspot).

to be parallel to its bright filaments (see Fig. 8 below). It is also worth mentioning that this stream of directions is parallel to the neutral line $H_\parallel = 0$. We have, therefore, a rotation by 90° of the vector field in the centre of our region when we pass from the map of 6 July to the map of 7 July, an effect which can be associated with the proton flare. Similar effects of the rotation of the vector field of $H_\perp$ associated with flares were observed earlier (Severny 1964). In Fig. 5 a composite map of directions of $H_\perp$ for the three days 5, 6, and 7 July is presented to illustrate the above-mentioned behaviour of the magnetic field. All six maps of $H_\perp$ obtained for 7 July are similar, including those for the lowest level 4808 Å. Differences in directions of the order of 30° which are often observed can be attributed to uncertainty in the determination of directions. Only for two points does the difference reach about 90° when comparing the map for 6103 Å and those for 5250 Å for 7 July (the three maps for 5250 Å for this date are practically identical). Therefore there were no appreciable changes in the vector field of $H_\perp$ during the morning hours of 7 July, and all observed changes must be attributed to the night 6–7 July, when the proton flare appeared (see Fig. 6).

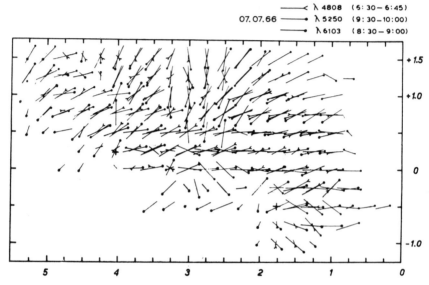

Fig. 6   The behaviour of the transverse component on 7 July, after the flare. Note that there are only minor variations in direction. Scale: 1 unit = 25″ of arc (zero corresponds to position of guiding sunspot).

4   The Total Vector of the Magnetic Field

Ten isogauss maps of values of $|\mathbf{H}|$ were constructed on the basis of observed maps of $H_{\parallel}$ and $H_{\perp}$ and empirical calibrations (Severny 1967). Examples of these maps are given in Fig. 7 showing the main process of the fission of large magnetic tubes of force into small pieces, the process observed recently by Gopasyuk (1967) for decaying groups.

It can also be seen from this figure that the isogauss contours (for a given strength) for 4808 Å are broader than for 5250 Å, indicating that magnetic flux and energy at the lower level are higher than at the upper. The same can be inferred from planimetry of the isogauss maps for 5250 Å and 4808 Å. We have $V(|\mathbf{H}|^2/8\pi) \simeq 2 \times 10^{35}$ ergs for 4808 Å and about 2×10^{33} for 5250 Å if the volume V is the same. This means that $|\mathbf{H}|$ is about ten times higher at the lower level. But the real difference between maximal |**H**| values at the corresponding points is not greater by more than a factor of about 3. On the other hand, the maximal value of the |**H**| field at the upper level 6103 Å is smaller by a factor of about 3 than the field at the level 5250 Å. The difference

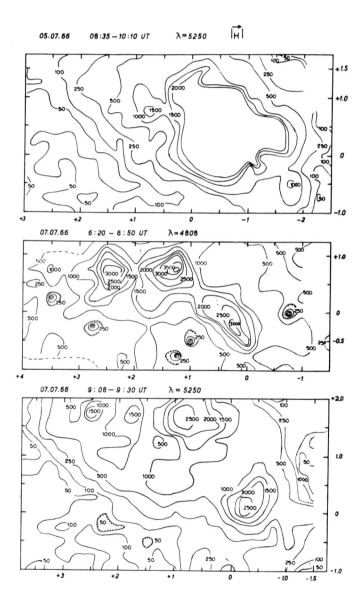

Fig. 7   Illustrating the process of fission of a large area occupied by a magnetic field into small pieces, over a period of time. Scale: 1 unit = 25″ of arc (zero corresponds to position of guiding sunspot).

by a factor of 10 between 4808 Å and 5250 Å derived from the energy $V(|\mathbf{H}|^2/8\pi)$ is, therefore, due to the larger area of isogauss contours on the map of 4808 Å (about 3 times larger). Thus we see that the magnetic field of the active region is concentrated at deep layers of the solar atmosphere.

The change of magnetic energy $V(|\mathbf{H}|^2/8\pi)$ can be followed for the 6103 Å level, for which we have maps for all three days 5, 6, and 7 July, and is shown in Fig. 4 (+ +); the increase of energy at 6.4 July is quite real. At the 5250 Å level we do not have a map for 6 July and Table 2 shows that there were no

Table 2   Values of $V(|\mathbf{H}|^2/8\pi)$ for the 5250 Å Level for the Period 5–7 July 1966

Date in July	5.34	5.39	7.39	7.41	7.43
$V(|\mathbf{H}|^2/8\pi)(10^{32}$ ergs)	10.1	22.2	17.7	20.9	15.5

appreciable variations of the energy $V(|\mathbf{H}|^2/8\pi)$ during the period in question, or that the initial value of energy was recovered (if we assume that on 6 July the energy attained a peak value which is large compared with these values). The most probable behaviour of the magnetic field as a whole is that the bulk of magnetic tubes of force are pushed up from below and then lowered, but as this process is rather slow the observed change in flux $F_S + F_N$ and energy $V(H_{\parallel}^2/8\pi)$ can in part be connected with the change of orientation of the magnetic field and the transformation of the $H_{\perp}$ field into a $H_{\parallel}$ field, and vice versa ($|\mathbf{H}|^2/8\pi \simeq$ const. for 5250 Å). The possibility of such a process is also indicated by the examination of the radial velocities in the active region before and after flares (Gopasyuk, Ogir, and Tsap 1963).

5   The Position of Proton Flares relative to Magnetic Fields and Electric Currents

At 0534 UT on 6 July the start of the flare 1b is recorded on Hα film of the Crimean coronagraph. The flare appeared as two small bright features—one coinciding practically with the neutral line $H_{\parallel} = 0$ and the other in the region of S polarity, near the "hill" B_S on the map of $H_{\parallel}$ taken for 6103 Å at 0500–0545 UT. Both these bright knots appeared in the middle of the same bright area occupied by the proton flare (Fig. 8). By using the copy of the Hα film obtained through the kindness of Dr. Banin (Sibizmiran) we were able to plot the area occupied by the proton flare (0030 UT) on the combined magnetic map, containing the main "hills" of the $H_{\parallel}$ field (A_S, B_S etc.) recorded on 7 July (0500–0530), the directions of $H_{\perp}$ recorded on the same day (0530–0600), and sunspots. This map can be constructed when the guiding sunspot can be identified and the E–W direction is known (Fig. 8). Although the start of the flare was not recorded it can be seen clearly that two main clouds or filaments of flare appeared simultaneously in regions of opposite magnetic polarity — the first, a cloud, is just to the north of neutral line $H_\parallel = 0$ and in contact with this line, and the second, a filament, is about 8″ to the south from the line $H_\parallel = 0$, in agreement with the recent results of Moreton and Severny (1966, 1968). Both filaments are parallel to the neutral line $H_\parallel = 0$ (see the similar cases described by Severny, 1963). The flare as a whole appeared in the region of crossing or bifurcation of directions of transverse field (in the middle of the map) as in this and other earlier investigations (Severny 1964, Moreton and Severny 1966, 1968). The position of the

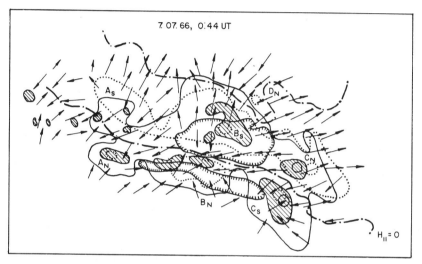

Fig. 8   The position of bright Hα clouds of flare (full line, with shading inside) with respect to the magnetic field (see text).

flare in relation to the distribution of vertical electric currents is of particular interest. The vertical currents of j_z are calculated from observed data on $H_\parallel$ and $H_\perp$ by the relation

$$\mathbf{j} = \frac{c}{4\pi} \operatorname{rot} \mathbf{H}$$

and the maps for 5, 6, and 7 July are given in Fig. 9, where black and white regions are regions of oppositely directed current density j_z.

The demarcation line between positive and negative currents is parallel to the line $H_\parallel = 0$ in the middle of the region and sometimes coincides with this line, so that, taking also into account the directions of $H_\perp$, the possibility can not be excluded that electric currents connect the magnetic regions of opposite polarity and form a pattern similar to the pattern of the magnetic lines of force. The maps also show clearly that both parts of the flare are just above the places with the strongest electric currents ($\geqslant 0.1$ G km^{-1}, j_z being measured in G km^{-1}) in agreement with the recent result of Moreton and Severny

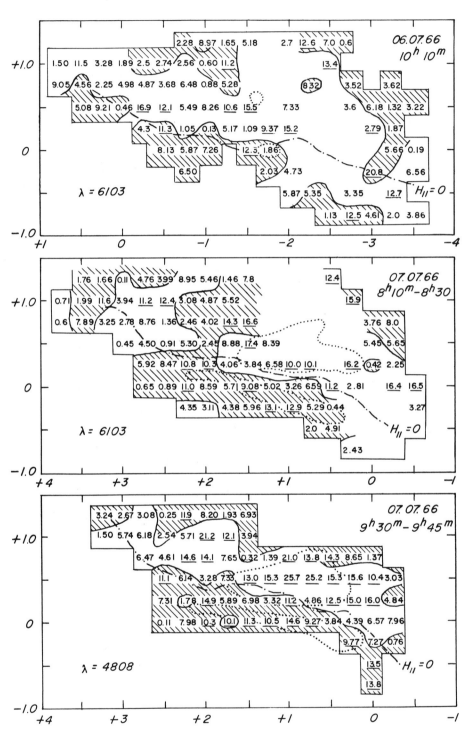

(1966, 1968), who found that about 80 per cent of flare knots coincide with points of strongest ($\geqslant 0.1$ G km^{-1}) electric current. This gives an additional support to the Alfvén and Carlquist (1967) theory of flares as interruptions in electric current filaments occurring at some critical values of electric current.

References

ALFVÉN, H., and P. CARLQUIST, 1967, Currents in the solar atmosphere and the theory of solar flares, *Solar Phys.*, **1**, 220–228.

BRUNS, A., N. NIKULIN, and A. SEVERNY, 1965, A new method of simultaneous registration of transverse magnetic field parameters, *Izv. Krȳm. Astrofiz. Obs.*, **33**, 80–85.

GOPASYUK, S., 1967, Temporal variations of the magnetic field in active solar regions, *Izv. Krȳm. Astrofiz. Obs.*, **36**, 56–68.

GOPASYUK, S., M. OGIR, and T. TSAP, 1963, Some peculiarities of active solar regions during flares, *Izv. Krȳm. Astrofiz. Obs.*, **30**, 148–160.

HOWARD, R., and A. SEVERNY, 1963, Solar magnetic fields and the great flare of July 16, 1959, *Astrophys. J.*, **137**, 1242–1250.

MICHARD, R., and I. RAYROLE, 1965, Observations systématiques des champs magnétiques des centres d'activité à l'Observatoire de Meudon, *Proc. IAU Symposium No. 22, Stellar and Solar Magnetic Fields* (North Holland Publ. Co., Amsterdam), pp. 169–172.

MICHARD, R., and T. TSAP, 1968, *Annls Astrophys.*, in press.

MORETON, G., and A. SEVERNY, 1966, Magnetic fields and flares in the region with CMP 20 September 1963, *Astr. Zh.*, **71**, 172.

—— 1968, *Solar Phys.*, **3**, 282–297.

NIKULIN, N., 1964, New details in the scheme of the magnetograph of the Crimean Astrophysical Observatory, *Izv. Krȳm. Astrofiz. Obs.*, **31**, 209–215.

SEVERNY, A., 1963, The location of great flares in magnetic fields of spot groups, *Izv. Krȳm. Astrofiz. Obs.*, **30**, 161–184.

—— 1964, Observations of transverse and longitudinal magnetic fields connected with solar flares, *Izv. Krȳm. Astrofiz. Obs.*, **31**, 159–199.

—— 1966, Magnetic fields at different layers of the solar atmosphere, *Astr. Zh.*, **43**, 465–479.

—— 1967, Calibration of records of a solar magnetograph, *Izv. Krȳm. Astrofiz. Obs.*, **36**, 22–50.

Fig. 9   The position of flare clouds (dotted line) with respect to the distribution of vertical currents j_z (shaded and white areas are regions of opposite j_z). Maximum values of electric current are underlined. Scale: 1 unit = 25″ of arc (zero corresponds to position of guiding sunspot).

2

Distribution of Magnetic Fields in Photospheric and Chromospheric Layers in the Active Region of 7 July 1966 and Their Correlation with the Flare Event of 8 July, 1253–1340 UT

G. Brückner*‡ and M. Waldmeier†

* University of Maryland, Department of Physics and Astronomy, College Park, Maryland, USA
† Eidgenossische Sternwarte, Zürich, Schmelzbergstrasse, Switzerland

Abstract

Longitudinal and transverse field components inside the very active region are determined with a spatial resolution of 2″ of arc by 2″ of arc measuring circular and linear polarization of the Fe I 5250 Å line. Also chromospheric fields are measured using the centre of the Hα line. The interesting peculiarities of the field distribution are (*a*) the very active region shows a tripolar structure; the adjacent region of opposite polarity does not show any coincidence with a spot structure on 7 July 1966, 1200 MET, (*b*) the transverse component of the magnetic field has its maximum along the neutral line, (*c*) large field gradients can be observed at the neutral line, (*d*) the Hα magnetic field distribution in chromospheric layers shows much weaker fields than the photospheric field distribution, (*e*) the flare event appeared at both sides of one neutral line.

The outstanding interest which has been shown in the very active sunspot group of July 1966 may justify a detailed analysis of the magnetic fields which could be measured in this group.

Magnetic field measurements have been made with the new magnetograph at the Locarno solar observatory owned by the Deutsche Forschungsgemeinschaft (Brückner 1968). This magnetograph records simultaneously the longitudinal and the transverse component of magnetic fields measured in the Fe I line 5250 Å. A detailed description of the instrument and of the data reduction procedure is given by Brückner (1968). Unno's theory of forming a Zeeman

‡ Now at Space Science Division, U.S. Naval Research Laboratory, Washington, D.C.

triplet in the solar atmosphere has been used to transfer measured polarization into magnetic fields. The magnetograph also has been used to record the longitudinal magnetic field component measured in Hα. This could not be done simultaneously, but a time difference of one hour may not influence seriously the comparison of the photospheric and chromospheric field patterns. It is obvious that this measuring procedure does not allow comparison of *fine-structure field differences* in 5250 Å and Hα as is possible by means of Severny's double magnetograph (Severny 1966a, b). The spatial resolution of the magnetograms was 2″ of arc by 2″ of arc. In 5250 Å the longitudinal component has been measured with an accuracy to ± 10 gauss, the transverse component to ± 70 gauss. The Hα measurements are accurate to within 10 gauss.

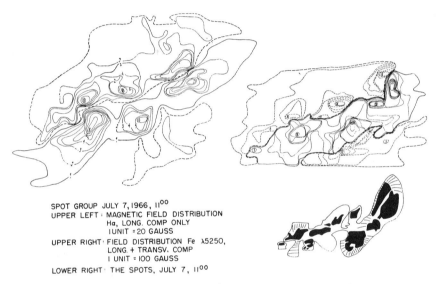

SPOT GROUP JULY 7, 1966, 11⁰⁰
UPPER LEFT : MAGNETIC FIELD DISTRIBUTION
        Hα, LONG. COMP ONLY
        I UNIT = 20 GAUSS
UPPER RIGHT· FIELD DISTRIBUTION Fe λ5250,
        LONG. + TRANSV. COMP
        I UNIT = 100 GAUSS
LOWER RIGHT · THE SPOTS, JULY 7, 11⁰⁰

Fig. 1   Magnetic field distribution (5250 Å and Hα) in the spot group, 7 July 1966, 1100 MET. Upper left: magnetic field distribution Hα longitudinal component only, 1 unit = 10 gauss; Upper right: field distribution Fe 5250 Å, longitudinal + transverse component, 1 unit = 100 gauss. Lower right: the spots, 7 July, 1100 MET.

Figure 1 shows the field distribution in the very active group, measured at 7 July, 1200 MET. The equal-gauss lines in 5250 Å represent the total field strength of both the longitudinal and the transverse component, in Hα only the longitudinal component. The transverse magnetic component in Hα was below the noise level of the magnetograph. A qualitative analysis shows that

a. There are tremendous differences of the photospheric and chromospheric field strength. The Hα fields reach only 160 gauss, while the photospheric fields go up to 2000 gauss. (There is a discrepancy between the

Locarno magnetograph measurements and the Crimea fields measured by means of the line splitting which can be explained by stray light which has not been corrected in our measurements. The seeing conditions during the 7 July measurements at Locarno have been moderate.)

b. Some parts of the region show opposite polarity of the Hα and 5250 Å fields. This is particularly true in the centre of the group, where the third polarity has a tendency to join the magnetic field region of the same polarity lacing the opposite polarity region. Also, one can observe opposite polarities of the Hα and 5250 Å fields in some parts of the two large preceding spots.

Figure 2 shows the 5250 Å field distribution and the spot group. A remarkable fact may be that the third polarity is not connected with visible spots. It is remarkable that the neutral line cuts the umbra of one of the preceding spots in two parts of opposite polarity.

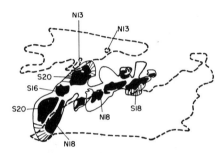

Fig. 2   Field strength and polarities (Fe 5250 Å), 7 July 1966, 1100 MET. Magnetic fields: Locarno.

One obtains a fairly detailed picture from Fig. 3. We have plotted the longitudinal and the transverse components of the magnetic field for three different cross sections. The transverse component reaches its maximum value of *c.* 1000 gauss on the neutral line at the cross section L4 and L7; this effect is not obvious to see at line L3. The field gradient of the longitudinal component at the neutral line varies between 0.05 and 0.1 gauss km^{-1} in good agreement with Severny's condition of 0.1 gauss km^{-1} for a flare-like situation. It has to be mentioned here that there is a time difference of 1 day between the magnetogram and the appearance of the first flare. It may be that the field gradient increased until the flare appeared.

Figures 4 and 5 show the structure of the flare overlapped with the magnetic pattern in 5250 Å and Hα. The flare appeared along the southern neutral line from one end to the other, but there is no brightening along the north neutral line, which shows the same magnetic values as the other. We want to mention this because some authors believe the third polarity has a strong influence on large proton flares. It may be that the 7 July proton flare has shown another structure from the "post-flare" of 8 July, which is shown here.

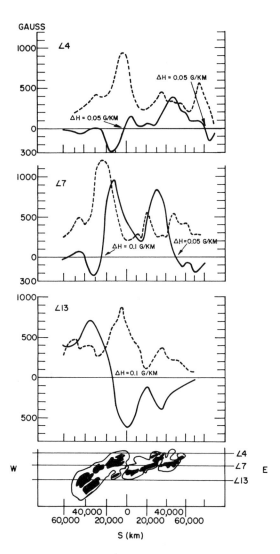

Fig. 3   Magnetic field cross sections of different parts
of the spot group, 7 July 1966, 1100 MET,
Fe 5250 Å.
– – – – Transverse component
———— Longitudinal component

The brightest point of the flare one can identify with the lacing spot of the
Hα field (Fig. 5).

Figure 6 shows the development of the flare event; all pictures are obtained
at Zürich. The seeing quality was moderate, but after the first very bright
phase of the flare, one can recognize different bright knots which are easy to

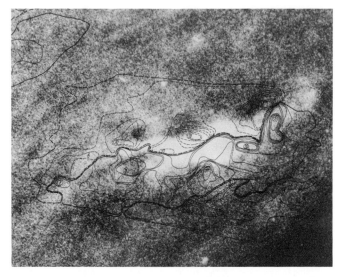

Fig. 4   Flare of 8 July 1966 and magnetic field distribution for 5250 Å, 7 July 1966.

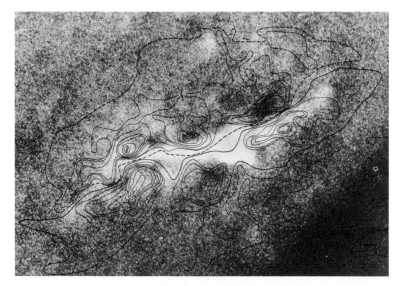

Fig. 5   Flare of 8 July 1966 and magnetic field distribution for Hα, 7 July 1966.

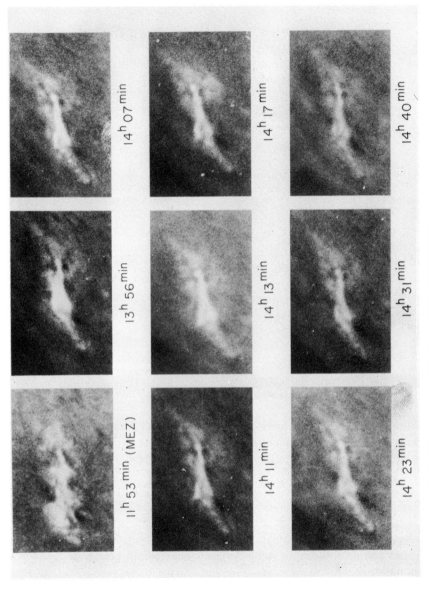

Fig. 6 Development of the flare, 8 July 1966 (Zürich).

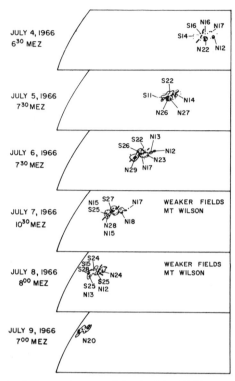

Fig. 7   Development of the spot group 4 to 9, July 1966; spots: Zürich, magnetic fields: Crimea and Mt. Wilson.

identify with the largest field gradients in the neighborhood of the large spots. The first picture shows the Hα plages before the flare occurred; the second to ninth pictures, different stages of the flare. Picture 2 was taken after the flare had started.

Figure 7 shows the development of the spot group as it was observed at the Zürich observatory. The given field strengths are the Crimea measurements, also, on 7 and 8 July, the Mount Wilson measurements. The changing polarity of the two southern spots from 6 July to 7 July may be wrong, but it can be an indication of the close neighborhood of opposite polarities inside one penumbra.

References

Brückner, G., 1968, Ein neuer Magnetograph zur simultanen Messung des longitudinalen und des transversalen Zeemaneffektes im Sonnenspektrum, *Z. Astrophys.*, **68**, 48–84.

Severny, A. B., 1966a, Magnetic field at different depths of the solar atmosphere, *Astr. Zh.*, **43**, 465–479.

—— 1966b, in *The Fine Structure of the Solar Atmosphere, Colloquium Anacapri*, Ed. K. O. Kiepenheuer (Franz Steiner Verlag, Wiesbaden), p. 109.

3

The Hα Plage associated with the Proton Flare of July 1966

C. Popovici and A. Dimitriu
Bucharest Observatory, Bucharest, Rumania

Abstract

The Hα plage was a new-born plage between two old Hα plages. Its development was slow and irregular at the beginning and accelerated rapidly on 3 July, when within some eight hours the plage took on its compact, oval form along the axis of the sunspot group. The area of the plage increased to a flat maximum by 6 July, three days before the maximum of the corrected area of the sunspot group; 12 hours before the proton flare the plage and the sunspot group took the characteristic A form, two parallel bright filaments extending from west to east symmetrical with the axis of the sunspot group and above the common penumbra of the spots, being brighter between the two principal spot umbrae of the group.

The Hα plage 20934 (McMath No. 8362) of the proton flare was a new one, born between plages 8361 and 8367 (8331), and was first seen at the east solar limb on 26 June 1967. The plage was from the beginning detached from the old, more important plage 8361, somewhat to the westward, and from the less extended and fainter plage 8367, which disappeared after 3 July. Initially, plage 8361 was more extended and brighter than plage 8362 but after 3 July it became less important. For the period 4–8 July, the plage 8362 dominated the entire solar disk (see also the Stanford 9.1-cm spectroheliogram).

On 28 June, the three bright filaments of the plage had a N–S orientation decreasing in brightness and extent from west to east. The points and filaments of the plage developed at the beginning in a somewhat confused, discontinuous, and irregular manner (Figs. 1*a* and *b*) until 3 July. At the end of

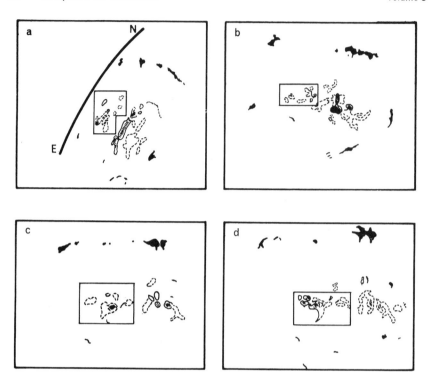

Fig. 1   Evolution of the Hα plage 20934:
    a. 27 June 1966, 1728 UT;   *b.* 1 July 1966, 0645 UT.
    c. 3 July 1966, 0748 UT;   *d.* 3 July 1966, 1853 UT.
    Shaded areas, most intense emission; dotted areas, least intense emission; solid
    black areas, filaments of 7 July and the principal spots of the group.

this period, the east filament began to be reinforced, especially in its southern
part, and extended in the E–W direction, roughly parallel to the solar

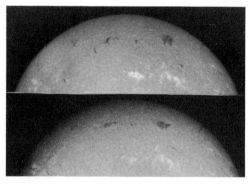

Fig. 2   Hα filtergrams for 3 July 1966.
    Top: Honolulu 1853 UT. Bottom: Bucharest 0748 UT.

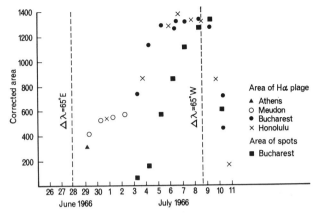

Fig. 3   Variation of the area of sunspots and Hα plage 20934.

equator. On 3 July, it took a compact oval form along the axis of the C-type spot group, which developed rapidly to an E-type group. The plage preserved this form until its disappearance on the west limb (10 July).

The most spectacular change in form, compactness, and intensity took place between 10 UT (Bucharest) and 18 UT (Honolulu) on 3 July (Figs. 1c, d, and 2) and the flare actively continued to increase into 4 July.

The corrected area of the Hα plage, which grew slowly until 3 July, had a very rapid growth from 3 to 5 July with a maximum about 6 July ($1400 \times 10^{-6} A_H$), remained constant until 8–9 July, and then decreased rapidly (Fig. 3). The corrected area of the whole sunspot group (Bucharest) grew until 9 July ($1400 \times 10^{-6} A_H$), two days after the proton flare, and decreased rapidly on 10 July ($615 \times 10^{-6} A_H$ Bucharest, $548 \times 10^{-6} A_H$ Kislovodsk); there is some uncertainty in the computed corrected area from $\Delta\lambda > 65°$ W.

The brightness of the Hα plage was greater at its west end between the two principal spot umbrae, where the proton flare occurred, and decreased

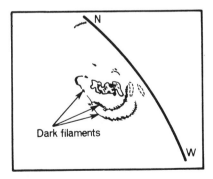

Fig. 4   Hα plage 20934, 7 July 1966, 1852 UT, showing dark filaments.
Shaded areas, most intense emission; dotted areas, least intense emission; solid black areas, filaments of 7 July and the two principal spots of the group.

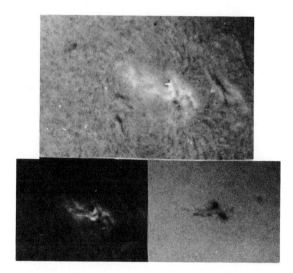

Fig. 5   Hα filtergrams of 6 July 1966, Bucharest 1153 UT.

gradually to the east end. This was the final form of the plage 12 hours before the proton flare, with two parallel bright filaments along the axis of the A-configuration sunspot group and above the penumbrae of the spots (Fig. 4) (Avignon *et al.* 1963). The plage filaments were very bright and this misled some observers who took them as a flare despite the little change in brightness. (For comparison, Fig. 5 is a photograph of the edge of Hα plage showing the filaments in relation to the spots and an overexposed Hα filtergram in which one can see the two filaments more clearly.) After the proton flare, the plage continued to be very bright.

The entire Hα plage region (8361, 8362, 8367) was ringed by the dark filaments for some four days (cf. Fig. 1*b*, 1 July). After the proton flare, a circular arc of very fine dark filaments bordered the plage to the southward, its eastern part being later much enhanced (8, 9, 10 July) and producing the eruptive prominence of 11 July.

Acknowledgments

We greatly thank observatories of Athens, Honolulu, and Meudon which sent us their Hα filtergrams for the period under consideration, thus completing our series of filtergrams and making this analysis possible.

Reference

AVIGNON, Y., M. J. MARTRES-TROPE, and M. PICK-GUTMANN, 1963, Identification d'une classe d'éruptions chromosphériques responsables des absorptions ionosphériques polaires, *C.R. Acad. Sci., Paris,* **256,** 2112–2120.

4

Birth and Development of the Calcium Plage associated with the Proton Flare of July 1966

T. Fortini and M. Torelli
Osservatorio Astronomico su Monte Mario, Rome, Italy

Abstract

Region 21034 may be considered as the fusion of two components born successively (with a difference in time of approximately 50 hours), 2° apart in longitude. The first part has developed in the extreme periphery of an expanding old region, at a rather slow rate. Its separation from the old region has been marked by the presence of a very dark supercellule. The second component has developed and merged with the first component more freely.

The largest spots after 4 July 1966 occupy the core of the region, a position rather unusual with respect to the general situation of spots in other regions.

On 25, 26 June 1966 at 33° N a large region which covered almost 30° in longitude was passing the east limb of the sun. It was an old expanding region and at this time the future region 21034 was a small and weak appendix rather than an individual entity (see Fig. 1). On 28 June and during 29 June small changes were observable in this appendix and in its surroundings. A dark oval, on the NW side, 50,000 km in length, was marked at the borders by bright features. It persisted for approximately 40 hours, breaking off between 30 June (1311 UT, Rome observation) and 1 July (0657, Paris observation). With the resolution time of the observations at our disposal we were unable to define the speed of this break-off which apparently defined the separation of the appendix from the main body of the region.

It is not easy to date exactly the birth of the region 21034 since on 28 and 29 June new elements were already brightening in it, accompanied by a general enhancement of the pre-existing calcium network. On 30 June the region appeared to have its own identity and a small spot had been observed in it in the afternoon. The development of the plage while new spots were forming in it proceeded in this phase at a rather slow rate. The brightening

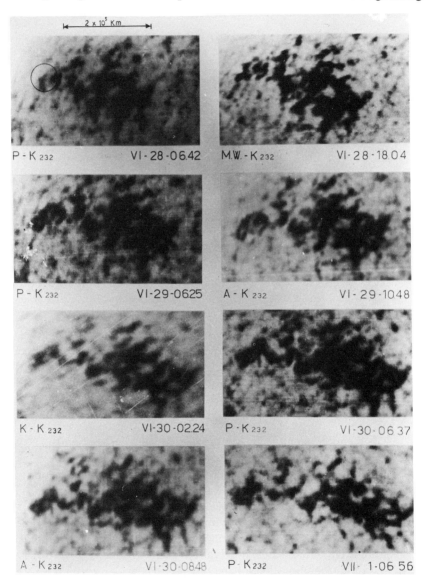

Fig. 1   A = Arcetri, K = Kodaikanal, M = Manila, MW = Mt. Wilson, P = Paris
(Features outlined in the circle: future region 21034)

proceeded along the borders of the supergranular cellules (Bumba and Howard 1965a) with successive expansion and weakening, particularly of the external parts. On 2 July, when a well-defined bipolar spot-group had developed in it (see Fig. 2), a new disturbance reached the solar surface, starting with a luminous grain (first observed at 1708, Mt. Wilson Observatory) at the junction of several supergranular cellules (cf. general observation by Bumba and Howard 1965b) 2° east in longitude of the newly formed region. Also in

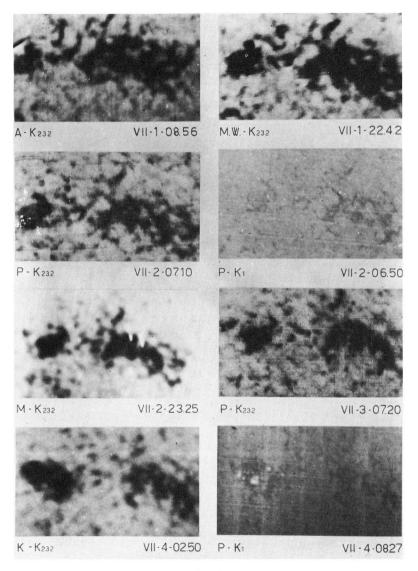

Fig. 2

this case the development proceeded with the lightening of the calcium network along the borders of the supergranular cells. The fusion of this component, where a second bipolar group of spots was present on 3 July, with the western part proceeded now at a fast rate. On 4 July the two components were one very bright body although the sunspots in it could still be divided into two separate groups. During 4 July the whole region slightly enlarged and the calcium pattern encircled two large supercellules, filled on 5 July by the main

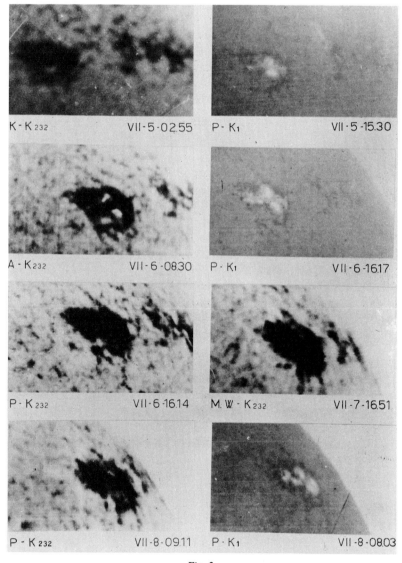

Fig. 3

spots of the group (Bumba 1965). These had developed a large penumbra and the area of the whole group was very large compared with the extension of the calcium area. The plage on 5 July and following days (Fig. 3) was characterized by the special configuration of the spots arranged in two close lines of components of opposite polarity. The calcium emission was very intense along the axis of the group.

Acknowledgments

We wish to acknowledge the cooperation of the V. Abastumani, Arcetri, Kodaikanal, Manila, McMath–Hulbert, Paris, and Mount Wilson Observatories. We sincerely regret that for showing the time sequence of the evolution of the region, in the preparation of the figures, we have not made the best choice of the observations of these Institutes.

References

BUMBA, V., 1965, Short note on the connection between the faculae network and sunspots, *Proc. IAU Symposium No. 22, Stellar and Solar Magnetic Fields* (North-Holland Publ. Co., Amsterdam), pp. 192–195.

BUMBA, V., and R. HOWARD, 1965a, A study of the development of active regions on the sun, *Astrophys. J.*, **141**, 1492–1501.

—— 1965b, Solar magnetic fields, *Science*, **149**, 1331–1337.

5

Birth and Development of the Sunspot Group associated with the Proton Flare of July 1966

P. S. McIntosh

Environmental Research Laboratories, Environmental Science Services Administration, Boulder, Colorado, USA

Abstract

The birth and early development of the sunspot group consisted of the successive formation of three pairs of spot clusters on the borders of three adjoining network cells. The rapid growth and merging of the last two pairs resulted in a configuration of parallel rows of spots of opposite polarity enveloped in one continuous penumbra. The region between these rows exhibited umbrae elongated parallel to exceptionally dark and thick penumbral filaments.

The discovery in recent years of supergranulation (Leighton, Noyes, and Simon 1962) coinciding spatially with both the chromospheric network and regions of magnetic fields (Simon and Leighton 1964) with strengths as high as several hundred gauss (Sheeley 1967) has brought a new outlook to the study of the origin of solar active regions. Bumba and Howard (1965) have associated the formation of new, small sunspots with the bright rings of facular granules that surround supergranule cells. Bumba and Howard also suggest that even the large, well-developed sunspot groups occupy spaces determined by the supergranulation pattern. The study of the sunspot group associated with the July 1966 proton event revealed a detailed correspondence between the spot birth and development and the network pattern.

The first sunspot to form appears on a photograph taken in the near-ultraviolet by Dezsö and shown schematically in Fig. 1 at top left. The photograph shows spots and faculae together over the entire solar disk. The illustration is based on a tracing made from the photograph by Debrecen observers. The pattern of Ca^+K_{232} emission on McMath spectroheliograms

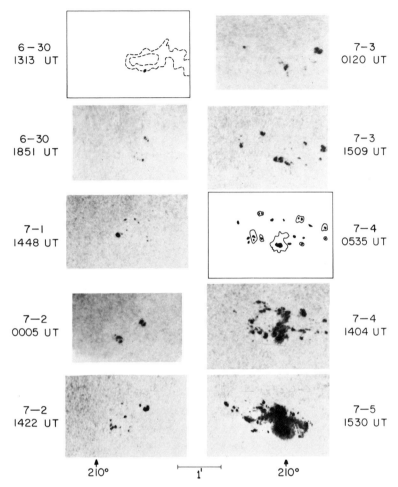

Fig. 1   The early development of the proton-flare sunspot group. The 210° longitude in
the Carrington system is indicated at the bottom of each column. North is up,
west to the right. The drawings are based on photographs taken by L. Dezsö,
Debrecen, Hungary. The dotted line outlines faculae visible at 3750 Å. Photograph at 30 June, 1851 UT, courtesy of Aerospace Corporation; all others
courtesy of Sacramento Peak Observatory, Air Force Cambridge Research
Laboratories.

is similar to the facular outline on the Debrecen tracing, so one can suppose
that the spot formed on the border of a network cell.

The early development of the sunspot group consisted of the successive
formation of three pairs of spot clusters. The first pair occurred with the
appearance of a second spot on the northern border of the facular ring by
1600 UT on 30 June. The other pairs followed at about 1.5 and 3.1 July. In
each pair the following spots were first to form. The interval between

formation of follower and leader for the last pair was 2–5 hours. The new spots formed among patches of faculae seen on the tracings from Debrecen. The distances separating the spot clusters were like the distances separating three adjoining network or supergranule cells. The initial separation of each pair (Fig. 2) was $19–24 \times 10^4$ km, well within the measured cell size of supergranules ($15–30 \times 10^4$ km) (Leighton, Noyes, and Simon 1962).

The increase in the separation of spot clusters of the two longer-lived pairs began at about 500 m s^{-1}. This rapid rate was observed for a few hours, then the rate decreased to about 200 m s^{-1}, in agreement with the rate of expansion of the calcium plage of about 250 m s^{-1}, reported by Bumba and Howard (1965).

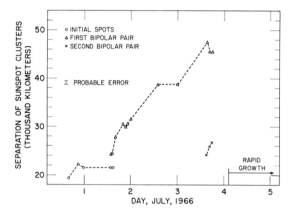

Fig. 2   Separation of pairs of sunspot clusters in the sunspot group.

In each pair the leader spots are farther from the equator than the followers, contrary to the normal occurrence. If differential rotation were the principal mechanism for relative spot motions, the follower spots would have approached the slower moving leaders. Since the spots separated, some other mechanism must be associated with the spot motions.

Observations from the Mount Wilson and the Crimean Astrophysical observatories showed that the last two pairs of spot clusters each formed a magnetic bipolar group arranged in the normal manner for northern hemisphere groups of cycle 20. The first pair of spot clusters was measured as all of one polarity, but the small size of these spots made measurement difficult.

The association of the spot development with the supergranulation was strengthened by the appearance of the group on 4 July. By this time many new spots had formed at such positions as to create two circles of spots joined by an area of growing penumbra. The pattern formed by the spots was duplicated in the calcium plage as observed on McMath–Hulbert Observatory patrol spectroheliograms. The cells in both white light and calcium were $19–22 \times 10^4$ km in diameter.

The formation of these spots and the appearance of penumbra in the central portion of the group marked the beginning of the most rapid growth for the region. The scattered umbrae at the north and south ends of the penumbra were of opposite magnetic polarity, making a delta configuration. From 4 to 6 July, these umbrae grew and coalesced, and the penumbra expanded along the circles of spots, eventually penetrating the circles.

By 6 July parallel rows of spots of opposite polarity had formed, extending in an east–west direction. Their darkness and close separation indicated strong magnetic fields and a steep magnetic field gradient. This basic configuration was maintained until west-limb passage.

The fine structure of the sunspot group was remarkable during this period of rapid growth. Many of the strong umbrae were elongated in the direction of neighboring penumbral filaments. On 4 and 5 July this elongation was primarily in a north–south direction, but on 6 July the orientation of elongated umbrae and penumbral structures was strongly east–west (McIntosh and Sawyer 1968). On this day, within 10 hours prior to the proton flare, the penumbral structure was unusually dark in the corridor between the rows of strong spots. McIntosh and Sawyer discuss the evolution of the region from 6 July to west-limb passage and present the measured areas of the group.

Acknowledgments

This study was made possible by white-light patrol films supplied by Dr. John W. Evans and Howard Demastus of the Sacramento Peak Observatory and by Dr. Thomas J. Janssens of the Aerospace Corporation, near-ultraviolet observations by Dr. Lorant Dezsö of the Debrecen Heliophysical Observatory, and calcium patrol spectroheliograms by Dr. Helen Dodson Prince of the McMath–Hulbert Observatory. Mr. John Allen was responsible for examining the white-light patrol films and making the copy negatives of the sunspot group.

This work was partially supported by NASA Contract R-102.

References

BUMBA, V., and R. HOWARD, 1965, A study of the development of active regions on the sun, *Astrophys. J.*, **141**, 1492–1501.

LEIGHTON, R. B., R. W. NOYES, and G. W. SIMON, 1962, Velocity fields in the solar atmosphere: I. Preliminary report, *Astrophys. J.*, **135**, 474–499.

MCINTOSH, P. S., and C. SAWYER, 1968, Evolution of the sunspot group after the proton flare of 7 July 1966, *Ann. IQSY*, this volume, Paper 23.

SHEELEY, N. R., 1967, Observations of small-scale solar magnetic fields, *Solar Phys.*, **1**, 171–179.

SIMON, G. W., and R. B. LEIGHTON, 1964, Velocity fields in the solar atmosphere: III. Large-scale motions, the chromospheric network, and magnetic fields, *Astrophys. J.*, **140**, 1120–1147.

6

Observation des éruptions à protons: l'évènement du 7 juillet 1966: Photométrie des raies coronales 5303 Å et 6374 Å

J.-L. Leroy

Observatoire du Pic-du-Midi, Bagnères de Bigorre, France

Abstract

From observations collected simultaneously at the stations of Lomnický štít, Kislovodsk, Pic-du-Midi and Wendelstein, we have plotted synoptic charts for the 5303 Å and 6374 Å radiations. The isophotes display the distribution and time evolution of these coronal emissions in the solar active region where a proton flare appeared on 7 July 1966.

La région solaire active où est apparue l'éruption à protons du 7 juillet 1966 est passée au bord solaire Est vers le 26 juin et au bord Ouest vers le 10 juillet. Les observations coronales effectuées aux alentours de ces dates et comportant la photométrie des raies 5303 Å et 6374 Å peuvent permettre de construire des cartes synoptiques qui donnent des indications sur la répartition et l'évolution des émissions coronales dans la région active considérée.

Nous avons donc établi, pour chacune des radiations 5303 Å et 6374 Å, deux cartes synoptiques correspondant aux deux passages au bord solaire indiqués plus haut. Ces cartes couvrent respectivement les périodes du 22 au 30 juin 1966 et du 6 au 14 juillet 1966. Elles sont construites à partir des documents fournis par les observatoires de Lomnický štít, de Kislovodsk, du Pic-du-Midi et de Wendelstein ce qui représente au total 19 observations pour la raie 5303 Å et 10 observations pour la raie 6374 Å (Fig. 1).

On a exprimé les mesures des diverses stations dans un même système d'unités en utilisant la méthode de comparaison des constantes décrite par M. N. Gnevyshev (1963). Cette méthode suppose que l'on connaisse les couronnes semestrielles moyennes observées par chacune des stations dont on veut comparer les échelles. Grâce à l'extrême amabilité du Docteur M. N.

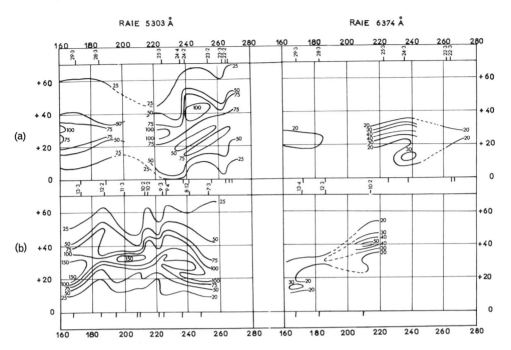

Fig. 1   Cartes synoptiques des émissions coronales à 5303 Å et à 6374 Å. (*a*) Passage au bord Est du 22 au 30 juin 1966. (*b*) Passage au bord Ouest du 6 au 14 juillet 1966.

Gnevyshev à Kislovodsk et du Docteur J. Sýkora à Lomnický štít ces moyennes ont été mises très rapidement à notre disposition et nous avons pu procéder à un raccordement qui présente le maximum de garanties que l'on puisse espérer obtenir dans un type d'opération de ce genre où les risques d'erreurs sont très grands (on se rappellera en particulier qu'une incertitude importante subsiste lorsque l'on a affaire à de très grandes intensités). Nous avons exprimé toutes les mesures dans l'échelle de l'Observatoire du Pic-du-Midi pour le milieu de 1966 car il se trouvait que les observations en provenance de cette station représentaient plus de la moitié du matériel disponible. Les chiffres portés sur les cartes représentent donc, suivant l'usage habituel, des millionièmes, dans l'échelle du Pic-du-Midi, de l'intensité de 1 Å du continu photosphérique, mesuré au centre du Soleil et au voisinage de la raie d'émission considérée.

Les cartes ont été tracées sur le canevas d'une projection de Mercator, la latitude étant comme d'habitude portée en ordonnée et la longitude en abscisse. On a indiqué par des petits segments les dates pour lesquelles des observations étaient disponibles. On remarquera que des lacunes importantes existent pour les deux passages au bord dans le cas de la raie 6374 Å et pour le passage au bord Est dans le cas de la raie 5303 Å.

L'existence d'un certain nombre des détails qui sont figurés sur les cartes est attestée par une seule observation et il est donc possible que la présence d'erreurs dans les mesures entraîne l'apparition de complications factices sur les isophotes. Nous avons pensé que les phénomènes associés à une éruption à protons pouvaient peut-être comporter des processus à variation rapide dans le temps et que par conséquent il était malgré tout préférable de conserver tous les détails des cartes. On peut espérer que des recoupements opérés à l'aide d'autres types d'observations permettront peut-être d'éliminer ulteriéurement ceux d'entre eux qui seraient illusoires.

Références

GNEVYSHEV, M. N., 1963, The corona and the 11-year cycle of solar activity, *Soviet Astr.*, 7, 311–318.

7

Coronal Data for the Period of the Proton Flare Event of July 1966

M. N. Gnevyshev
Astronomical Observatory, Pulkove, USSR

Abstract

Distribution curves of the coronal line intensity at 5303 Å and 6374 Å are given for the period of the July 1966 proton flare.

The coordinates of the flare were

$$\phi = +34° \qquad \lambda = 210°$$

The date of the limb passages of the point were

26 June at the east limb, 10 July at the west limb.

For all days of limb passages and for four days before and after, the distributions of the coronal line intensity at 5303 Å (Fig. 1) and 6374 Å (Fig. 2) are given. The intensities were measured at 40″ distance from the limb in absolute units.

The vertical line shows the latitude of the flare.

The dates of limb passages are enclosed in a box. The coronal measurements of Pic-du-Midi (P), Kislovodsk (K) and Lomnický štít (L) were used. If the position angles were corrected the curves are drawn with a broken line. In all cases the flares were not at the place of maxima of coronal intensity but near to it.

All coronal data were prepared by Mrs. R. S. Gnevysheva.

For Figures see overleaf.

47

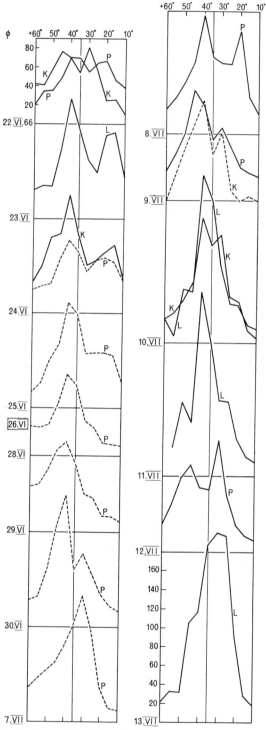

Fig. 1 Coronal line intensity distribution curves at 5303 Å.

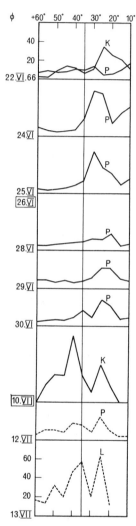

Fig. 2 Coronal line intensity distribution curves at 6374 Å.

48

8

Coronal Electron Densities during the Period of the July 1966 Proton Flare

G. Newkirk, Jr.*, R. T. Hansen†, and S. Hansen†

*High Altitude Observatory, National Center for Atmospheric Research, Boulder, Colorado, USA
†Kamuela, Hawaii, USA

Abstract

K-coronameter observations during the interval June–September 1966 are used to construct five electron density models of the corona above the proton flare region. These models are compared with others for the corona above active regions. The observations following the proton flares of 10 July and 5 September show the presence of a unique low elevation condensation in the corona. The possibility that this condensation is the direct contribution of material expelled by the flares is examined.

I Basic Data

Using the K-coronameter (Wlérick and Axtell 1957) maintained by the High Altitude Observatory on Mauna Loa, Hawaii, at an altitude of 11,150 ft (3400 m), we have secured observations of the electron corona above the proton flare region (PFR) of July–September 1966 over the range $1.125 \, R_\odot \leqslant R \leqslant 2R_\odot$ from the center of the disk. Favorable weather allowed an almost uninterrupted sequence of high-quality measurements which extend from the birth of the region in the corona in early July 1966 to its subsidence in mid-September. The corona above the PFR will be discussed from three standpoints — its general morphological development during the period, the construction of models of electron density distribution, and the possibility of a direct contribution of coronal material by the flares.

The basic data from the K-coronameter consist of measurements of the quantity pB made as the instrument scans about the sun at a given height above the solar limb. Here p is the polarization tangential to the limb and B

the radiance of the corona in units of 10^{-8} times the radiance of the center of the solar disk. The procedures of calibration and reduction of the raw output have been discussed previously (Newkirk, Curtis, and Watson 1958). Throughout this series of observations the scanning aperture had a diameter of $1.35'$ of arc ($2.12 \times 10^{-2} R_{\odot}$) and the probable error in a given measurement is about 0.5–1.0×10^{-8}. A statistical analysis of the data gathered over several years shows, as well, a systematic asymmetry of the observations in which features at the west limb are recorded as 10–20 per cent higher than those at the east limb.

2 General Description of the Corona above the PFR

An example of some of these data appears in Fig. 1, which shows the superposition of several polar plots of pB at east-limb (24–28 June) and at west-

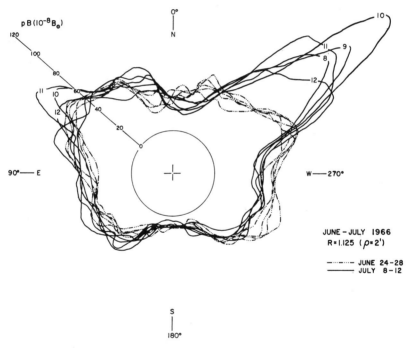

Fig. 1   A superposition of radial plots of the K-coronameter signal pB for the limb passages of the PFR on 24–28 June and on 8–12 July for a scan height of $R = 1.125R_{\odot}$. Dates for the individual traces in July are indicated.

limb passage (8–12 July) of the region. We have found that the data of 24–28 June are also representative of the undisturbed corona present during 1966. The most obvious feature of these graphs is the dramatic increase in the density of the corona which occurred above the PFR sometime between

27 June and 10 July. In spite of any temporal variation which may have occurred during the interval 8–12 July, the date of limb passage appears to be unambiguously established as 10 July 1966. In addition, the data display considerable real density structure within the enhancement. Important though this structure may be, it will be ignored in the development of our models for the electron density distribution.

The development of the corona above the PFR can best be seen in synoptic maps (Fig. 2) in which contours of the coronal signal pB at a given scan height are displayed on a rectangular projection of the solar disk. Although account must always be taken of the fact that a given coronal feature is seen for several days about limb passage and thus the contours are distended in longitude, this representation shows the concentration of coronal material at both $1.125 R_\odot$ and $1.5 R_\odot$ above the active region and its relation to the proton flares. Clearly, the region was indistinguishable from the quiet corona at the east limb passage of 27 June, was well developed by 10 July, and generally maintained its identity until the limb passage of 19 September. The subsidence in middle August may be associated with the temporary decrease in surface activity as reported by Dodson and Hedeman (1968). We also note that the center of gravity of the coronal enhancement migrated south and east between the limb passages of 10 July and 26 July.   (*Fig.* 2 overleaf.)

3 Electron Density Models

Models for the distribution of electron density above active regions have been determined from eclipse observations (e.g. Saito and Billings 1964), from a combination of radio and optical data (Christiansen *et al.* 1960), from the average characteristics of several regions observed with the K-coronameter during the last sunspot maximum (Newkirk 1961), and from the average characteristics of radio bursts (e.g. Malitson and Erickson 1966). Our present data are of such a quality and extent that we can determine a *sequence* of models which describe the evolution of the region during its entire lifetime. Hopefully, these individual models are more realistic than the previously mentioned averages and will yield insight into the fundamental processes governing the development of active regions in the corona.

The techniques for translating polarimetric observations of the corona into electron density have been discussed extensively in the literature (van de Hulst 1950) and need not be repeated. The models are developed to fit the several properties of the observations:

    a. The radial profile of the "background corona" or that component which is independent of longitude (Fig. 3, p. 54).

    b. The radial profile of pB along the axis of the PFR seen at limb passage (Fig. 3).

    c. The variation with projected latitude of pB at a given scan height when the region is at limb passage (Fig. 4, p. 55).

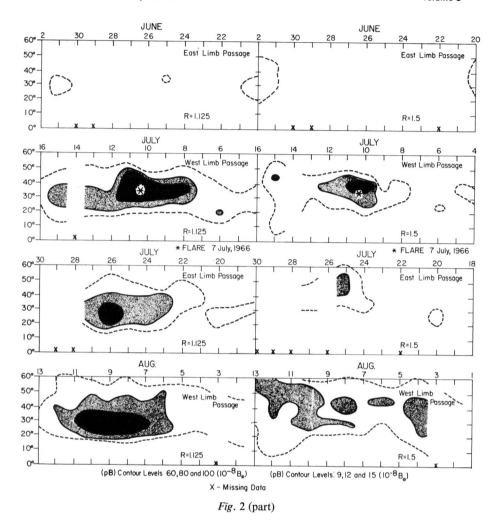

Fig. 2 (part)

  d. The variation of pB at a given scan height on the axis of the region as it passes over the limb (Fig. 5, p. 56).

How these various observations are related to the parameters of the models and the origin of particular choices of parameters will now be discussed.

  For mathematical convenience the electron density distribution in the corona above the active region is described by

$$N_{(R)} = N_S(R) + \left[N_0 \exp\left(-\frac{R-1}{F} \right) + CN_S(R) \right] \exp\left(-\frac{x^2}{S^2} - \frac{y^2}{b^2 S^2} \right) \quad (1)$$

where $N_S(R)$ is the spherically symmetric, time-independent component, the portion in brackets represents the excess electron component along the axis

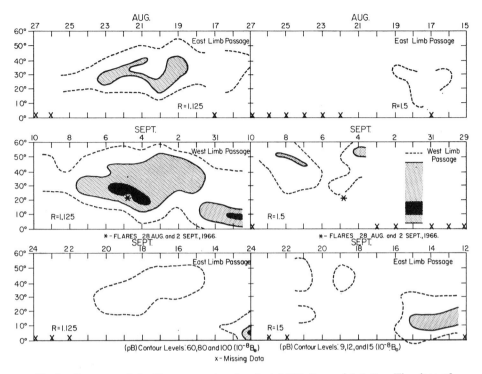

Fig. 2   Contours of the K-coronameter signal at 1.125 $R_\odot$ and 1.5 $R_\odot$. The date of observation appears as abscissa (longitude) while heliographic latitude appears as ordinate. The position of the proton flares is indicated by a star.

above the active region and the factor exponential in x and y represents the decrease of density away from the axis. The coordinate y is perpendicular to the axis of the region at distance R (in units of the solar radius) and lies in the meridional plane while x is perpendicular to this plane. The quantities N_0, C, and F are constants. The dispersion parameter S is taken as

$$S = 0.4 \exp\left(-\frac{(R - 1.5)^2}{1.375}\right) \qquad (2)$$

following the work of Hata and Saito (1966) and of Bohlin (1967) on the distribution of material in coronal streamers, while the parameter b is included to allow the possibility that the region may be more spread out in longitude than in latitude or vice versa. The term $N_0\, e^{-(R-1)/F}$ facilitates description of the appearance, immediately following the proton flares, of additional electrons characterized by an abnormally steep gradient of density with height.

Clearly, the observations at our disposal are insufficient to establish uniquely the various parameters of the electron distribution in the region.

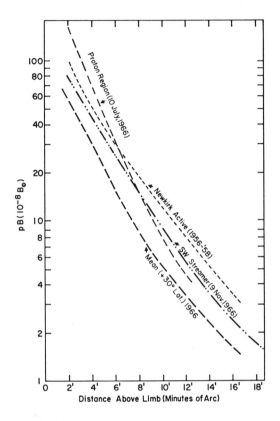

Fig. 3   The decrease with height of pB from the mean of all observations at latitude 30°N during 1966 is compared with the radial profile of the PFR and other coronal features located at the limb. The corona above the PFR displayed a markedly higher gradient in pB than either the mean corona, the southwest streamer observed at the limb on 9 November 1966 and seen so spectacularly at the eclipse of 12 November 1966, or the average region described by Newkirk (1961) during the last sunspot maximum.

For example, an entire family of models with different dependence of axial density and dispersion with height may satisfy both the axial radial profiles and the variation of pB on the axis at limb passage. Within the scope of the present work we have not investigated the accuracy with which the parameters are set and can state only that the models are consistent with the observations.

3.1   The Spherically Symmetric Component

The simplest parameter of Eq. (1) to determine is the spherically symmetric component N_S. To this end we take as the corona in which the PFR is immersed the mean of all data gathered at latitude 30° N during 1966 and notice that the profile of pB against R is adequately described by

$$(pB)_S = 0.8(pB)_Q \qquad (3)$$

where $(pB)_Q$ are the values suggested (Newkirk 1961) for the undisturbed corona during the last sunspot maximum. The electron densities N_S for the spherically symmetric component (Table 1) are thus similarly reduced by the factor 0.8 compared with the period 1956–1958 but are still larger by a factor

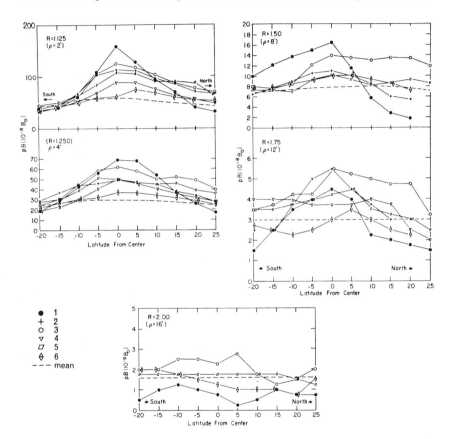

Fig. 4 The variation of pB with latitude at a given scan height with the region at the limb. The means of all observations during 1966 (dashed lines) are taken to represent the spherically symmetric corona in which the region is immersed.

	—R = 1.125—		—R = 1.50 —		—R = 1.250—		—R = 1.75—		—R = 2.0—	
	Date	Center	Date	Center	Date	Center	Date	Center	Date	Center
1	10 July	+35°	10 July	40°	10 July	30°	10 July	35°	9 July	35°
2	26 July	+25°	27 July	40°	26 July	30°	25 July	40°		
3	10 Aug.	25°	10 Aug.	30°	10 Aug.	30°	10 Aug.	35°	10 Aug.	35°
4	23 Aug.	25°			23 Aug.	30°	23 Aug.	30°		
5	5 Sept.	25°	5 Sept.	30°	5 Sept.	30°	5 Sept.	30°	5 Sept.	30°
6	19 Sept.	25°	19 Sept.	40°	19 Sept.	30°	19 Sept.	40°	18 Sept.	35°

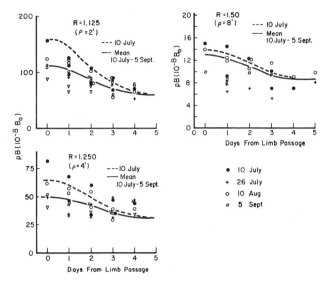

Fig. 5 The variation of pB at a given scan height on the axis of the region as a function of time from limb passage. The variations predicted by our models for 10 July and for the mean of all limb passages from 10 July through 5 September are indicated.

of 1.7 over the van de Hulst model for sunspot maximum (Allen 1963). This selection of the data for $(pB)_S$ could be debated extensively with little resolution. Although it is true that such data include the PFR, the influence of this particular region in some 220 days of observation is small. Alternatively, we

Table I   Coronal Electron Densities, July–September 1966

$R(R_\odot)$	N_S	$N_A + N_Q$	N (along axis) (10^7 cm^{-3})					
			10 July	26 July	10 Aug.	23 Aug.	5 Sept.	Mean*
1.000	(72)	(167)	(254)	(154)	(192)	(154)	(179)	(154)
1.125	23	57	82	53	67	53	58	53
1.250	9.6	24	28	20	25	20	21	20
1.375	4.6	11	12	9.8	12	9.8	8.9	9.8
1.500	2.6	6.1	6.3	5.6	7.0	5.6	4.6	5.6
1.625	1.6	3.5	3.6	3.4	4.2	3.4	2.7	3.4
1.750	1.0	2.1	2.3	2.2	2.8	2.2	1.7	2.2
1.875	0.70	1.4	1.5	1.5	1.9	1.5	1.1	1.5
2.000	0.50	0.9	1.1	1.1	1.3	1.1	0.8	1.0

*10 July–5 Sept.
N_S = spherically symmetric component
N_A = average active enhancement 1956–1958 (Newkirk 1961)
N_Q = quiet component 1956–1958 (Newkirk 1961)
( ) = extrapolated values

might have selected as the base level the values of pB averaged over the same interval for 30° S latitude.

Arguing against this latter choice is the fact that during 1966 activity in the southern hemisphere was considerably less than in the northern hemisphere.

3.2   The Axial Electron Density above the PFR

The basic observations used to determine the parameters for the axial electron density were the radial profiles of the *excess* signal

$$pB - (pB)_\mathrm{S}$$

of the region observed at successive limb passages. The accuracy of the fitting of these data by models characterized by the parameters listed in Table 2 can be judged from Fig. 6. Inspection of Table 2 shows that three of the limb passages as well as the mean of all five passages could be adequately represented by electron distributions following the same decrease in density with height as displayed by the spherically symmetric component, i.e. $N_0 = 0$. However, the data of 10 July and 5 September, both of which followed the outbreak of proton flares by 3 days, required an additional component which was largely restricted to heights below 1.5 $R_\odot$ ($\rho = 8'$).

Table 2   Parameters for Coronal Electron Densities,
July–September 1966

Date	C	N_0 (cm^{-3})	$F(R_\odot)$
10 July	1.14	10^9	0.1
26 July	1.14	0	—
10 Aug.	1.66	0	—
23 Aug.	1.14	0	—
5 Sept.	0.59	6.5×10^8	0.1
Mean, 10 July–5 Sept.	1.14	0	—

The total axial electron densities above the region inferred for each of the limb passages are contained in Table 1 and Fig. 7. Although they are not plotted in Fig. 7 to avoid confusing an already cluttered graph, the electron densities $N_\mathrm{A} + N_\mathrm{Q}$ (Table 1) inferred from an average of several rather randomly selected active regions (Newkirk 1961) are remarkably close to the gross structure of the PFR. Since the background corona was somewhat less dense in 1966 than at last sunspot maximum, we conclude that the PFR represented a larger perturbation in the corona than was represented by that average model.

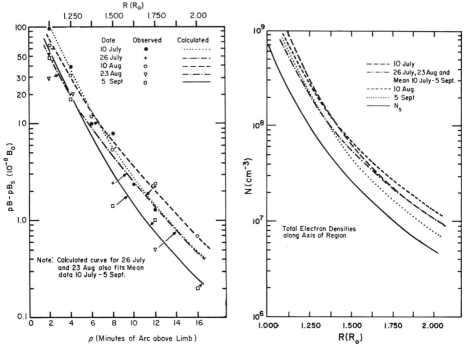

Fig. 6 The radial profiles of the excess signals produced by the PFR above the spherically symmetric background as calculated by our models are compared with the observations. For clarity arrows connect the individual observations with the appropriate curves.

Fig. 7 Total electron densities along the radial axis of the PFR for the various limb passages. Note the presence of an additional low elevation concentration of electrons on 10 July and 5 September immediately (by 3 days) following the proton flares.

3.3 Electron Densities away from the Region Axis

The parameters S and b govern the decay of electron density away from the axis of the active region. Although the data do not truly allow an independent evaluation of $S(R)$ and b, we must test if the values chosen are consistent with our observations. The variation of pB at a particular scan height on the axis as the region is carried over the limb is such a test for S, albeit not a particularly sensitive one. We have compared (Fig. 5) the calculated variation for the models of 10 July and for the mean model with the observations at $R = 1.125$, 1.250, and 1.50 with the conclusion that the data appear to be adequately represented. The values of S given by Eq. (2) and the other parameters then allow the calculation of contours of equal electron density (Fig. 8) in the neighborhood of the active region.

Information concerning the parameter b can be gained more directly from the variation of pB with latitude when the region is observed at limb passage (Fig. 4). It can be demonstrated that for such a region the excess signal at some position y away from the axis will be

$$(pB)_y - (pB)_s \sim (pB)_0 \exp\left(-\frac{y^2}{b^2 S^2}\right) \tag{4}$$

where $(pB)_0$ = signal on the projected axis of the region. Examination of the profiles shown in Fig. 4 shows that the region is not symmetric about the axis

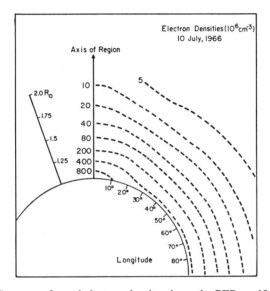

Fig. 8   Contours of equal electron density above the PFR on 10 July 1966.

and that b must have one value b_+ for y's measured to the north and another b_- for those measured to the south. Variation in S in time may well be present but cannot be reliably extracted from the data. We estimate that for $R \leqslant 1.5\ R_\odot$

$$b_+ S \sim 0.35\ R_\odot, \quad b_- S \sim 0.17\ R_\odot$$

For $R = 1.25\ R_\odot$ Eq. (2) yields $S = 0.38\ R_\odot$ and suggests

$$b_+ \sim 1.0, \qquad b_- \sim 0.5$$

3.4   Contribution to the Corona by Proton Flares

Even though these models represent a better picture of the temporal development of an active region than has been available in the past, they still leave many questions unanswered. For example, we cannot say with any assurance whether the proton flare of 7 July 1966 occurred at the base of an active region streamer as represented by our model for 10 July or whether the flare itself contributed significantly to the corona. The coronal environment for the proton flares of 28 August and 2 September is similarly uncertain. However, as noted earlier, the observation on 10 July and 5 September of a unique, low-elevation coronal condensation suggests that the proton flares in fact did eject material into the corona.

Ample evidence exists for the expulsion from flares of high-energy particles which are both trapped in the solar atmosphere (e.g. the particles responsible for Type IV bursts) and ejected into interplanetary space (e.g. the particles responsible for polar cap absorptions). The close correlation found by Bruzek (1964 a, b) between the ejection of high-energy particles from a flare and the appearance of a system of slowly expanding loop prominences suggests that some of the ejected material finds its way into the corona, later to condense and return to the surface in the descending knots of the prominences. Whether the condensed material in the loops originates in the streams of high-energy particles or in the dense coronal condensation which also accompanies loop prominence systems (Waldmeier 1950) is yet unknown. Jefferies and Orrall (1965) have found direct evidence that at least part of the material visible in Hα originates from streams of particles with energies of the order of 12 keV.

The present data, in addition to a similar observation (Newkirk et al. 1959) following a large flare on 9 June 1959, constitute the evidence that the same mechanism which releases high-energy particles also forms a slowly expanding "bubble" of dense coronal gas. All three of these events followed major flares with loop prominences and all showed expanding condensations to be contained within 250,000 to 440,000 km of the surface two to three days after the flare. Assuming that the expansion originated at the time of outbreak of the same flare which generated the loop prominences, we find (Table 3) a remarkable similarity between the mean velocity of expansion for the

Table 3   Expansion Velocities of Flare-Associated Coronal Condensations and Loop Prominence Systems

Event	v (km s^{-1})
9 June 1959	2.9
10 July 1966	1.6
5 Sept. 1966	1.4 (Proton flare of 2 Sept. taken as source)
Mean	2.0
Loop prominence systems mean (Bruzek 1964a)	2

condensation and that determined by Bruzek (1964a) for the latter stages of loop prominence systems. We thus conclude that the expanding series of loop prominences and the expanding condensation represent different aspects of the same phenomenon brought on by the emergence of a magnetic dome from the lower atmosphere.

The present data allow a quantitative test of whether the coronal material contained within the expanding magnetic dome could be the direct contribution of the flare. Since only the component described by

$$N_{\mathrm{L}} \equiv N_0 \exp\left(-\frac{R-1}{F} - \frac{x^2+y^2}{S^2}\right) \tag{5}$$

appears to have any direct connection with the flares, we calculate its contribution to the condensation. Integration of N_{L} in cylindrical coordinates yields the total content of electrons

$$M_{\mathrm{L}} \gtrsim 2\pi \int_{z=0}^{\infty} dz \int_0^{\infty} N_{\mathrm{L}} r\, dr = \pi S^2 F N_0 \tag{6}$$

where $z = R - R_\odot$, $r^2 = x^2 + y^2$. Thus, with $S = 0.4R_\odot$, $F = 0.1R_\odot$, $N_0 = 10^9 \text{ cm}^{-3}$, $M_{\mathrm{L}} \sim 2 \times 10^{40}$ electrons for the total contribution. To compare this content with that of a "typical" limb flare, for which Zirin (1966) gives

$$N_{\mathrm{e}} \sim 10^{11} \text{ cm}^{-3}$$

we assume the flare to be a hemispherical dome of radius 50,000 km and find

$$M_{\mathrm{flare}} \sim 3 \times 10^{40} \text{ electrons}$$

Since a large flare can be expected to have a volume up to an order of magnitude higher, we conclude that the proton flares contained sufficient mass and may have been the source of the material in the expanding condensation.

Acknowledgments

We wish to recognize the assistance of Charles Garcia in making many of the K-coronameter observations used in this study and to thank J. David Bohlin for the use of his computer program for calculating the K-coronameter signal to be expected from a coronal region of arbitrary density structure.

References

ALLEN, C. W., 1963, *Astrophysical Quantities* (Athlone Press, London).
BOHLIN, J. D., 1967, Structure, dynamics and evolution of solar coronal streamers (Thesis, University of Colorado).
BRUZEK, A., 1964a, On the association between loop prominences and flares, *Astrophys. J.*, **140**, 746–759.
—— 1964b, Optical characteristics of cosmic-ray and proton flares, *J. Geophys. Res.*, **69**, 2386–2387.

CHRISTIANSEN, W. N., D. S. MATHEWSON, J. L. PAWSEY, S. F. SMERD, A. BOISCHOT, J. F. DENISSE, P. SIMON, T. KAKINUMA, and H. DODSON-PRINCE, 1960, A study of a solar active region using combined optical and radio techniques, *Annls Astrophys.*, **23**, 75–101.

DODSON, H. W., and E. R. HEDEMAN, 1968, Some patterns in the development of centers of solar activity, 1962–66, *Proc. IAU Symposium No. 35, Structure and Development of Solar Active Regions*, Ed. K. O. Kiepenheuer (Reidel Publ. Co., Dordrecht, Holland), pp. 56–63.

HATA, S., and K. SAITO, 1966, The flattening, total light, brightness distribution and polarization of the solar corona, *Ann. Tokyo Astr. Obs.*, 2nd series, **10**, 16–52.

VAN DE HULST, H. C., 1950, The electron density of the solar corona, *Bull. Astr. Insts, Neth.*, **11**, 135–150.

JEFFERIES, J. T., and F. Q. ORRALL, 1965, Loop prominences and coronal condensations. I. Non-thermal velocities within loop prominences; II. The source of mass and energy and a model of the loop prominences mechanism, *Astrophys. J.*, **141**, 505–518, 519–525.

MALITSON, H. H., and W. C. ERICKSON, 1966, Observations of type III and type IV solar radio bursts at 26.3 Mc/s, *Astrophys. J.*, **144**, 337–351.

NEWKIRK, G., 1961: The solar corona in active regions and the thermal origin of the slowly varying component of solar radio radiation, *Astrophys. J.*, **133**, 983–1013.

NEWKIRK, G., G. W. CURTIS, and D. K. WATSON, 1958, Observations of the solar electron corona, Sept. '56–Jan. '58, 48 pp., *IGY Solar Activity Report Series* (World Data Center A) No. 4 (High Altitude Observatory, University of Colorado, Boulder, Colorado).

NEWKIRK, G., G. W. CURTIS, D. K. WATSON, R. MANNING, and J. SHELBY, 1959, The inner solar corona during June 1959, *Nature, Lond.*, **184**, 1308–1309.

SAITO, K., and D. E. BILLINGS, 1964, Polarimetric observations of a coronal condensation, *Astrophys. J.*, **140**, 760–777.

WALDMEIER, M., 1950, Polar maps of the solar corona, *Z. Astrophys.*, **27**, 24–41.

WLÉRICK, G., and J. AXTELL, 1957, A new instrument for observing the electron corona, *Astrophys. J.*, **126**, 253–258.

ZIRIN, H., 1966: *The Solar Atmosphere* (Blaisdell, Waltham, Mass.).

9

The Slowly Varying Component of the Radio Emission during the Period of the July 1966 Proton Flare

H. Tanaka, T. Kakinuma, and S. Enome
The Research Institute of Atmospherics, Nagoya University, Nagoya, Japan

Abstract

The paper presents the results of observations made over the period of the proton flare of July 1966 with radio interferometers in various parts of the world over a wide range of frequencies between 1420 and 17000 MHz.

A radio source was observed on 1 July and increased in intensity until the time of the proton event, after which it decayed gradually. The source was more obvious on 9400 MHz than on 4000 MHz in confirmation of observations by the authors in 1964, and it is proposed that proton flares should be predicted by an increase to or above unity of the ratio of the flux density of the slowly varying component at 9400 MHz to that at 4000 MHz.

I Introduction

In this paper we show the results of observations made with interferometers over a wide range of frequencies between 1420 and 17000 MHz. We shall confine ourselves to the description of observed materials. Discussion may be possible only after surveying all the data such as optical and X-ray data, etc.

The half-power beamwidths of the various interferometers are listed in Table 1, and the observed values of flux densities, polarizations, half-power widths, and positions of the source are summarized in Tables 2–5 and Figs. 1–5.

Table I   Beamwidth of Radio Interferometers

Station	Wavelength (cm)	Beamwidth	
Sydney	21	$3' \times 3'$	(Pencil beam)
Sydney	21	$2'$	(Fan beam)
Ottawa	10.7	$1.2'$	(Fan beam)
Stanford	9.1	$3.1' \times 3.1'$	(Pencil beam)
Toyokawa	7.5	$4.5'$	(Fan beam)
Nançay	3.2	$4.5'$	(Fan beam)
Toyokawa	3.2	$1.1'$	(Fan beam)
Mitaka	1.7	$4'$	(Fan beam)

Table 2   Total Flux Density and Flux Density of the Slowly Varying (S) Component (in units of 10^{-22} W m^{-2} Hz^{-1})

Date July	Time UT	Flux Density Total	S-comp.	Time UT	Flux Density Total	S-comp.
		1420 MHz			**2800 MHz**	
3	0201	66	3.9	1519 40.0s	96.0	3.73
4	0118	66	4.7	1524 14.8s	101.2	8.90
5	0157	62	6.4	1545 51.5s	101.6	11.1
6	0114	66	8.0	1533 25.9s	105.0	15.8
7	*			1529 23.1s	109.0	17.1
8	0202	71	9.7	1529 36.6s	111.0	15.7
9	0202	72	8.7	1529 43.7s	105.0	11.3
10	0119	70	7.0	1530 08.4s	104.0	9.84
11	0115	70	4.9	1530 23.4s	106.0	4.39
12				1534 54.1s	100.0	~1

* Burst in progress

Date July	Time UT	Flux Density Total	S-comp.	Time UT	Flux Density Total	S-comp.
		3300 MHz			**4000 MHz**	
3	2000–2100	96	5.3	0254		
4	2000–2100	101	12.3	0255	106	7.0
5	2000–2100	102	14.0	0255	110	11.0
6	2000–2100	106	20.8	0255	112	18.6
7	2000–2100	109	21.9	0255	132	35.0*
8	2000–2100	111	20.2	0255	123	25.6
9	2000–2100	104	13.1	0256	130	31.2*
10	2000–2100	105	14.6	0256	115	16.2
11	2000–2100	105		0256	107	12.9
12				0256	108	11.0
13				0256	104	8.2

* Postburst increase

Table 2   (continued)

Date July	Time UT	Flux Density Total	S-comp.	Time UT	Flux Density Total	S-comp.
	9400 MHz (Toyokawa)			9400 MHz (Nançay)		
2	0254	251	0.2			
3	0254	250	1.1			
4	0255	251	1.8	1155 26s		3.2
5	0255	260	11.0	1155 36s		14.4
6	0255	272	19.3	1155 46s		23.8
7	0255	284	34.5*	1155 56s		26.2
8	0255	272	26.1	1156 06s		24.4
9	0256	272	44.4*	1156 15s		12.8
10	0256	265	14.4	1156 24s		10.5
11	0256	257	4.1	1156 33s		8.5
12	0256	255	0.7	1156 41s		3.9

* Postburst increase

17000 MHz

Date July	Time UT	Flux Density S-comp.
2	0245	2.1
3	0245	*
4	0245	2.1
5	0245	4.3
6	0246	12.9
7	0246	18.4†
8	0246	10.5
9	0246	19.8†
10	0246	*
11	0246	7.2
12	0246	7.1
13	0247	16.2

* No observation
† Postburst increase

2 Development

On careful examination of the records the radio source can be identified as a hump superposed on an adjacent source at 1420 MHz on 1 July 1966. On 2 July it could be recognized at 9400 MHz, but not so easily at 17000 and 4000 MHz. On the next day, 3 July, it could be clearly discerned at all frequencies.

In the decimetre wavelength range the daily values of flux density of the source increased rather gradually and steadily, reaching their maximum around 8 July, and then slowly decreased. At shorter wavelengths, on the

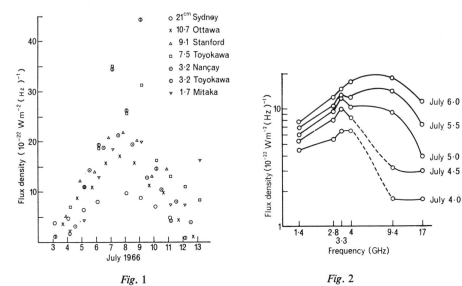

Fig. 1   *Fig.* 2

Fig. 1   Variations of the flux density of the slowly varying component in units of 10^{-22}W m^{-2} Hz^{-1}. Values for 1420 MHz are derived from fan-beam scan.

Fig. 2   Variation of spectrum of the slowly varying component. Values used in this figure are estimated by linear interpolation of observed values. Slightly high values at 3300 MHz might be due to the effect of negative side lobes of a crossed antenna pattern, although smoothing, which consists of replacing each value by the average of the nine values centred upon it, has been done.

Table 3   Daily Variation of Degree of Polarization

Date July	4000 MHz %	9400 MHz %
3	∼0	∼0
4	9.5R	13.3R
5	4.5R	23.5R
6	3.2R	14.9R
7	4.7R*	14.7R*
8	5.0R	13.8R
9	4.5R*	11.1R*
10	5.4R	12.7R
11	1.5R	∼0
12	1.6L	∼0
13	3.4L	

* Postburst increase

Table 4   Position of the Source

The position of the source is given by the distance from the centre of the disk and the position angle of the direction of scanning measured eastwards from the geographic north, i.e. tilting of the rotation axis of the sun is not taken into consideration.

Date July	2800 MHz D*	2800 MHz P.A.†	4000 MHz D	4000 MHz P.A.	9400 MHz D	9400 MHz P.A.	3300 MHz D‡
2					3.0′E	270°	
3	2.8′W	282°15′			0.3E	270	2.2′W
4	5.4	281 42	2.8′W	270°	2.4W	270	4.5
5	7.6	279 05	5.6	270	4.4	270	7.1
6	10.0	280 34	8.3	270	7.4	270	9.5
7	12.4	281 02	10.6	270	9.9	270	11.4
8	13.7	280 58	12.4	270	11.5	270	12.6
9	13.9	280 54	13.1	270	12.2	270	13.0
10	14.4	280 50	13.5	270	12.5	270	13.1
11	14.8	280 45	12.5	270	13.2	270	12.5
12	14.0	280 13	12.9	270			13.5
13			13.5	270			

* Distance from the centre of the disk.
† Position angle measured eastwards from the geographic north.
‡ Pencil-beam

Table 5   Observed Half-Power Width of the Source (in minutes of arc)

Date July	1420 MHz	2800 MHz	3300 MHz	4000 MHz	9400 MHz
3		2.33	5.0(4.7)		1.4
4	5.1(6.1)	2.28	4.7(4.9)	5.2	2.3
5		2.28	4.6(4.7)	5.0	1.8
6	4.8(6.3)	2.38	4.6(5.1)	4.9	1.6
7		2.49	4.6(4.6)	5.0	1.9
8		2.38	4.4(4.6)	5.2	2.1
9		2.42	4.6(4.8)	4.7	1.9
10	2.9(6.2)	2.11	4.9(5.3)	5.1	2.3
11		1.90	5.0(6.0)	6.5	2.6
12		2.29	4.9(6.0)	5.1	
13				5.5	

Main figures: east–west extent
Figures in parentheses: north–south extent

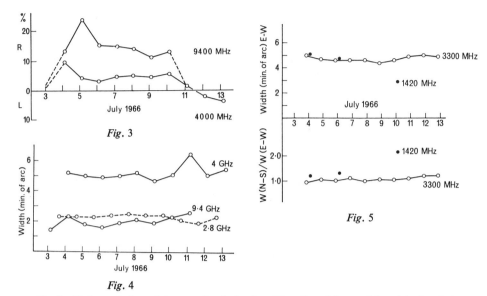

Fig. 3

Fig. 4

Fig. 3   Daily variation of degree of polarization. Here R and L stand for right-handed and left-handed circular polarizations respectively. Sense of polarization corresponds to the north polarity of the "following spot". Reversal of the sense of polarization towards the west limb at 4000 MHz may be spurious owing to the mixing of another source as mentioned in the text.

Fig. 4   Variation of observed width of the source measured from fan-beam scan. Widths at 2800 MHz are not E–W extent, since observations were not made at local noon as shown in Table 3.

Fig. 5   Variation of observed size (E–W extent) and ratio of N–S extent to E–W extent derived from pencil-beam map.

other hand, the values remained low for the first few days, and then exhibited a rapid increase until the time of occurrence of the proton event (see Figs. 1 and 2).

After the bursts of 7 and 9 July a gradual decay of the radio source began, while another radio source following to the east of the relevant source developed rapidly. After 10 July it became difficult to separate these sources with interferometers of ordinary resolving power.

3 Comments

Tanaka and Kakinuma (1964) have proposed the use of the ratio of the flux density of the slowly varying component at 9400 MHz to that at 4000 MHz for the prediction of the solar proton flare: when this ratio is equal to or greater than unity there is a high probability that a solar proton event will occur. In the present case, as seen in Table 2 or in Fig. 1, the flux ratio was about unity on 5 and 6 July, and indeed a solar proton event took place. A closer examination reveals that the peak of the radio-frequency spectrum shifted to higher frequencies as the radio source developed (Fig. 2); this upholds the choice of 9400 and 4000 MHz as reference frequencies.

The degree of polarization of the source was rather weak at both 9400 and 4000 MHz in comparison with the values found by Swarup *et al.* (1963) except for 4 July at 4000 MHz and 5 July at 9400 MHz. It may be worth mentioning that from that day a rapid enhancement of the flux density began at each of these two frequencies.

The observed half-power width of the source was about 2.3′ at 2800 MHz and about 2′ at 9400 MHz. These values are normal compared with those observed by Swarup *et al.* (1963).

If we make the assumption that the source had the same north–south extent as east–west, the maximum brightness temperature was about 1.4×10^6 °K at 2800 MHz and about 2.6×10^5 °K at 9400 MHz.

The structure of the source was very simple at both 2800 and 9400 MHz. It consisted of neither a bipolar source nor a composite source, although Kundu (1959) had indicated that a typical source on 3.2 cm wavelength is usually composed of two regions, a very intense region of small diameter $(\lesssim 1.5')$ and a less intense region of larger diameter $(\sim 5'–8')$. Polarization measurements at 9400 MHz showed a predominance of radiation of right-handed circular polarization over almost the entire region of the source.

The height of the source was difficult to determine since, as the source was born near the central meridian, large errors are inevitable.

No abnormal radio observations were obtained, but, as has been reported in this series of papers, this active region was associated with a sunspot of delta configuration, and in order to study an active region with such a sunspot configuration, radio interferometers with much higher resolving power may be necessary. This matter must therefore await future study.

Acknowledgments

We are indebted to the observatories of Ottawa, Stanford, Sydney, Nançay, and Tokyo for furnishing original records.

References

KUNDU, M. R., 1959, Etude interférometrique des sources d'activité solaire sur 3 cm de longueur d'onde, *Paris Symposium on Radio Astronomy*, Ed. R. N. Bracewell (Stanford University Press, Stanford), pp. 222–236.

SWARUP, G., T. KAKINUMA, A. E. COVINGTON, G. A. HARVEY, R. F. MULLALY, and J. ROME, 1963, High-resolution studies of ten solar active regions at wavelengths of 3–21 cm, *Astrophys. J.*, **137**, 1251–1267.

TANAKA, H., and T. KAKINUMA, 1964, The relation between the spectrum of slowly varying component of solar radio emission and solar proton event, *Rep. Ionosph. Space Res. Japan*, **18**, 32–44.

10

Remarks on the Slowly Varying Component of Solar Radio Emission during the Proton Flare Period of July 1966

A. Krüger

Heinrich Hertz Institute for Solar–Terrestrial Physics, German Academy of Sciences, Berlin-Adlershof, German Democratic Republic

Abstract

The centre of activity which produced the proton event of 7 July 1966 was characterized by an unusual increase of the slowly varying (S) component of solar radio emission at short centimetre waves. One day before the proton event a monotonic spectrum was present indicating a rapid growth of electron density. However, such a monotonic increase of the spectrum of the S-component towards higher frequencies is not in every case a necessary condition for the occurrence of proton flares, as comparisons with the development of the S-component in August and September 1966 show.

The centre of activity No. 21034 (McMath plage No. 8362) which produced the proton event of 7 July 1966 was characterized by an unusual increase of the slowly varying component of solar radio emission (to be called the S-component). This increase occurred after a period of relative quietness of solar microwave radiation for more than one month.

The behaviour of the S-component is illustrated by the dynamic spectrum of Fig. 1 which has been drawn for the period of May–August 1966 by means of daily single-frequency observations of the stations Nagoya (NAG), Ottawa (OTT), Kislovodsk (KIS), and of the Heinrich-Hertz-Institut, Berlin-Adlershof (HHI). From a comparison with the Zürich sunspot numbers it follows that the occurrence of active regions with a large energy exchange is more clearly reflected by the characteristics of the S-component than by the sunspot number.

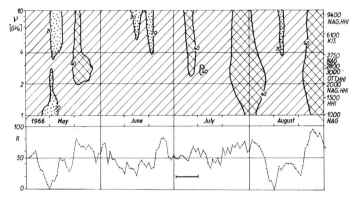

Fig. 1   Dynamic spectrum of the S-component and definite Zürich sunspot numbers during the period May–August 1966.

Figure 2 represents the measurements of daily means of flux density for different frequencies in the centimetre and lower decimetre range in comparison with the time–latitude distribution of sunspot groups on the visible solar hemisphere. In this figure the occurrence of the proton flare is denoted by a circle. It can be seen that the main part of the radio emission of the

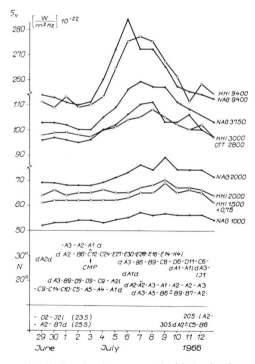

Fig. 2   Daily means of radio flux density compared with the development of spot groups.

S-component during the time under consideration was due to the centre No. 21034. As a remarkable fact a strong increase of the emission in the upper centimetre region was observed.

The latter point is clearly expressed in Fig. 3, where the spectrum of the S-component on the day before the proton event is compared with the average spectra of June and July 1966. A predominance of radiation in the centimetre range is present on that day.

In Fig. 4 the development of the spectrum of the S-component is shown in more detail. On the days before 5 July 1966 the typical spectral maximum near 10 cm wavelength is present, indicating the influence of magnetic fields. After that day the radiation of the S-component rapidly increased covering

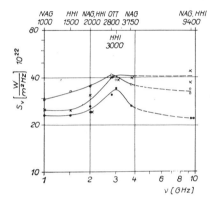

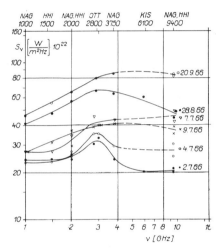

Fig. 3   Spectra of the S-component (dots — monthly mean for June 1966; open circles — monthly mean for July 1966; crosses — daily mean for 6 July 1966).

Fig. 4   Spectra of the S-component on different days.

the effect of a spectral maximum and leading to a monotonic spectrum increasing towards higher frequencies. This may be regarded mainly as an effect of a rapidly increased electron density.

It seems, however, that such an increase of density within a coronal condensation is only one necessary condition for the production of energetic solar events. As shown in Fig. 4, non-monotonic spectra of the S-component can also be connected with proton events. This was the case on 28 August 1966. It seems plausible that the existence of stronger magnetic fields does not conflict with the occurrence of proton flares.

More detailed conclusions are obtained on the basis of interferometric measurements from which it is possible to distinguish between different centres of activity on the sun and to study their fine structure.

Figure 5[1] shows such interferometric records of the stations Nançay at 9400 MHz and Sydney at 1420 and 720 MHz. For comparison the observations of Nançay at 169 MHz are included there, showing the influence of noise storm centres which exhibit no clearly expressed relation to the S-component. From Fig. 5 the development of the centre of activity and its predominance at centimetre waves is again evident. Further investigations dealing with high-resolution measurements have been treated by Gelfreich (private communication), Banin *et al.* (1968), Tanaka *et al.* (1968).

Acknowledgments

We would like to thank Drs. A. Boischot and A. Watkinson for sending copies of their interferometer records, shown in Fig. 5.

References

Banin, V., L. D. de Feiter, A. D. Fokker, M. J. Martres, and M. Pick, 1968, On the development and activity of the active region associated with the proton flare event of 7 July 1966, *Ann. IQSY*, this volume, Paper B.

Tanaka, H., T. Kakinuma, and S. Enome, 1968, The slowly varying component of the radio emission during the period of the July 1966 proton flare, *Ann. IQSY*, this volume, Paper 9.

[1] For Fig. 5 see following pages 74–77.

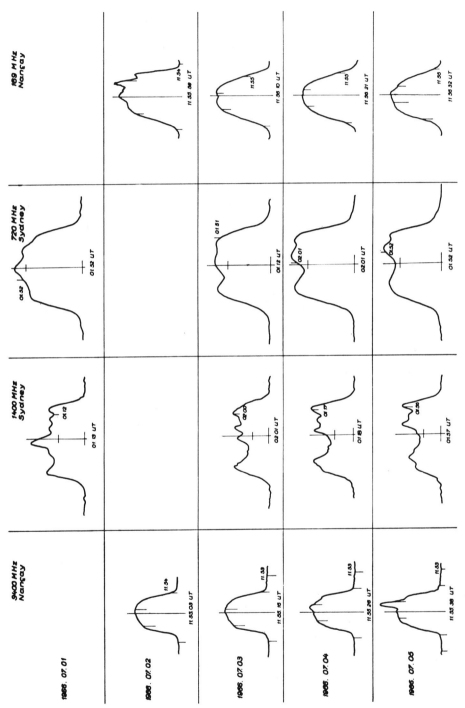

Fig. 5 Interferometer scans of the sun obtained at Nançay and Sydney during the proton flare period of July 1966.

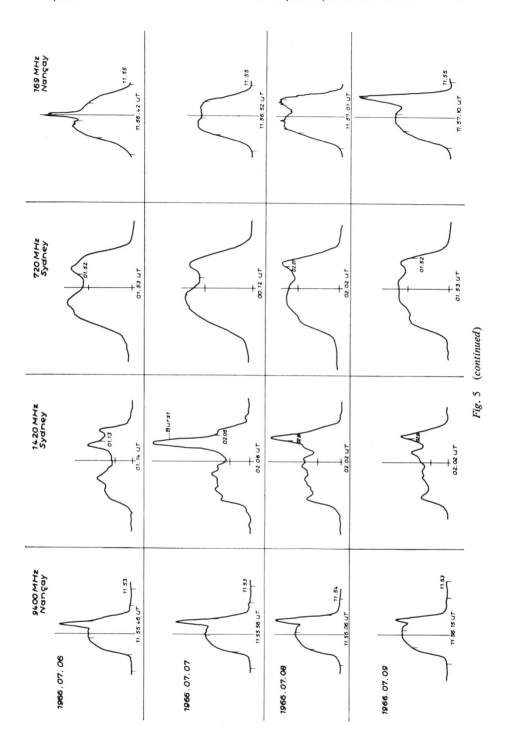

Fig. 5 (continued)

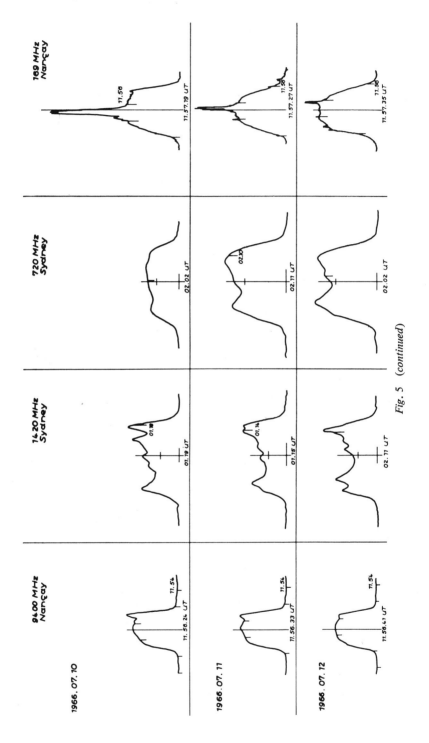

Fig. 5 (continued)

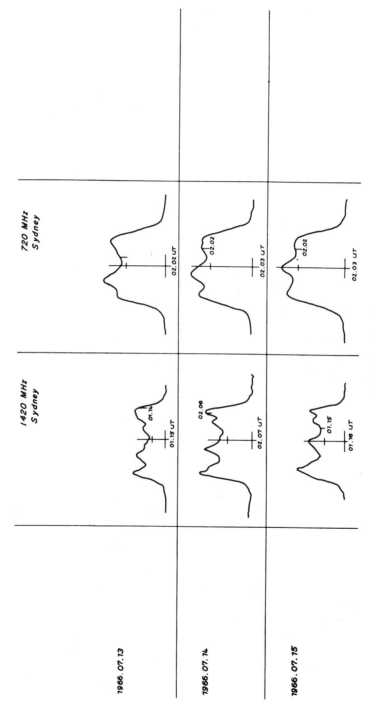

Fig. 5 (continued)

11

The Slowly Varying Component of Solar X-Ray Emission in the Period 1–15 July 1966

H. Friedman and R. W. Kreplin

E. O. Hulburt Center for Space Research, Naval Research Laboratory, Washington, D.C., USA

Abstract

Solar X-ray monitoring by the Naval Research Laboratory's SOLRAD 8 Satellite (1965–93A) has provided a history of the sun's X-ray emission for the particularly interesting period of early July 1966. The activation of plage region 8362 began on 4 July as indicated by increasing emission in the 0–8, 8–20, and 44–60 Å bands. By 6 July, X-ray flux levels had increased by factors of 15, 5, and 1.6 in the 0–8, 8–20, and 44–60 Å bands respectively.

The NRL SOLRAD 8 Satellite, known also as 1965–93A, Explorer 30, and IQSY Solar Explorer, was instrumented to measure solar X-ray emission in bands from 0.5 to 60 Å. Two ultraviolet photometers were also flown to measure radiation in the region of the Lyman α line.

All measurement instrumentation aboard the satellite has operated properly from launch, 18 November 1965, until the present time. Although the spin axis orientation system failed in early September 1966, this in no way affected the measurements to be considered in this paper. However, a malfunction of the data storage system and digital transmitter about a month after launch prevented acquisition of continuous X-ray emission histories during this interval.

Acquisition and transmission of analog data were performed continuously, consequently recordings of the solar X-ray emission could be made only when the satellite was within range of a telemetry receiving station. Telemetry transmissions in this period were recorded by the NASA system of STADAN stations and from the Navy stations at Hybla Valley, Virginia, and Point Mugu, California.

The satellite instrumentation has been described in a report entitled, "Final Data and Calibrations for the Explorer 30 (NRL SOLRAD 8) X-ray Monitoring Experiment (1965–93A)" which was distributed to those scientists and institutions interested in using the satellite's real-time transmission in their own solar physics programs.

The interval from 1 July to 11 July was marked by a build-up to an unusually high level of solar activity for this period of the solar cycle. This build-up is illustrated in Fig. 1. Between 1 and 3 July X-ray emission levels were found to be 0.1 erg cm^{-2} s^{-1} in the 44–60 Å band, 3×10^{-3} in the 8–20 Å band, 10^{-4} in 0–8 Å and below the detection threshold of the 0.5–3 Å photometer, about 5×10^{-6} erg cm^{-2} s^{-1}, based on gray body spectral distributions of 2×10^{6} °K and 0.5×10^{6} °K (Kreplin 1961). These levels

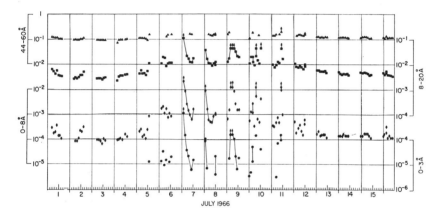

Fig. 1   Build-up of solar activity during period 1–11 July 1966.

are considerably higher than observations made at solar minimum; in fact in the 44–60 Å band they are about a factor of five greater than the levels of June, July, and August 1964 (Kreplin and Gregory 1966).

On 4 July we observed the first indications of increasing X-ray emission. The increase continued through 5 July with considerable variability observed from pass to pass. Levels continued to increase on 6 July, showing 1–8 Å flux levels fluctuating even during the period of one telemetry pass (approximately 10 minutes). The emission spectrum also became much harder as indicated by "on scale" readings made by the 0.5–3 Å Geiger–Müller (GM) counter photometer. Variability was also observed in this band.

On 6 and 7 July an effort was made to collect and process all data obtained from participants in the solar monitoring program and merge it with the data from our customary sources. These data are plotted in Fig. 2 and will be described in more detail in Papers 20 and 31.

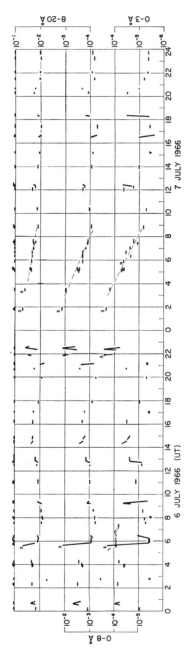

Fig. 2 8–20, 0–8, and 0–3 Å X-ray emission history for 6 and 7 July. The small bars at the top of the figure represent intervals when the satellite was within range of a telemetry ground station. The symbol S indicates saturated photometer signals and N indicates a noisy telemetry record.

The increase in X-ray emission which began on 4 July is attributed to the activation of plage region 8362. The solar rotation carried this region over the limb on 10 July but it is not until 13 July that all traces of activity disappear from the X-ray records.

References

KREPLIN, R. W., 1961, Solar X-rays, *Annls Géophys.*, **17**, 151–162.
KREPLIN, R. W., and B. N. GREGORY, 1966, Solar monitoring during the IQSY, *Space Research VI*, Ed. R. L. Smith-Rose (Spartan Books, Washington), pp. 1011–1021.

12

Flares in the Active Region during the Proton Flare Period of July 1966

A. Bruzek

Fraunhofer Institute, Freiburg im Breisgau, Federal Republic of Germany

Abstract

Flare activity began on 3 July and had maximum intensity from 6 July to 9 July. However, no really large event (importance 3 or 4) took place on the visible hemisphere. Three class 2B flares only occurred on the disk, the proton flare of 7 July being the most important event. Probably a great flare occurred behind the west limb on 11 July. A total of 78 subflares, 35 importance 1 flares and three importance 2B flares were observed in this active region from 2 July to 11 July.

All minor flares as well as the origin and the brightest parts of the major flares lay close to spots, mainly inside the spot group in the rather narrow lane between the two rows of spots of opposite magnetic polarity. Only the major flares produced parts outside the spot group. Parallel strands were formed at least in rudimentary shape in a number of flares.

I Introduction

This report is based on data and information which were generously supplied by a number of observatories collaborating in the proton flare project: Meudon Observatory (Service Solaire) kindly provided the complete flare lists compiled from the reports of the observatories engaged in the international flare patrol. Lockheed Observatory and Sacramento Peak Observatory sent copies of flare patrol films for the periods 1–8 July and 8–10 July, respectively. Prints covering the most important and many minor events were kindly provided on request by the observatories Arcetri (9 July event), Haleakala (7 and 9 July events, many minor flares from 6 to 10 July),

McMath–Hulbert (8 July event and a number of small flares), Meudon (8 July event).

The present paper starts with a general survey of the flare activity in the region (Sec. 2) and discusses then the shape and position of the flares which are believed to be important characteristics for the proton emission (Sec. 3). Section 4 reviews the flares preceding and following the proton flare. Sections 5 and 6 give a description of the two other importance 2B flares of the region (8 and 9 July). These flares are compared with the 7 July event in order to find special features related to the proton emission. Section 7 is a short note on the flare activity on the west limb.

2   General Remarks on the Flare Activity

Flare activity started definitely with a number of subflares on 3 July when the spot group began growing. The activity attained a fairly high level on 6 July as far as the number of flares and hours of flare activity are concerned.

Table I   Number of Flares according to Importance Class and Total Time of Flare Activity for each day from 1–11 July 1967 in the Active Region

Importance	S	1	2	3	ΣN	Σt
July 1						
2	1				1	0h32m
3	5				5	3 11
4	8	3			11	5 26
5	17				17	6 43
6	11	5			16	11 47
7	7	7*	1		15	11 24
8	7	7	1		15	12 54
9	12	3*	1		16	12 33
10	9	9			18	9 23
11	1	1		1†	3	5 02
ΣN	78	35	3	1	117	

* post-flare activity, subdivision into individual flares doubtful
† limb event

From 6–9 July flare activity in the active region, although partly of low importance, occurred during a total of about 12 hours per day. Table 1 reviews the occurrence of flares of different importance classes during the period 1–11 July. The last two columns (headed ΣN and Σt) give the total number of flares and the total time of flare activity for each day regardless of importance. Figure 1 shows the occurrence of flares of importance S, 1 and $\geqslant 2$ for half-day periods.

Besides the proton flare of 7 July (McCabe and Caldwell 1968) and the great limb event of 11 July (Valníček *et al.* 1968) only two other major flares occurred in the associated active region: the flares of 8 July, 1200–1330 UT and of 9 July, 0230–0520 UT, both importance 2B flares. It is noteworthy that 7 July, 1338–1756 UT was a period of no flare activity and that the next importance 1N flare did not appear in the active region before 8 July, 0022 UT, i.e., there were almost 11 hours without any flares of importance 1 or more. Another period of only subflare activity followed the second largest flare of the active region from 9 July, 1005 UT to 10 July, 0122 UT, a period of about 15 hours (see Fig. 1).

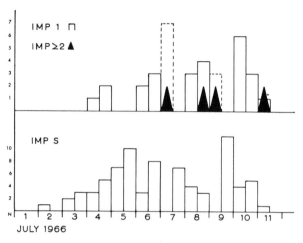

Fig. 1   Total number of flares of different importance classes for half-day periods. Note the lack of importance 1 flares in the periods following the 7 and 9 July 2B flares.

It should be emphasized that the reduced activity observed in the above two cases cannot be accounted for by the systematic observational effect discussed by Dodson and Hedeman (1964) because the quiet periods had already started before the end of the period of increased number and importance (05–16 UT). Thus, the observations after the 7 and 9 July flares show that important flares may be followed, after a slow and intermittent decrease of activity, by a relatively quiet period of 12 hours or more. Such post-flare quiet periods have also been observed with a number of other important flares in recent years. A possible interpretation of this observation would be that after large flares a period of recovery is required until another important flare can be produced.

Absorption features related to the flare activity were observed in many cases: a number of flares were accompanied by dark filaments of high velocity in the line of sight according to reports of the observatories cooperating in the international Hα flare patrol. The Lockheed flare patrol film shows numerous surgelike ejections mainly on 4 July, and Dodson (1968) reports conspicuous, amorphous absorption as well as Doppler-shifted filamentary absorption on 6 July preceding the 7 July proton flare.

The only case of flare-induced filament activation detected in the photographic material at hand occurred with the 9 July flare (see Sec. 6). No flare was preceded by the activation or the sudden disappearance of a prominent dark filament.

3 Position and Shape of the Flares

Almost all flares occurred completely inside the spot group between rather close spots. Only the three major disk flares had parts outside the spot group proper.

It is rather difficult to find the exact position of flares relative to the spots in the Hα filtergrams because many spots are invisible in the Hα centre. Fortunately Hα $\pm$ 0.5 Å and Hα $\pm$ 1.0 Å photographs were provided by Sacramento Peak Observatory. These "wing filtergrams" show the spots clearly (Fig. 3) but trace the brightest parts only of the flares (which are sometimes called the "cores" of the flare). These flare cores appeared in all cases close to spot umbrae, frequently between umbrae of opposite magnetic polarity. This tendency is well known also from other flare observations. In the active region under investigation the position of the cores was different for different flares, i.e. no spot was preferred significantly, not even in the same "family" of flares.

Two different basic shapes may be distinguished in the disk flares of the present active region, i.e. the flares may be classified into two "families" according to shape. The first family comprises the flares of the period 6–8 July (early UT hours of the day) including the 7 July proton flare; the second began with the major flare of 8 July noon and ended on 9 July with the flares immediately following the major 9 July flare. Examples are given in Fig. 2. The flares of the first family started with a number of small bright points close to spot umbrae (Fig. 2, frames c and d); these points expanded and merged to form two bright filaments or one bright strand along the dividing line of magnetic polarities. In many cases the strand turned to the northern leader spot which at that time was covered partly by a large, bright spot (frame b). The characteristic components of flare family 2 are two close bright knots covering from the beginning more or less large parts of the sunspots (Fig. 2, frames e and f, Figs. 3 and 4). The differences between the two families, however, are not very important. They may be partly or completely apparent differences only, which are due to the changing projection, depending on the position of the region on the solar disk.

Parallel strands, which are characteristic for many proton flares, were visible in a number of cases but were not a conspicuous feature. It is almost certain that the two strands, as far as they existed at all, could not be

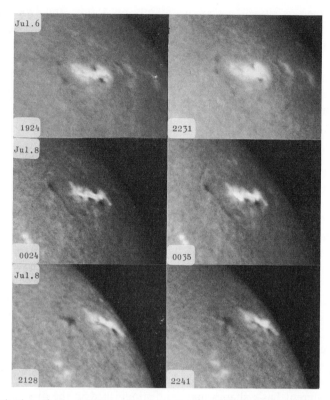

Fig. 2   Selection of minor flares representing the two flare families (see text): *a*, 6 July, 1924 UT, normal Hα plage; *b*, 6 July, 2231, flare 1B, 2220–2255, maximum 2230 UT; *c* and *d*, 8 July, 0024 and 0035, flare 1N 0022–0114, maximum 0035 UT; *e*, 8 July, 2128, flare 1N 2057–2205, maximum 2103 and 2128 UT; *f*, 8 July, 2241, flare 1N 2226–2340, maximum 2240. Haleakala Observatory photographs.

distinguished in each flare because of overlapping due to close proximity and unfavourable projection.

As for the height of the flares we can get some information from limb observations. The flares of 10 July which occurred immediately on the solar limb were fairly low features with heights less than 10,000 km. This value may be considered typical for the minor flares of the active region.

4   Flare Activity preceding and following the Proton Flare

The most important flare of this active region was the proton flare of 7 July (McCabe and Caldwell 1968). The flares preceding it were of minor importance (Fig. 1 and Dodson 1968). Many of the 6 July flares had approximately the same basic configuration as the proton flare itself. For instance the

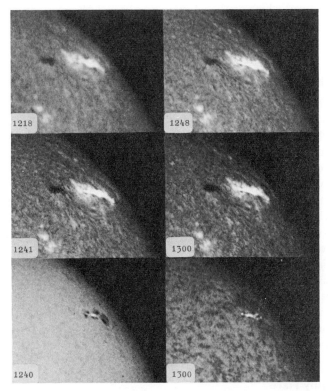

Fig. 3   2B flare 8 July. Precursor 1200, main flare 1236–1330, maximum 1248. Frames *c* and *f* are taken at distances 1 and 0.5 Å from the centre of Hα respectively; they show the position of the brightest flare knots between the spots. Sacramento Peak Observatory photographs.

flare 6 July, 2220–2255 UT had at its maximum at 2230 UT the same shape (Fig. 2, frame *b*) as the proton flare at 0030 UT. The proton flare, however, was very much brighter even at this early stage of development (maximum occurred 0040 UT) and it expanded strongly. Obviously, the place of origin and the initial shape of both flares were the same regardless of their final size and importance. Apparently the essential optical characteristics for a proton flare are brightness and vigorous development rather than place of origin and initial shape.

According to the reports of the co-operating observatories the proton flare was followed by a long enduring importance-1 flare activity lasting until about 1300 UT. It is not clear whether that was merely a post-flare period of enhanced plage brightness (or brightness fluctuations) which faded very slowly or whether distinct flares with a new sudden brightening occurred. The flare reports which are based mainly on visual observations give neither onset nor ending times in the majority of cases listed between 0420 and 1300 UT.

5   The 8 July Noon Flare

The first major flare following the 7 July proton flare occurred on 8 July (Fig. 3). It started with an importance-SN precursor at 1200 UT. The flash of the main flare began at 1236 UT, and maximum was attained at 1248 UT. A bright strand extended from the rear spot of the group more or less along the magnetic axis (i.e. the dividing line between north polar and south polar spots), passed between north polar and south polar umbrae of the leader spot and ended in a conspicuous circular dark marking — which definitely was not a spot! — preceding the spot group. At maximum a kind of bright mound had developed near the leader; by then the northern (i.e. the south polar) row of umbrae was covered almost completely by the flare while the southern (north polar) spots remained still partly visible in Hα. With a maximum corrected area of 5.2 square degrees that flare was the smallest of the three major disk flares. It attained, however, a brightness of 220 per cent of the local continuum. The brightest part was located in the centre of the spot group between north polar and south polar umbrae (see wing filtergrams, Fig. 3, frames c and d).

6   The 9 July Flare

The second largest disk flare of the active region occurred on 9 July. The event may be divided into two parts: a precursor flare of importance 1B which started at 0230 UT and the main flare of importance 2B beginning at 0306 UT. The precursor consisted of a bright region in the western and central part of the spot group quite similar to the preceding flares of 8 July (Fig. 2, frames e and f). In addition, a bright knot appeared after 0234 UT east of and close to the largest follower spot and grew and brightened slowly.

After 0310 UT both these regions brightened and expanded rapidly partly merging (Fig. 4). All large spots but the southern leader (which had north polarity) were covered by the flare within a few minutes. Between 0311 and 0316 UT the small dark filament east of the flare faded slightly, having minimum opacity between 0312 and 0314 UT. Obviously it was made a "winking filament" by the flashing flare. It reappeared in a slightly modified shape after 0320 UT.

At flare maximum (0325 UT) the central and western parts had become two mounds and at 0329 UT a bright spherelike knot started rising towards the sun's limb. Gradually, it became a typical knot of a loop prominence. At 0340 UT and again at 0420 UT bright extensions of the flare region were

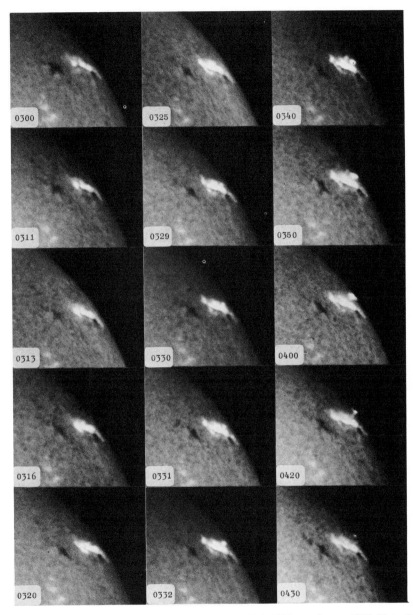

Fig. 4   2B flare July 9. Precursor 0230, main flare 0306–0520, maximum 0330. Note the faint dark filament east of the active region 0313 and 0316 UT, and the appearance of rising bright knots (loop prominence tops) after 0325. The flare is divided into two parallel strands after 0340. Haleakala Observatory photographs.

visible projected against the disk; these may be considered as branches of a loop prominence. At 0420 the top knot was already outside the disk. The average velocity of the apparent ascending motion of the loop tops was 5 km s^{-1} between 0330 and 0420 UT. The flare was clearly split into two strands parallel to the axis of the spot group after 0340 UT. This was a typical case of loop prominence evolution as described by Bruzek (1964). The loop prominence system continued growing outside the limb at a speed reduced to 2 km s^{-1} and was still observed after 1000 UT (for detailed discussion of the limb event see Valníček et al. 1968). The main flare on the disk was reported as ending at 0520 UT. However, a number of observatories reported flare activity of importance 1 or even higher until about 1100 UT; this may or may not have been a long-enduring tail of decreasing post-flare activity related to the loop prominence system.

Comparing the 9 July flare with the 7 July proton flare (McCabe and Caldwell 1968) we find appreciable differences in shape and development which may partly be due to the different arrangement of the spots. Surprisingly, the 9 July flare looked more like a proton flare as these have been observed in past years (Ellison et al. 1961, Avignon et al. 1964, Bruzek 1964) than the 7 July flare did. According to reports of observatories the areas of the two flares were about the same size at maximum brightness. The 7 July flare, however, was much brighter and it expanded more and for a longer period, eventually covering all spots for at least one hour. Again brightness and rate of expansion appear to be the decisive characteristics of the proton flare.

7 Limb Flare Activity (9–11 July)

The 9 July flare was followed after 1200 UT by numerous but quite unimportant flares; only subflares were observed quite close to the western limb of the sun.

On 10 July the active region passed the solar limb and a large number of minor flares (subflares and importance-1 flares) occurred on the limb. They formed mounds or humps of variable shapes which probably originated on the rear side of the sun. They attained visible heights of not more than 10,000 km. The only feature of larger height was a spike or very narrow loop ($h = 17,000$ km) observed between 1800 and 1806 UT (see also Valníček et al. 1968).

The very last event observed in this active region was the large eruptive prominence of 11 July, 0904–1052 UT (Valníček et al. 1968). It was preceded by importance-1 flare activity starting as early as 0604 UT.

References

AVIGNON, Y., M. J. MARTRES, and M. PICK, 1964, Identification de classes d'éruptions chromosphériques associées aux émissions de rayons cosmiques et à l'activité radio-électrique, Annls Astrophys., 27, 23–28.

BRUZEK, A., 1964, On the association between loop prominences and flares, *Astrophys. J.*, **140**, 746–759.

DODSON, H. W., 1968, The behavior of the active region prior to the proton flare of 7 July 1966 based on λ-sweep records, *Ann. IQSY*, this volume, Paper 21.

DODSON, H. W., and E. R. HEDEMAN, 1964, Problems of differentiation of flares with respect to geophysical effects, *Planet. Space Sci.*, **12**, 393–418.

ELLISON, M. A., S. M. P. MCKENNA, and J. H. REID, 1961, Cosmic ray flares, *Dunsink Obs. Publs*, **1**, 53–88.

MCCABE, M. K., and P. A. CALDWELL, 1968, Optical observations of the proton flare of 7 July 1966, *Ann. IQSY*, this volume, Paper 24.

VALNÍČEK, B., G. GODOLI, and F. MAZZUCCONI, 1968, The west limb activity on 9, 10, 11 July 1966 as observed in the Hα line, *Ann. IQSY*, this volume, Paper 16.

13

Photographie en Hα, Hβ et D₃ de la protubérance active du 9 juillet 1966

J.-L. Leroy

Observatoire du Pic-du-Midi, Bagnères de Bigorre, France

Abstract

We have obtained photographs of the large active solar prominence of 9 July 1966, through different monochromatic filters, which enable us to study separately characteristic emissions from hydrogen (Hα and Hβ) and helium (D₃). One cannot find any important difference between prominence images obtained from these various radiations.

Le 9 juillet 1966 nous avons photographié la grande protubérance active visible au bord Nord-Ouest du Soleil. Les observations ont été effectuées entre 9 heures et 11 heures T.U. environ, à l'aide d'un coronographe de 20 centimètres d'ouverture et de filtres interférentiels isolant respectivement les radiations Hα, Hβ et D₃ avec une sélectivité d'une dizaine d'ångströms.

Les planches jointes montrent des séries d'images en Hα, Hβ et D₃ obtenues à intervalles rapprochés de façon que l'on puisse comparer la répartition des émissions, dans les différentes radiations considérées, malgré l'évolution rapide de la protubérance.

On voit sur ces photographies que les émissions en Hα, Hβ et D₃ semblent provenir des mêmes régions de la protubérance à la précision près de nos observations. Cette constatation est particulièrement significative dans le cas des images en D₃ et en Hβ obtenues à 0921 et à 0922 car les différences d'aspect qui pourraient provenir de la saturation des émissions doivent être ici assez réduites.

Les images précédentes sembleraient donc impliquer l'homogénéité de la protubérance active considérée pour les détails d'une dimension supérieure ou égale à 2″ environ (soit 1500 kilomètres dans la protubérance). La même propriété avait déjà été mise en évidence dans le cas des protubérances quiescentes.

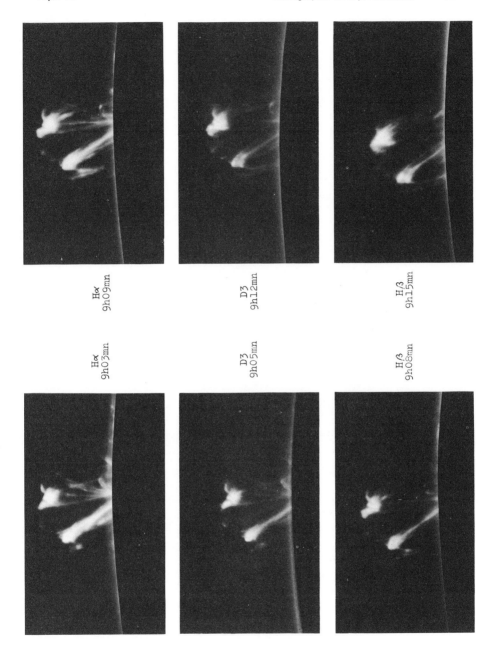

Hα
9h09mn

D3
9h12mn

Hβ
9h15mn

Hα
9h03mn

D3
9h05mn

Hβ
9h08mn

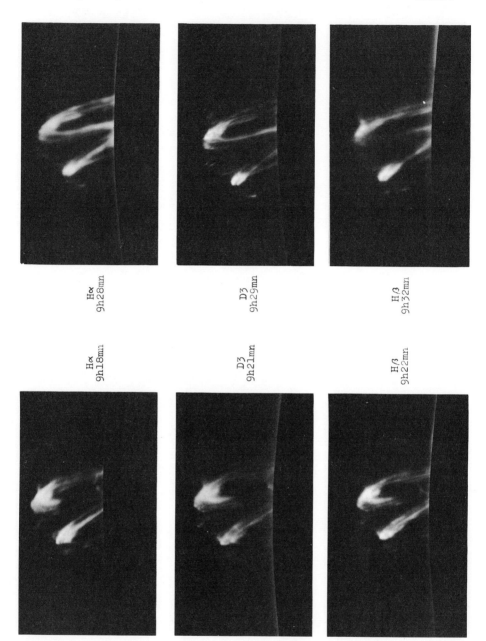

Hα
9h28mn

D3
9h29mn

Hβ
9h32mn

Hα
9h18mn

D3
9h21mn

Hβ
9h22mn

9 Juillet 1966

ECHELLE : 1 mm = 2"5 environ

Hα
9h49mn

D3
9h58mn

Hβ
10h01mn

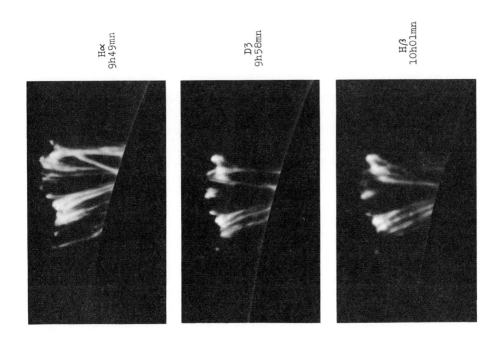

14

Active Prominences of 9 and 11 July 1966

E. A. Gurtovenko, N. N. Morozhenko, and A. S. Rakhubovsky

Main Astronomical Observatory of the Ukraine, Academy of Sciences, Kiev, USSR

Abstract

The spectra of active prominences on 9 and 11 July 1966 have been analysed.

The main peculiarity of the spectral line profiles is their loop-like shape which reveals the existence of large and complicated movements in the prominences under investigation.

The physical conditions in the prominences are found to be the same as in quiescent prominences, but there is a sharp difference between them for turbulent velocities in the prominences of 9 and 11 July 1966: these were very large and were of the same order of magnitude as those which occur in limb-flares. This "microturbulence" does not correspond to the normal distribution of velocities.

I General Description of the Events

1.1 Introduction

Following the International Proton Flare Project programme, we carried out detailed observations of the active region No. 21304 in July 1966. Our results of spectral observations and a spectral analysis of the two active prominences which occurred in this region on 9 and 11 July are presented in this paper.

The prominence observations were made with an $H\alpha$ filter and with a solar spectrograph, its dispersion being 1.2 Å mm^{-1} in the second, and 0.8 Å mm^{-1} in the third order (Gurtovenko and Didytchenko 1960). Both these prominences had the same coordinates: $\phi = +40°$, $\lambda = +90°$.

1.2   The Prominence of July 9

Cinematographic observations were carried out from 0632 to 1402 UT. During this period the prominence substantially changed in intensity and shape. Some examples of Hα filtergrams are shown in Fig. 1, and we particularly draw attention to the great brightness in the early phase and to the bright coronal condensed knots occurring later on and existing for a fairly long time.

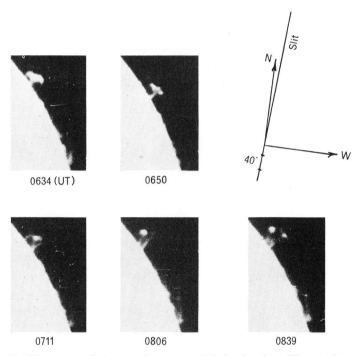

0634 (UT)   0650

0711   0806   0839

Fig. 1   Hα filtergrams of the prominences on 9 July showing different phases of its development.

The measured intensity of the brightest prominence knots shows that they would be observed as weak bright points in projection on the disk in the early phase of the prominence development.

Spectral observations were made from 0655 to 0727 UT in Hα–H_{12}, H and K (Ca II) and D_3 (He I) lines. Since no emission was observed visually in the D_1 and D_2 lines of Na I, we did not make any spectral recording of the metal-line profiles. Emission was observed in the H, K, D_3, and H–H_8 lines, only the emission of the brightest knot being visible in the H_8 line. The absence of metal-line emission is to be considered as a characteristic feature of this prominence; of course, one has to take into account that the spectral observations were not carried out in the maximum phase of its development.

Spectrograms of the prominence in different lines are show in Fig. 2 and corresponding drawings of the shape of the prominence and of the position of the slit based on the Hα filtergrams can be seen in Fig. 3. The lines have the form of a loop with a broad short-wave branch, which passes into a "cap" extending along the dispersion. At 0657 the slit passed over two bright knots *a* and *b* (Fig. 3). The *a* knot had a small radial velocity, but above the knot the velocity increased with the height, and therefore this part was rather weak on the Hα filtergram. The *b* knot belongs to the "cap"; it has almost no radial velocity as a whole, but inside it a dispersion of radial velocities within $+60$ to -40 km s^{-1} is present.

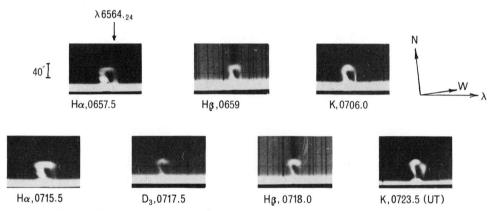

Fig. 2   The most intense lines in the spectrum of the prominence on 9 July.

The long-wave branch of the Hα line has a constant radial velocity of $+60$ km s^{-1} at all heights. This branch is overlapped by the telluric line 6564.24 Å, as one can see in Fig. 2. It can be supposed that this weak and fairly narrow long-wave branch originated in a homogeneous cloud of steam or gas, rising up with a constant velocity. This general character is common to all the lines and, as one can see from Fig. 2, it did not change substantially during the whole of the period investigated.

This loop-like shape of the spectral lines shows that we have here a loop-prominence system which forms in the course of some major flares. We can refer here to Banin's (1966) observation of a major flare close to the limb associated with a loop-prominence system, in which the shape of spectral lines was formed exactly as we have observed in this event.

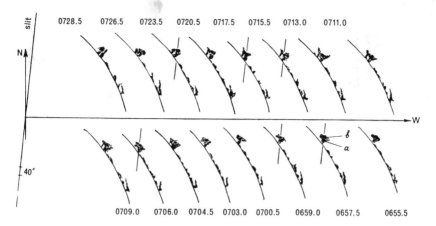

Fig. 3   Structures of the 9 July prominence according to Hα filtergrams during the
period when spectra were photographed. The position of the slit is indicated.

1.3   The Prominence of 11 July

Hα filtergrams were obtained from 1108 to 1230, hence the first phase of the
prominence development was not recorded. Several examples of the filtergrams are shown in Fig. 4. The most characteristic features of this prominence
were explosion-like changes and the appearance of high coronal knots
connected with the photosphere by weak threads of gaseous material.

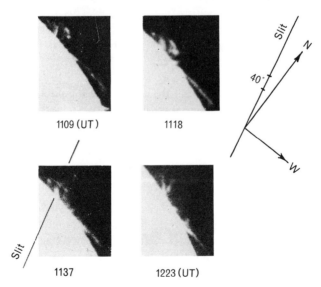

Fig. 4   Hα filtergrams of the prominence on 11 July showing different phases of its
development.

Spectral observations were carried out in Hα–H$_8$, H, K, and D$_3$ lines from 1125 to 1215, when the prominence was already decaying. The emission was rather weak, and ceased to be visible already in the Hδ line; again no metal-line emission could be discovered.

Spectrograms of the prominence obtained in different lines and demonstrated in Fig. 5 show a great variety of radial velocities in different knots of

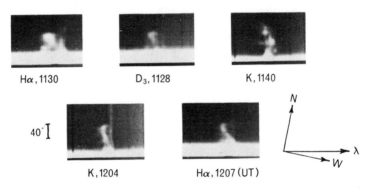

Hα, 1130   D$_3$, 1128   K, 1140

40° I   K, 1204   Hα, 1207 (UT)

Fig. 5   The most intense lines in the spectrum of the prominence on 11 July.

the prominence, which confirms its explosion-like character in the early stage of its development. After 12 h this character is less pronounced, and the lines are more compact and stable. At that time, one can detect in the H and K lines, and less clearly in the Hα line, a narrow long-wave component, which corresponds to a radial velocity of $+40$ km s^{-1}. This shape is somewhat similar to the loop-like form in the prominence of 9 July, which is somewhat astonishing after the stormy character of the prominence in the earlier phase of its development. Of course, the *a* "cap", so characteristic for the loop-type prominence of 9 July, is missing here. We are inclined to suppose that this similarity of the line shapes in both the prominences points to the existence of a stable magnetic field configuration in the active region which regulates to some extent the character of gas motions in the active prominences.

2   Spectrophotometric Observations

2.1   Introduction

Since with our equipment it is not possible to obtain simultaneous photographs of several spectral regions, all the lines were photographed at different times within a time interval of 1 to 5 minutes. Repeated pictures of identical lines showed that the prominence of 9 July developed relatively slowly, and therefore we could investigate the mean profiles of each of the lines, compiled from all the photographs obtained. Five photometric tracings were made in each spectral line as indicated in Fig. 6.

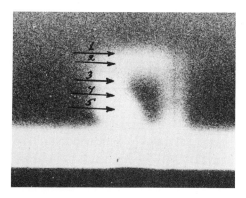

Fig. 6   A scheme of the five photometric tracings made in the prominence of 9 July.

The development of the prominence on 11 July was much more complex, and the procedure adopted at the first event could not be applied in this case. In the later fairly stable phase of the prominence, three photometric tracings were made of each line.

2.2   Results of Measurement

The resulting profiles of the Hα line in the spectrum of the 9 July prominence are shown in Fig. 7. As one can see from this, the profiles of the two components of the line can be easily separated in profiles 3, 4, and 5, in profile 2 this separation is uncertain, and in profile 1 it is entirely impossible.

In the case of the 11 July prominence we obtained line profiles of the various bright knots. From these line profiles we tried to deduce the equivalent width A, the optical thickness τ_0 and the Doppler half-width $\Delta\lambda_D$. The results are shown in Table 1 for the prominence of 9 July and in Table 2 for the prominence of 11 July.

The optical thickness of the Hα, H, and K lines was deduced from a graph of the dependence of the central intensity I_0 or τ_0, constructed on the basis of tables published by Yakovkin and Kostik (1966) for resonance lines. Due to the complex form of the line profiles, however, the resulting τ_0 values have to be considered as an approximation only. Since this method can only be applied to resonance (H and K) or resonance-like (Hα), we have not deduced any τ_0 values for higher lines of the Balmer series. The optical thickness in the D_3 (Table 1) was estimated by comparison with this line in quiet prominences. It is found to be quite small, of the order of 10^{-1} to 10^{-2}.

The value of $\Delta\lambda_D$ for the Hα line was deduced from the line wings. Since its value decreases as one approaches the line core, one has to consider the data given in Tables 1 and 2 merely as parameters which indicate the mean value of the characteristic velocities. In other lines, which were found optically thin, $\Delta\lambda_D$ was deduced from the line half-widths.

The equivalent widths A in Tables 1 and 2 are given in ergs. In the Hα line, they have been corrected for self-absorption. Using the formula

$$A = -\frac{N_k A_{kl} h\nu}{4\pi} \tag{1}$$

we have deduced the populations N_k, of the upper levels of hydrogen, helium,

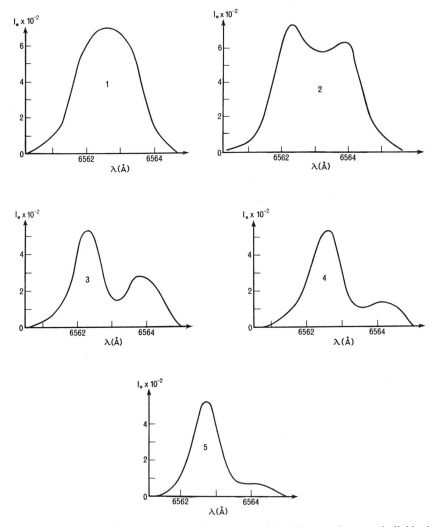

Fig. 7   Hα lines profiles in the prominence on 9 July. The numbers on individual profiles correspond to the different tracings shown in Fig. 6.

Table 1   Equivalent Width A, Optical Thickness τ_0, and Doppler Width $\Delta\lambda_D$, as deduced from Spectra of the Prominence on 9 July 1966

Line	Tracing	A (blue) (10^5ergs)	A (red) (10^5ergs)	τ_0 (blue)	τ_0 (red)	$\Delta\lambda_D$ (blue)	$\Delta\lambda_D$ (red)
Hα	1	7.76	—	1.91	—	0.957	—
	2	6.41	3.02	2.62	1.35	0.713	0.584
	3	2.52	0.767	1.33	0.30	0.530	0.742
	4	3.24	0.377	1.65	0.13	0.548	0.693
	5	2.92	0.214	1.56	0.09	0.518	0.677
Hβ	1	0.670	—	—	—	0.615	—
	2	1.140	0.118	—	—	0.700	0.361
	3	0.354	0.215	—	—	0.354	0.450
	4	0.361	0.079	—	—	0.353	0.313
	5	0.434	0.084	—	—	0.414	0.217
Hγ	1	0.166	—	—	—	0.505	—
	2	0.330	0.088	—	—	0.488	0.391
	3	0.076	0.171	—	—	0.304	0.332
	4	0.059	0.037	—	—	0.202	0.132
	5	0.161	0.024	—	—	0.287	0.169
Hδ	1	0.082	—	—	—	0.446	—
	2	0.024	—	—	—	0.330	—
	3	0.026	0.010	—	—	0.108	0.326
	4	—	—	—	—	—	—
	5	—	—	—	—	—	—
Hϵ	1	0.130	—	—	—	0.379	—
	2	0.170	—	—	—	0.456	—
	3	—	—	—	—	—	—
K	1	0.498	—	0.43	—	0.470	—
	2	1.073	0.447	0.95	0.44	0.431	0.362
	3	0.540	0.200	0.71	0.30	0.265	0.304
	4	0.448	0.155	0.79	0.35	0.226	0.160
	5	0.605	0.139	0.79	0.37	0.307	0.132
D$_3$	1	0.542	—	0.075	—	0.586	—
	2	0.615	0.361	0.085	0.045	0.586	0.533
	3	0.305	0.192	0.044	0.030	0.566	0.497
	4	0.230	0.073	0.052	0.025	0.364	0.337
	5	0.166	0.034	0.039	0.110	0.475	0.331

and ionized calcium. The populations N_1, of the lower levels, were deduced from the τ_0 values and are therefore somewhat uncertain. The values found for N_1 and N_k are given in Tables 3 and 4.

Table 2 Equivalent Width A, Optical Thickness τ_0, and Doppler Width $\Delta\lambda_D$ as deduced from Spectra of the Prominence on 11 July 1966

Line	Time	Tracing	A (blue) (10^5ergs)	A (red) (10^5ergs)	τ_0 (blue)	τ_0 (red)	$\Delta\lambda_D$ (blue)	$\Delta\lambda_D$ (red)
Hα	1125	2	4.44	1.78	1.6	0.74	0.66	0.825
		1	3.00	0.74	0.67	0.27	1.23	1.14
	1129	2	1.27	3.10	0.65	0.88	0.56	0.89
		1	5.04	0.52	1.83	0.30	0.79	0.62
	1130	2	—	4.44	—	1.66	—	0.65
		1	1.76	1.02	0.83	0.58	0.49	0.68
		3	1.70	—	0.30	—	1.04	—
	1207	2	1.44	—	0.60	—	0.77	—
		1	1.12	0.314	0.59	0.23	0.70	0.49
Hβ	1127	2	0.575	0.190	—	—	0.82	0.56
	1127.5	—	0.420	0.142	—	—	0.53	0.62
K	1134	2	0.324	0.300	0.18	0.28	0.45	0.74
		1	0.690	—	0.46	—	0.65	—
	1140	2	0.300	0.330	0.28	0.25	0.34	0.66
		1	0.700	—	0.37	—	0.69	—
	1204	2	0.270	0.087	0.31	0.17	0.36	0.28
		1	0.308	0.138	0.29	0.16	0.41	0.42
		3	—	0.166	—	0.14	—	0.43
	1216	2	0.470	—	0.40	—	0.46	—
		1	0.308	0.101	0.26	0.11	0.48	0.38
		3	—	0.690	—	0.10	—	0.30
D$_3$	1126	2	0.445	0.085	—	—	0.98	0.64
	1128	—	0.238	0.051	—	—	0.52	0.38

Table 3   Populations of Different Quantum States of Hydrogen, Helium and Ionized Calcium

Tracing	Hydrogen							Ionized Calcium			Helium
	$10^{-19}N_1$	$10^{-13}N_2$	$10^{-10}N_3$	$10^{-10}N_4$	$10^{-10}N_5$	$10^{-10}N_6$	$10^{-10}N_7$	$10^{-12}N_1$	$10^{-9}N_2$	$10^4(N_2/N_1)$	$10^{-9}N$
					Blue components						
1	3.20	1.34	7.32	2.45	1.82	2.19	6.35	4.05	0.84	2.06	2.81
2	3.22	1.35	3.05	4.20	3.60	5.73	1.52	8.10	1.80	2.22	3.20
3	1.19	0.50	2.38	1.29	0.84	0.70	—	3.77	0.90	2.39	1.58
4	1.57	0.66	3.05	1.33	0.64	—	—	3.49	0.75	2.15	1.19
5	1.43	0.60	2.75	1.60	1.75	—	—	4.83	1.01	2.09	0.86
					Red components						
1	—	—	—	—	—	—	—	—	—	—	—
2	1.36	0.573	2.86	1.55	0.960	—	—	3.16	0.744	2.35	1.87
3	0.38	0.160	0.72	0.80	0.644	0.296	—	1.80	0.332	1.85	1.00
4	0.15	0.065	0.36	0.29	0.404	—	—	1.11	0.259	2.33	0.38
5	0.10	0.043	0.20	0.41	0.262	—	—	0.98	0.232	2.37	0.18

Table 4   Population of Quantum States and Values of Turbulent, v_t, and Radial, v_r, Velocities, as deduced for the Prominence of 11 July 1966

Line	Time	Tracing	$10^{-12}N_k$		$10^{-10}N_i$		v_t(km s^{-1})		v_r(km s^{-1})	
			blue	red	blue	red	blue	red	blue	red
Hα	1125	2	7.7	4.4	4.20	1.7	30.2	37.7	16.0	13.7
		1	6.0	2.2	2.80	0.7	56.2	52.1	8.8	20.0
	1129	2	2.7	5.70	1.20	3.20	25.7	40.4	19.8	14.3
		1	10.5	1.30	4.75	0.49	36.0	28.4	10.8	16.6
	1130	2	—	7.80	—	4.18	—	29.2	—	10.0
		1	3.00	2.90	1.66	0.96	22.4	30.7	16.0	11.7
		3	2.30	—	1.60	—	48.0	—	6.7	—
	1207	2	3.40	—	1.36	—	35.1	—	11.7	—
		1	3.00	0.82	1.06	0.30	31.8	22.4	8.1	11.5
Hβ	1127	—	—	—	2.11	0.70	51.0	34.5	6.1	14.4
	1127.5	—	—	—	1.56	0.52	33.0	37.8	10.2	13.0
K	1134	2	3.10	2.91	0.054	0.050	34.2	34.2	19.5	6.4
		1	7.30	—	0.115	—	50.4	—	8.7	—
	1140	2	2.70	4.10	0.050	0.055	25.9	50.1	21.5	7.1
		1	6.60	—	0.116	—	52.5	—	11.3	—
	1204	2	2.50	1.00	0.045	0.014	27.1	21.3	3.9	11.2
		1	2.90	1.50	0.051	0.023	31.2	31.8	11.9	8.5
		3	—	1.40	—	0.028	—	33.0	—	10.5
	1216	2	4.10	—	0.078	—	35.1	—	1.3	—
		1	3.50	1.40	0.051	0.017	36.6	29.0	10.0	8.9
		3	—	0.77	—	0.011	—	22.9	—	11.5
D₃	1126	—	—	—	0.230	0.044	49.8	32.1	3.2	20.7
	1128	—	—	—	0.123	0.026	26.5	19.3	—	—

2.3　Electron Temperature

Knowing the populations of different levels in hydrogen atoms we have tried to deduce the electron temperature using the Saha–Boltzmann equation

$$b_s N^+ n_e = \frac{N_s}{S^2} \frac{(2\pi m k)^{3/2}}{h^3} T^{3/2} \exp\left(-\frac{\chi_s}{kT_e}\right) \tag{2}$$

where b_s is a parameter characterizing deviations from thermodynamic equilibrium in the population of an s-level.

It is well known (Thomas and Athay 1965) that $b_s \gg 1$ for low levels and it tends to 1 as s increases. We used this characteristic feature of the b_s factors to deduce the electron temperature.

The right-hand part of Eq. (2) — let us denote it by C — can be calculated with known N_s values and for an assumed value of the electron temperature T_e. Then one can plot C against the ionization potential of the sth level, χ_s and after extrapolating this dependence to $\chi_s = 0$, we can find the C-value for which $b_s = 1$. Or, in other words, we find the value of $N^+ n_e$ for the assumed value of T_e. This value can be inserted into the equation of ionization equilibrium

$$N_1 \Phi_1 + N_2 \Phi_2 = N^+ n_e \sum R_s \tag{3}$$

and from here the population N_1 of the ground state can be found. In Eq. (3) one takes into account only radiative processes, since these are predominant in prominences. The photo-ionization coefficient Φ_s is given by

$$\Phi_s = W \frac{8\pi}{C^2} \kappa_s \nu_s{}^3 \mathrm{Ei}\left(\frac{\chi_s}{kT_s}\right) \tag{4}$$

with W denoting the dilution coefficient ($W = 0.3$ has been adopted here), κ_s is the absorption coefficient and T_s the Planck's temperature at the limit of the spectral series considered. We have adopted $T_1 = 6900°$ according to Hirayama (1963) and $T_2 = 6000°$. The ionization from the levels $s \geqslant 3$ has been neglected to determine $\sum R_s$ we have included individual R_s values according to Cillie (1932) up to $s = 30$.

As soon as we know N_1 we can easily find T_e from the equation

$$\frac{N_2}{N_1} = \frac{b_2}{b_1} \frac{I_2}{I_1} \exp\left(-\frac{h\nu}{kT_e}\right) \tag{5}$$

assuming $b_1 = b_2$. This assumption is well founded, due to the high optical thickness of the Lyman α line (Yakovkin 1963).

The T_e value thus obtained, of course, does not agree with the value assumed at the beginning. It is clear, however, that when applying this method successively, one gets the final value of T_e by successive approximations. The resulting T_e's for the prominence of 9 July are shown in Table 5.

Table 5   Values of Turbulent, v_t, and Radial, v_r, Velocities, and Electron
Temperature T_e as deduced for the Prominence of 9 July 1966

Tracing	v_t (H) (km s^{-1})	v_t (Ca II) (km s^{-1})	v_t (He) (km s^{-1})	v_r (H) (km s^{-1})	v_r (Ca II) (km s^{-1})	v_r (He) (km s^{-1})	T_e (°)
			Blue components				
1	35.2	36.0	28.5	0.0	0.0	0.0	7800
2	32.3	33.0	28.5	10.6	8.4	15.6	7500
3	19.5	20.2	27.5	25.0	28.2	23.4	7800
4	20.5	17.2	16.2	18.8	23.6	10.3	7900
5	20.0	23.4	22.5	12.7	16.0	7.7	7300
			Red components				
1	—	—	—	—	—	—	—
2	22.8	27.6	25.7	50.4	38.7	37.5	7600
3	21.2	23.2	23.9	45.4	54.0	53.0	7600
4	23.1	12.2	14.6	49.1	55.5	58.5	7300
5	22.1	10.1	14.3	49.8	59.3	63.5	—

2.4   Turbulent and Radial Velocities

Turbulent velocities have been deduced from the well-known formula

$$c^2\left(\frac{\Delta\lambda_D}{\lambda}\right)^2 = \frac{2RT_e}{\mu} + v_t^2$$

where the first term on the right-hand side is negligibly small, for the value
found for T_e, $\simeq 8000°$. Thus the lines are predominantly broadened by nonthermal, turbulent motion. For computing v_t we used the $\Delta\lambda_D$ values given in
Tables 1 and 2. The radial velocities v_r were estimated according to the shift
of the emission lines as compared with the corresponding Fraunhofer lines.
Both the resulting values of v_t and v_r are given in Tables 4 and 5.

The turbulent velocities deduced in both prominences are quite high. In
the loop prominence of 9 July the turbulent velocities reach their maximum
value in the "cap" and decrease towards the photosphere. In the 11 July
prominence, too, turbulent velocities are smaller in tracings nearer to the
photosphere (tracing 1), in the earlier phase of development. Later on, v_t no
longer seems to depend on the altitude. Since the line profiles differ from the
Doppler profile, we can conclude that turbulent velocities varied along the
line of sight.

3   Conclusions

   a. The prominences investigated seem to be only links in the chain of the
active limb events, which originated at one place in the active region during
its development.

b. In the quiet phase of their development they possess a complex loop structure, which indicates that there exist some movement-trajectories characteristic of a formation of loop-prominence systems in the active region.

c. From consideration of the type of spectrum, the prominences belong to "non-metallic" prominences with a moderate number of hydrogen lines.

d. The temperature, population of quantum states, density of gas, and the mechanisms of excitation are similar to the conditions one finds in quiescent prominences.

e. The prominences studied, however, differ strongly from the quiescent type by having substantially higher turbulent velocities, which do not obey the normal velocity distribution.

References

BANIN, V. G., 1966, *Izv. Krȳm. Astrofiz. Obs.*, **35**, 190.

CILLIE, G. G., 1932, *Mon. Not. R. Astr. Soc.*, **92**, 82.

GURTOVENKO, E. A., and E. I. DIDYTCHENKO, 1960, *Izv. Glav. Astr. Obs., Kiev*, **3**, No. 2.

HIRAYAMA, T., 1963, *Publs. Astr. Soc. Japan*, **15**, 104.

THOMAS, R., and R. ATHAY, 1965, *Fizika Solnechnoi Chromosfery*, (published by "Mir", Moscow).

YAKOVKIN, N. A., 1963, *Bull. Soln. Dann.*, No. 8, 167.

YAKOVKIN, N. A., and R. I. KOSTIK, 1966, *Astrofizika*, **2**, 379.

15

Polarization Measurements of the Proton Flare on 11 July 1966

G. Stiber

Lund Observatory, Lund, Sweden

Abstract

In the search for different sources of the continuous emission in solar limb objects, a programme for determining polarization has been carried out at the Swedish Solar Observatory at Anacapri, Italy, by the present author. The spectacular event on 11 July 1966 was found to have a polarization lower than that predicted by the theory of electron scattering. By special instrumental arrangements, the probable electron density was measured to be about 3×10^{11} electrons cm^{-3}. This value agrees well with the degree of polarization when we consider that the non-polarized contribution to the continuous spectrum from the free–free and free–bound transitions of hydrogen increases with increasing electron density. The plane of polarization was found to be in good agreement with that to be expected if electron scattering were responsible for some of the continuous spectrum.

On the suggestion of Professor Öhman, the f/13 12-cm Lyot coronagraph at Anacapri was equipped in 1965 with special devices in order to make it possible to record polarization effects in limb events. The main purpose was to investigate whether mechanisms other than Thomson scattering might contribute to the continuous spectrum. For instance, could the formation of H⁻ give some continuous emission? A $\lambda/2$ plate which could be turned in four positions and a fixed polaroid were mounted behind the collimating lens in the coronagraph. This arrangement gave four planes of polarization, one coinciding with the north–south direction and the others differing 45° from each other. A green filter combined with an interference filter for 5303 Å gave a transmission band of about 100 Å centred at 5320 Å. The occulting disk had a 1-mm hole near the limb and behind this a neutral filter was placed. In this way a photometric standard was introduced.

Four recordings in rapid succession were thus needed for complete determination of the polarization. The best series of the 11 July event was secured at 0924–0929 UT with an exposure time of $\frac{1}{2}$ sec, and all the measurements belong to this series. The photometric analysis of the films was made with the microphotometer of the Lund Observatory. When measuring the films the problem was how to compare the intensity of corresponding points on four negatives. Several methods were tried and that finally selected was to let the motor of the self-recording photometer work in the east–west direction

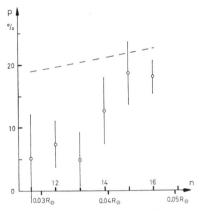

Fig. 1   True polarization of the flare spray on 11 July 1966, 0924–0929 UT plotted against the height above the solar limb. The dashed curve represents pure electron scattering.

Fig. 2   The vibrational angle ψ of the polarized light (defined according to the text) plotted against the height above the solar limb.

over the negatives. Since the steep increase in intensity at the extreme limb was visible on every recording, one and the same point in the flare could be found by way of a photometric procedure giving an arbitrary scale (n) corresponding to the "height above the limb". When all the four intensities were available for a certain point in the flare, the degree of polarization was calculated. The weakest intensities were omitted to avoid large probable errors. Hence only intensities exceeding or equal to 10 per cent of that of the solar stray light at the same point were accepted. Nevertheless, 23 points in the flare area had intensities strong enough in all the four planes of vibration. Figure 1 shows the true polarization with the mean errors plotted against the height above the limb, here also transformed into the unit $R_\odot$. The dashed curve is the degree of polarization of a prominence according to Baumbach's (1938) formula for pure electron scattering. Figure 2 shows the vibrational angle ψ, of the polarized light, also plotted against the height above the limb. ψ is measured counterclockwise starting from the north. Calculation of the weighted mean value of ψ gives $\bar{\psi} = 49°$ and this value together with the tangential angle is indicated in Fig. 2, where also the mean errors can be seen. From Fig. 2 the conclusion might be drawn that the polarized light arises from electron scattering.

Reference is made to a more extensive publication (Stiber 1968) where a detailed photometric study of the continuous emission of the flare is presented. In addition, calculations are presented of the continuous emission from free–free and free–bound transitions of hydrogen at 5320 Å (H^- is not taken into account). When the electron density reaches the magnitude here considered, this emission is considerable and may well account for the discrepancy in Fig. 1 between the measured and the theoretical degree of polarization. In fact, if the discrepancy is interpreted as due to superimposed non-polarized emission, one finds that this emission may have the same intensity as that of the polarized component. Theoretical calculation from Aller (1963) then gives an electron density of $N_e = 4.1 \times 10^{11}$ electrons cm^{-3} if an electron temperature of 10^4 °K is assumed. The estimation of the electron temperature does not influence the calculations very much, however. For instance, to get $N_e \simeq 10^{13}$ an electron temperature of 10^5 °K would be needed. When comparing this result with the results obtained from the measurements of the absolute intensity of the flare spray, good agreement is found: taking the maximal value of the flare intensity measured, 1.9×10^{-4} in units of the intensity of the solar centre, one finds $N_e = 2.5 \times 10^{11}$ electrons cm^{-3} if the flare had an extension of 2×10^9 cm along the line of sight. This distance was estimated from the negatives, as the flare was assumed to have axial symmetry.

From these measurements and from Fig. 1 the probable electron density can thus be estimated to be 3×10^{11} electrons cm^{-3}. The degree of polarization is on the average 10 per cent at heights of 0.03–0.05 $R_\odot$ above the solar limb. The tendency of the polarization to increase with the distance from the limb in Fig. 1 might be explained by the fact that in the outer parts of the flare the electron density is lower and so the pure electron scattering will have a larger influence. The plane of vibration of the polarized light is found to be parallel to the tangent of the limb. This clearly indicates electron scattering as one source of the continuous emission.

In view of the general difficulties in recording this event in white light our investigation will perhaps serve rather as a pointer for future work than as one describing very accurately the physical state in flare sprays.

References

ALLER, L. H., 1963, *Astrophysics, The Atmospheres of the Sun and Stars*, 2nd edn (Ronald Press Co., New York), pp. 188–189.
BAUMBACH, S., 1938, Die Polarisation der Sonnenkorona, *Astr. Nachr.*, **267**, 273–296.
STIBER, G., 1968, Measurements of polarization and electron density in the flare spray on July 11, 1966, *Ark. Astr.*, **4**, 571–586.

16

The West-Limb Activity on 9, 10, 11 July 1966 as observed in the Hα Line

B. Valníček*, G. Godoli†, and F. Mazzucconi‡

* Ondřejov Observatory, Czechoslovakia
† Catania Astrophysical Observatory, Sicily
‡ Arcetri Astrophysical Observatory, Italy

Abstract

An analysis of the limb activity is given. The most important phenomena are the loop system, observed on 9 July, and the eruptive prominence of 11 July.

By comparison of simultaneous observations with different bandwidth filters it was possible to establish the position of the phenomenon in three-dimensional space and thus to establish the twisted form of the 11 July phenomenon. From observations of radial velocity the unambiguous direction of motion could be determined.

The uniform inclination of all the phenomena confirm the conclusion that above the active region there exists one constant system of magnetic fields.

The analysis of velocity changes is important in connection with form changes of the prominence.

1 Participating Observatories, Review of Observational Material

All available observational material has been obtained from the observatories of Bucharest, Catania, Crimea, Freiburg, Kharkov, Kiev, Pic du Midi, Rome, Sacramento Peak, and the People's Observatory of Prague. We have used this material to complete the Arcetri and Ondřejov observations.

Table 1 shows the types of instrument used and the description of the material, the dates and number of observations and the pass-band width. Information on the pass-band width is important when the Doppler velocity

Table I   Principal Characteristics of Instruments Used and Description of the Material

Observatory	Instrument	Band Width	Date of Observations	Number of Pictures
Arcetri	Halle filter	0.5 Å	9 July	14
			10 July	14
			11 July	33
Bucharest	Halle filter	0.75 Å	9 July	40
			11 July	6
Catania	Halle filter	0.5 Å	9 July	28
			10 July	36
			11 July	31
Crimea	Filter Lyot–Ohman	0.5 Å 1.8 Å	11 July	12
	Spectroheliograph	0.15 Å	11 July	2
Freiburg	Halle filter	0.5 Å 1.0 Å	11 July	4
Kharkov	Spectroheliograph Spectrohelioscope	0.2 Å	11 July	7
Kiev	Filter Lyot–Ohman	1.0 Å	9 July	12
			11 July	10
Ondřejov	Filter Lyot–Solc	0.75 Å	9 July	15
			11 July	21
	Coronagraph Filter Solc	8 Å	11 July	48
Pic du Midi	Coronagraph Filter Lyot	10 Å	9 July	18
Prague	Coronagraph Filter Solc	8 Å	9 July	33
Rome	Filter Halle	0.75 Å	9 July	14
			10 July	55
			11 July	21
Sacramento Peak	Coronagraph Filter Lyot	4 Å	9 July	965
			10 July	184
			11 July	10

is great for rapid variations in a phenomenon could vanish because of a narrow pass band. To complete the series of photographic and spectro-helioscopic observations we have obtained also from the Kiev Observatory drawings of the west limb for 9 and 11 July.

The times of observation for each day are represented in Fig. 1 where the density of lines indicates the density of observations.

Fig. 1   Times of observations.

The character and quality of observations naturally depend on the instrument used. Pictures obtained by small patrol instruments demonstrate only the larger features and fine detail cannot be seen. Much better results are observed by coronagraphs or by telescopes with a larger image. The superiority of the coronagraph for limb observation is beyond any doubt.

For our work we have as far as possible obtained enlarged pictures of uniform scale (1 mm = 5000 km) so that the diameter of the sun's disk is 278 mm. Such uniform enlargement is useful for the evaluation of pictures, and many of the participating observatories have been able to prepare the material in this size.

2   Positions of Active Phenomena

2.1   The Loop System observed on 9 July

The base of the loop system was situated in the northern part of the 21034 group, as can be seen in pictures obtained at Ondřejov Observatory with a narrow pass-band filter. An associated 2B flare was observed at Athens Observatory (0425–0512 UT, 34°N 74°W) and another flare 1N at Arcetri (0805–1005 UT, 35°N 78°W). Because the centre of the active region is in latitude 33°N, it seems that the northern part of the 21034 group is identical with the position of the flares and loop. For this phenomenon we also have at our disposal drawings from Kiev, made at 1359 UT. Pictures from Sacramento Peak record a decreasing activity in the same region in the late afternoon, and a small amount of activity in the southern part of the region. No other limb activity can be found for this day in this region from the material which is in our hands.

Only a diffuse, faint prominence, with slowly changing form, exists in the position 23–25°N. The intensity was not high and the changes observed here seem not to be connected with the loop system.

2.2   The Situation of 10 July

The observational material for 10 July is relatively limited. The limb activity was generally diminished. It seems that one small activity appeared in the prominence situated at 23°N, in the same place as the diffuse prominence was observed on 9 July.

Activity of the same type as on the preceding day appears in the position of the 21034 group with faint loops, later activated, and evidently connected, as we shall see, with the flare 1N observed in the same group in Arcetri, Catania and Istanbul at 0905–1002. At Sacramento Peak a surge-like activity was observed at the position of the loops at 1744–1820 with maximum probably later than 1820.

2.3   The Situation of 11 July

In the early morning the 21034 group was situated on the limb. A subflare, observed here in Ondřejov at 0418–0443, was accompanied by a small loop at latitude 35°N. This phenomenon remains almost constant until 0750, when new activity appears. This activity, according to Arcetri, Kharkov, and Ondřejov observations, begins with an activation of the prominence, culminating at 0900 UT in an eruptive prominence at latitude 35°N, and in the northern part of the 21034 group. The development of the prominence was directed towards the north, to the latitude 50–55°N. The activity finished here after 1400 UT. It seems that one flare of great importance situated behind the limb must have been associated with this event.

3   Detailed Description of Limb Phenomena

3.1   The Activity of 9 July

In the photograph obtained at 0551 at Ondřejov (Fig. 2) the loop system is represented as a structure connected, as we have said, with the northern part of the active region. The width of the base of the loops is around 50,000 km and the height reaches 60,000 km (35,000 km above the limb). The system of loops slowly changes form and grows. In the first phase, which ends at 0830 UT, the northern part of the loop system is brighter; later the southern part is brighter. The jump at 0730–0800 in the graph of Fig. 3, in which the height

Fig. 2   The loop system of 9 July, 0551 UT (Ondřejov).

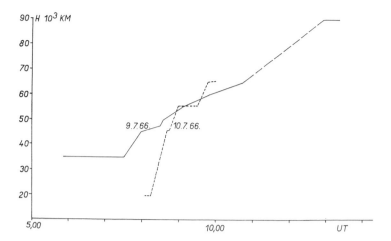

Fig. 3   Height of the loop systems of 9 July (full line) and 10 July (dashed line).

of the system has been plotted against time, corresponds to the brightening in the northern part of the loops.

Seen through the birefringent filters of Pic du Midi (pass band 10 Å) (Fig. 4) and of Prague Observatory (pass band 8 Å) the loop system shows distinct filaments without bright spots. These are not visible with the narrow pass-band filter, which only shows the loops as composed of a few bright spots without clear filamentary connection with the active centre on the sun. This fact implies the existence of radical velocities of the filament greater than 50 km s^{-1}.

The narrow pass-band filter observations are from Arcetri and Ondřejov. With the Arcetri 0.5 Å filter (Fig. 5) the loop filaments are not seen at all;

Fig. 4   The loop system of 9 July, 1006 UT (Pic du Midi).

with the Ondřejov 0.8 Å filter the loop filaments ascending directly from the active region as emission filaments begin to be seen.

Unfortunately, coronagraph observations from Prague Observatory and from Pic du Midi give uncertain results of height measurements because of incorrect centring of the sun's image. But large-scale pictures from Pic du Midi allow us to follow the very detailed structure of the loop system. It is

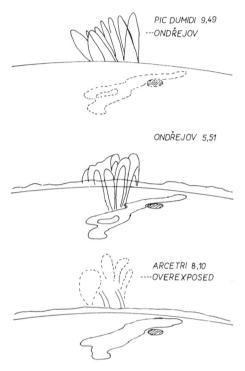

Fig. 5   Sketches of the loop system of 9 July (*c.* 0500–1000 UT) according to Pic du Midi (10 Å pass band), Ondřejov (0.8 Å pass band), Arcetri (0.5 Å pass band).

also possible to measure the inclination of individual loops, and in this way it is possible to determine more precisely the part of the centre of activity which is connected with the loops. It is actually situated in the centre of the flare field, nearer to the northern part of the centre of activity.

3.2   The Activity of 10 July

Four flares occurred during 10 July in the region considered, but only one seems to be connected with limb phenomena. At 0920 UT, faint loops, which had been present above the active region since 0842 became brighter, reaching an intensity maximum at 0950–0955 UT.

The Arcetri observations show a small flare-like phenomenon in the active region, beginning at 0915 and finishing before 0925 UT. This subflare seems to be associated with the jump in the height of the loops after 0930 (Fig. 3) and with a displacement of the loop of 10,000–12,000 km in a northerly direction. At 1030 UT the Rome filtergrams showed one small surge in the same region. All these results are recorded and integrated by the Kharkov spectrohelioscope observations. According to these observations, three places on the limb in the 21034 group have been active: 32°N (0843–0937 UT, flare-like), 30°N (0905–0930 UT, small active prominence), 35°N (0842–0952 UT, loops).

The inclination of the loop axis, measured at 0950 UT is 55°.

A new surge-like phenomenon occurred in this region at 1744–1820. The surge was inclined in the same direction as the axis of the loop system, but the inclination was greater: 70°.

3.3   The Activity of 11 July

The limb activity in the region considered continued with a small bright prominence in the same position as on the preceding day and with a small surge in the northern part (35°N) at 0517 UT. The activity was renewed after 0700 UT, when some small brightening can be found in the southern part. At 0800 UT the northern part also underwent variations. By this time the whole part of the limb above the active region remained bright and changeable. At 0905 the northern part was very bright and a few minutes later a very important eruptive phenomenon clearly began.

At the beginning, the phenomenon was divided in two parts, which developed separately (Fig. 6). One part developed approximately in a direction parallel to the limb and toward the observer. The other part, which was the main one, developed in a direction inclined at 40° to the limb, with a velocity reaching in the first phase 300 km s^{-1}. After a sudden drop to 100 km s^{-1} the velocity again grew to 380 km s^{-1}. A remarkable occurrence in this phase is that the phenomenon also grew in the direction perpendicular to the initial direction, forming one gigantic blast, reaching more than 100,000 km in diameter. In filtergrams for 0.8 Å (Fig. 7) we can see the bright prominence separated by the dark absorption strip of the chromosphere. At a later phase (Fig. 8) we can see that the main part of the prominence is always behind the limb, but the part which is spreading nearly parallel to the limb is moving towards the observer. This means that this part is displaced in the direction of a line from the plane of the principal part of the prominence to the observer.

The detailed study of filtergrams of Arcetri and Catania (0.5 Å pass band) and coronagraph pictures of Ondřejov (8 Å pass band) leads us to an interesting conclusion: the initial phase of the phenomenon is visible with the narrow-band filter in the same form as it is with the wide-band filter of

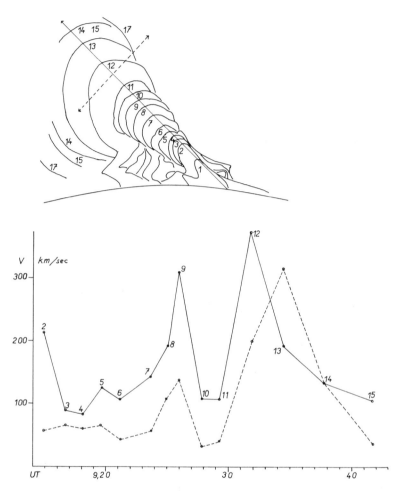

Fig. 6   Development of the two parts of the 11 July eruptive prominences and velocity changes of the main part.

the coronagraph (Figs. 9 and 10). But the blast is visible only partially in the narrow-band filter. The complete form can be seen only in the coronagraph, in which we find that the blast continues into the very dense part in the apparent direction towards the limb. We must conclude that this part, visible only with wide-band filters, has a radial velocity which is beyond the limit of visibility in narrow-band filters.

This fact is well documented by spectrohelioscopic observations of Kharkov and Ondřejov observatories. The strong blue asymmetry (Fig. 11) indicates motion of the prominence mass towards the observer. It is a velocity of the same order as was measured in the first stage of the blast-forming, from which it appears that the process is actually a continuation of the phenomenon.

Fig. 7   The beginning stage of the 11 July phenomenon, 0912 UT. Notice the absorption strip of the chromosphere. Ondřejov Observatory, 0.8 Å filter.

In this way we conclude that the blast phenomenon was in reality a twisted prominence, which started in a direction parallel to the plane of the disk and after completing a twist returned to the chromosphere in a direction nearly perpendicular to the initial direction. The twisted part later disappeared at the limb in the new direction, as can be seen from drawings representing the comparison of Arcetri, Catania, and Ondřejov pictures (Fig. 12).

The phenomenon ended at 1100 UT. At 1117 only a small group of surges and a small prominence remained. It seems that the limb activity above the 21034 group for this rotation ended with this phenomenon.

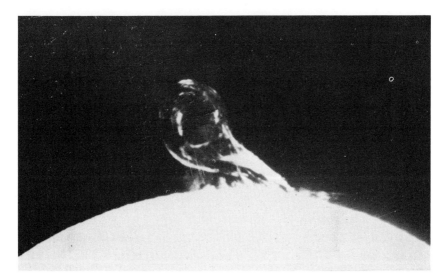

Fig. 8   The blast-forming stage of the 11 July phenomenon, 0934 UT. Ondřejov Observatory, 0.8 Å filter.

Fig. 9   Maximum intensity stage of the 11 July phenomenon, 0947 UT. Ondřejov
Observatory, 0.8 Å filter.

4   Concluding Remarks

The limb activity during the transit of the proton flare region across the
limb is characterized by the formation on 9 and 10 July of loop prominences
and by 11 July a great eruptive prominence. The form of this phenomenon

Fig. 10   Maximum intensity stage of the 11 July phenomenon, 0949 UT. Ondřejov
Observatory coronagraph, 8 Å filter.

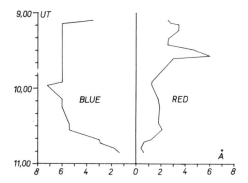

Fig. 11   Variations of the Hα line-width on the 11 July eruptive prominence (Kharkov Observatory).

seems to demonstrate the existence of complex magnetic fields above the active region.

The coherence in inclination of all phenomena (the system of loops of 9 July, the isolated loop of 10 July, and finally, the eruptive prominence of 11 July) seems to be very important. In all cases this inclination was between 40° and 60°. It appears that above the active region there always exists one constant system of magnetic fields, which hampers the motion of all prominence-type phenomena in directions other than the preferred direction.

The development of the phenomenon of 11 July is interesting because of the sudden change in velocity and the ensuing formation of the blast. The consequent general decrease of the activity, which on 11 July is probably associated with this extremely energetic process, leads to the situation where the magnetic force is overcome by the kinetic energy of the prominence mass in twisted motion.

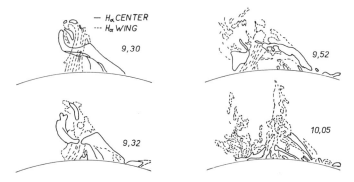

Fig. 12   Sketches of the eruptive prominence of 11 July (*c.* 0930 UT) according to Arcetri (0.5 Å pass band), Ondřejov (8 Å pass band) and Kharkov spectrohelioscope.

17

Radio Bursts associated with Active Region McMath No. 8362 of July 1966

O. Yudin* and K. Kai†‡
* Radiophysical Research Institute, Gorky University, Gorky, USSR
† Tokyo Astronomical Observatory, Tokyo, Japan

Abstract

Observational data of radio bursts associated with an active region McMath No. 8362 in the range 1.76 cm–13.5 m are given for the period 2–11 July 1966. In the period preceding the proton event of 7 July, the noticeable increase of number and intensity of radio bursts at 3 cm wavelength range is greater than that in other wavelength ranges. After the proton flare on 7 July in the active region 8362 some comparatively greater bursts were observed: on 8 July at 0030 UT and 1706 UT, on 9 July at 0230 UT, and on 11 July at 0912.5 UT.

The region 8362[1] which produced the proton flare at 0020 UT on 7 July began to develop activity on 3 July. In Table 1 observational data of radio bursts[2] associated with this active region in the wavelength range 1.76 cm–13.5 m are given for the period 30 June–11 July. Practically continuous solar observations were possible in all frequency ranges due to participation of a great number of observatories in the proton flare project (PFP) programme. For the analysis observational data obtained in the following observatories were used: Astrophysical Observatory Potsdam (AOP), Research Institute of Atmospherics, Nagoya University (NAG), University of Bologna (BOL),

---

‡ Now at Division of Radiophysics, C.S.I.R.O., Epping, Sydney, N.S.W., Australia.
[1] Numbering of regions is made according to the data of McMath-Hulbert Observatory.
[2] In a number of cases bursts observed at nearly the same frequencies at different observatories show appreciable differences in duration, maximum time and intensity. This fact may be explained by the differences in sensitivity and stability of receiving apparatus.

Radiophysical Research Institute, Gorky University (GOR), University of Hawaii (HAW), Heinrich Hertz Institute (HHI), Kiel University (KIEL), Kislovodsk Observatory (KIS), National Bureau of Standards (NBS), Nera Station (NERA), National Research Council (OTT), Ondřejov Observatory (AOO), Crimean Astrophysical Observatory (SIM), Tokyo Astronomical Observatory (TOK), New Copernicus University (TOR), Royal Observatory Belgium (UCC), Ussurijsk Observatory (USS), Astrophysical Observatory Arcetri (ARC), High Altitude Observatory (HAO), Sagamore Hill Observatory (SGM), Pennsylvania State University (PEN), Hiraiso Radiowave Observatory (HIR). (Tables appear following text and references.)

Since the different observatories use somewhat different classifications of radio bursts, the types of bursts shown in Table 1 have been modified to a common system, though some inaccuracies are possible. For the centimetre and decimetre range ($\lambda \leqslant 50$ cm, $f \geqslant 600$ MHz) the classification given in *Solar–Geophysical Data* (1966) and described by Covington (1951, 1959) is used. All indications are given according to the URANE code (daily flux level and outstanding phenomena). Additional indications have been introduced as follows: Great Burst 10, Rise only 11, Fall only and Absorption 12. For the decimetre and metre range the determination of burst types is based on the classification described in *Solar–Geophysical Data* (1966, p. 27) and by Dodson *et al.* (1953).

As is known, a precise coincidence of radio bursts with flares does not always take place, especially in the case of weak events. We may more confidently single out a group of bursts and flares associated with it. In Table 2 there are given the averaged data characterizing starting, maximum, and ending times for both groups of radio bursts and flares in Hα.[3] The table contains the group of bursts which are well identified with the proper flares in the region 8362, and certain groups of bursts which may be associated with the flares in other active regions. In certain cases we were successful in singling out bursts whose association with flares in other regions was established (such bursts are not included in Table 1). In some cases two or more flares occurring in different active regions (including the region 8362) were observed simultaneously with a burst; thus it is impossible to say confidently that the bursts observed are associated with a definite active region. Such events are indicated in italics in Table 1. It is seen that most bursts for the period 6–10 July are associated with flares in the region 8362 since during this period all solar activity was in this region. Until 5 July only occasional bursts with small intensity were observed, but after 1200 UT on 5 July bursts began to occur more frequently. At the same time the frequency of flare occurrence in the region 8362 increased. On 6 July the solar activity continued increasing. In Fig. 1 the histogram shows the change of the number of bursts and flares for 3-hour intervals. The histogram of the number of bursts (*c*) has a maximum at 1200–2400 UT on 6 July. Most of them were observed at $\lambda = 3$ cm

[3] The range of scattering of individual values may be of the order of 10–15 minutes.

(*d*), with the maximum within 1200–1500 UT. In the range $\lambda = 8.0$–10.0 cm, on the other hand, the total number of bursts is less (*e*) though observations were carried out continuously. The total number of flares in the region 8362 (*b*) and that of flares of importance equal to or greater than 1 (*a*) do not show such appreciable maxima. In the same figure histograms of total energy of bursts (for 3-hour intervals) are given both at 3 cm (*f*) and at 8–10 cm (*g*). From these diagrams it is seen that about one day before the proton flare, the energy of radio bursts started to increase, especially at 3 cm. The decrease

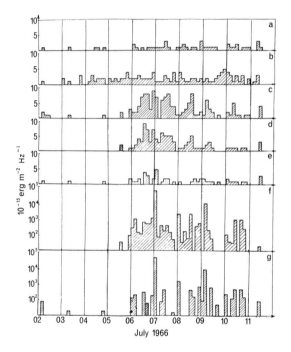

Fig. 1   Comparison of numbers of bursts and flares. *a*. number of flares in region 8362 (importance 1); *b*. number of flares in region 8362; *c*. number of bursts; *d*. number of bursts (range 3 cm); *e*. number of bursts (range 8–10 cm); *f*. total energy of burst (range 3 cm); *g*. total energy of bursts (range 8–10 cm).

of solar activity was less rapid than its rise. After the proton flare on 7 July in the active region 8362 some comparatively greater bursts associated with chromospheric flares were observed: (*a*) on 8 July a burst at 0030 UT associated with an importance 1B flare at 0028 UT; (*b*) on 8 July a burst at 1706 UT associated with an importance 2N–2B flare at 1710 UT; (*c*) on 9 July a burst at 0230 UT associated with an importance 3B flare at 0230 UT; (*d*) on 11 July a burst at 0912.5 UT associated with an importance 4N–3+ flare at 0904 UT. A burst at 0230 UT on 9 July is the next greatest to that

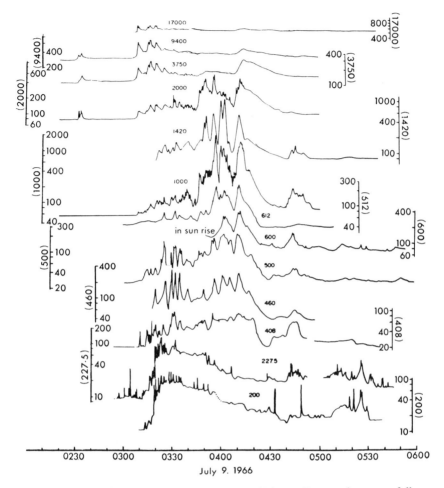

Fig. 2   Single-frequency records of the 9 July 1966 burst. Frequencies are as follows:
17000 (TOK), 9400 (NAG), 3750 (NAG), 2000 (NAG), 1420 (KIEL), 1000
(NAG), 612 (TOK), 600 (UCC), 500 (HIR), 460 (KIEL), 408 (TOK), 227.5
(TOK), 200 (HIR).

associated with the proton flare on 7 July. Detailed descriptions of the latter
event are given in other articles of this series (Stewart 1968, Enome 1968,
Kai 1968). Single-frequency records of the July 9 burst and a dynamic
spectrum drawn from single-frequency records are given in Figs. 2 and 3,
respectively.

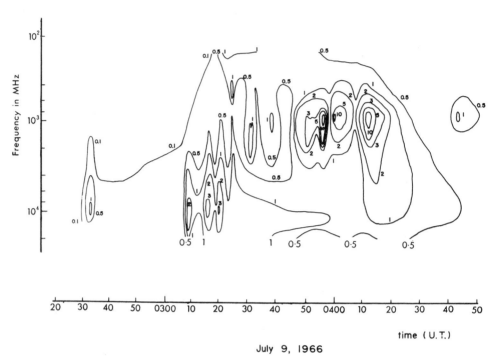

July 9, 1966

Fig. 3   Dynamic spectrum of 9 July 1966 burst. Flux densities are given in units of 10^{-20}W m^{-2}Hz^{-1}.

Acknowledgments

The authors are very grateful to all international colleagues from different observatories for their observational data which composed the main content of the present paper.

References

COVINGTON, A. E., 1951, Some characteristics of 10.7 cm solar noise, II, *J. R. Astr. Soc. Can.*, **45**, 49–51.

—— 1959, Solar emission at 10 cm wavelength, *Paris Symposium on Radio Astronomy*, Ed. R. N. Bracewell (Stanford University Press, Stanford, California), pp. 159–165.

DODSON, H. W., E. R. HEDEMAN, and L. OWREN, 1953, Solar flares and associated 200 Mc/sec radiation, *Astrophys. J.*, **118**, 169–196.

ENOME, S., 1968, Single-frequency bursts observed in Japan during the proton event of 7 July 1966, *Ann. IQSY*, this volume, Paper 27.

KAI, K., 1968, The complete Type IV burst associated with the proton event of 7 July 1966, *Ann. IQSY*, this volume, Paper 28.

Solar–Geophysical Data, 1966, (Descriptive Text and Index), *IV Solar Radio Waves*, Jan. 1966, Institute for Telecommunication Sciences and Aeronomy of the ESSA, Boulder, Colorado, pp. 21–29 (Government Printing Office, Washington, D.C.).

STEWART, R. T., 1968, The dynamic spectrum of the proton event of 7 July 1966, *Ann. IQSY*, this volume, Paper 25.

Table 1　Solar Radio Emission: Outstanding Occurrences 2–11 July 1966

(1)	(2)	(3)	(4)	(5)	(6)	(7)	(8)	(9)	(10)
					Time		Flux Density		Polariza-
Date	Freq.	Station	Type	Start Time	of Max.	Duration	$(10^{-22}\mathrm{W\,m^{-2}Hz^{-1}})$		tion
July	(Hz)			(UT)	(UT)	(min)	Peak	Mean	0, l, r, L, R
02	3750	TOY	3	0500.0	0520.2	40.0	5.0	2.0	0
	2000	TOY	3	0500.0	0520.0	40.0	2.0	1.0	0
	260	AOO	1	0525.0	0642.0	145.0	15.0		
	260	AOO	0	0835.0	0913.0	57.0	15.0		
	127	TOR	2	1124.0	1135.0	34.0	4.0		
03	3000	HHI	3	0714.5	0725.0	24.5	2.0	0.8	
	2000	HHI	3A	0714.5					
			1	0714.5	0715.9	3.0	1.5	0.9	
	1500	HHI	3A7		0725.0	19.0	2.0	0.8	
			1	0714.5	0715.8	3.0	2.0	0.8	
04	2800	OTT	3	1920.0	2000.0	195.0	2.2	1.1	
05	9400	HHI	1	1344.0	1344.6	2.5	6.0	1.0	
	9400	HHI	1	1350.0	1350.8	4.0	5.5	1.5	
	9100	GOR	3	1349.0	1350.0	9.0	8.5	4.0	
	2800	OTT	12	2100.0	2150.0	65.0	−2.6	−1.3	
	9400	NAG	3	2223.0	2229.2	25.0	12.0	4.0	r
	2800	OTT	1	2238.0	2240.0	5.0	1.2	0.6	
06	9400	NAG	37	0036.0	0040.0	70.0	11.0	4.0	0
	3750	NAG	37	0036.0	0040.0	55.0	3.0	2.0	0
	17000	TOK	17	0152.6	0152.8	1.0	29.0		r
	9400	NAG	37	0315.0	0415.5	115.0	22.0	5.0	0
	9100	GOR	3A	0321.0	0534.0	159.0	30.0	8.0	
			1	0359.0	0400.5	2.0	5.0	3.0	
			1	0414.5	0415.5	6.5	10.0	2.0	
	3750	NAG	3	0335.0	0400.4	85.0	8.0	3.0	0
	17000	TOK	274	0533.8	0534.4	4.0	140.0		r
			4			11.0	24.0		r
	9400	NAG	2	0533.0	0534.3	20.0	45.0	15.0	l
	9100	GOR	2	0533.5	0534.2	1.5	32.0	16.0	
	17000	TOK	1	0629.7	0629.9	3.0	48.0		r
	9400	HHI	3	0629.0	0629.7	30.0	19.0	4.0	
	9400	NAG	3	0629.0	0629.8	10.0	11.0	4.0	l
	9100	GOR	3	0629.0	0629.7	9.0	13.0	5.0	
	3000	HHI	3	0627.0	0640.0U	55.0U	4.0		
	2000	HHI	3	0642.5	0648.0	20.0	0.6	0.3	
	9400	HHI	1	0805.0	0807.0	7.0	8.5	3.0	
	9100	GOR	1	0805.0	0807.0	5.0	10.0	5.0	
	3000	HHI	1	0805.0	0807.5	7.0	1.0	0.6	
	9400	HHI	37	0815.0	0818.5	19.0	8.5	3.0	
	9100	GOR	3	0814.0	0816.2	14.0	10.0	5.0	
	9100	GOR	1	0842.0	0842.7	2.0	5.0	2.5	
	111	AOP	8	0914.8	0914.9	0.1	120.0	20.0	
	9400	HHI	3	1013.5	1017.0	13.5	5.0	3.0	
	9100	GOR	1	1014.0	1014.5	6.0	5.0	2.5	
	9400	HHI	3A7	1039.0	1044.0	21.0	9.0	3.0	
	9100	GOR	3A	1033.0	1049.2	37.0	8.0	3.5	
	9400	HHI	1	1049.0	1049.4	2.0	12.0	3.5	
	9100	GOR	1	1049.0	1049.2	1.0	7.0	3.5	
	127	TOR	2	0952.0	1044.0	206.0	17.0	2.0	
	23	AOP	3	1033.3	1033.4	0.3	2000.0	700.0	
	9400	HHI	3		1320.0U		8.0		
	9100	GOR	3	1258.0	1303.2	33.0	13.0	7.0	
	8800	SGM	3	1154.0	1304.0	98.0	20.4	10.0	
	4995	SGM	3	1154.0	1304.0	96.0	7.0	3.5	
	3000	HHI	3	1310.0	1316.0	24.0U	1.0	0.6	
	2695	SGM	3	1154.0	1322.0	106.0	5.4	2.5	
	9400	HHI	24	1301.0	1304.0	36.0	31.0	4.0	
	9100	GOR	2	1302.5	1303.2	2.5	26.0	13.0	
	8800	SGM	2	1301.0	1303.8	4.5	17.0	4.2	
	9400	HHI	3A	1347.0		100.0			
	3000	HHI	3A		1435.0U		3.0	1.0	
	2695	SGM	3	1355.0	1458.0	75.0	4.8	2.4	
	9400	HHI	1	1351.4	1352.6	2.0	9.5	3.0	
	9100	GOR	1	1351.0	1351.7	3.0	9.0	4.5	
	8800	SGM	17	1351.5	1351.7	5.5	8.5	2.2	
	9400	HHI	1	1354.5	1355.5	2.0	11.0	4.0	
	9100	GOR	37	1355.0	1355.7	13.5	9.0	4.5	
	3000	HHI	1	1355.0	1355.5	3.0	3.0	1.0	
	2000	HHI	1	1355.0	1355.5	1.0	0.6	0.3	
	10700	PEN	2	1400.0	1403.8	1.1D	34.0	17.0	
	4995	SGM	3	1340.0	1403.0	27.0	7.0	3.5	
	2000	HHI	3		1400.0		2.0	0.6	
	9100	GOR	1	1412.0	1413.2	6.5	14.5		
	8800	SGM	1	1412.5	1413.4	1.8	13.6	4.3	
	4995	SGM	1	1412.5	1413.3	1.8	5.3	1.5	
	2000	HHI	U		1412.0				
	10700	PEN	1	1451.2	1451.5	2.0	7.2	3.6	

(1)	(2)	(3)	(4)	(5)	(6)	(7)	(8)	(9)	(10)
06	10700	PEN	1	1454.4	1455.0	1.4	7.2	3.6	
	2700	PEN	1	1454.6	1455.1	1.3	1.5	0.7	
	10700	PEN	1	1512.4	1513.2	1.5	4.9	2.4	
	9400	HHI	3A	1545.5		100.0			
	8800	SGM	3A	1545.0	1550.0	22.0	3.4	1.6	
	3000	HHI	3	1539.0	1626.0	106.0	3.0	1.0	
	2695	SGM	3A	1545.0	1550.0	22.0	2.4	1.2	
	2000	HHI	3	1542.0		96.0	0.6	0.3	
	9400	HHI	14	1545.5	1546.0	14.5U	9.5	4.0	
	8800	SGM	1	1545.9	1546.0	0.6	6.7	2.5	
	2695	SGM	1	1545.3	1545.7	0.9	1.8	0.4	
	8800	SGM	1	1548.1	1548.2	0.4	6.7	1.5	
	2695	SGM	1	1548.2	1548.9	1.1	2.4	0.6	
	9400	HHI	1	1639.5	1640.0	5.5	7.0	3.0	
	9400	HHI	1	1647.5	1648.0	3.5	6.0	2.0	
	606	SGM	8	1717.5	1718.0	0.6	53.9	8.0	
	8800	SGM	3	1755.0	1833.5	64.0	34.5	8.0	
	8800	SGM	3	1909.0	1914.6	23.0	6.9	1.0	
	8800	SGM	3	1937.0	1939.5	30.0	17.3	4.0	
	8800	SGM	3	2009.0	2031.2	53.0	34.5	8.0	
	10700	PEN	1	2115.6	2117.2	2.2	7.3	3.7	
	10700	PEN	3	2130.0	2131.1	12.4	31.8	15.6	
	8800	SGM	1	2131.5	2132.0	5.5	12.1	3.0	
	10700	PEN	1	2149.0	2150.0	3.4	14.7	7.3	
	9400	NAG	3	2150.0	2151.5	13.0	37.0	10.0	l
	8800	SGM	3	2150.0	2151.6	24.0	27.6	6.0	
	2700	PEN	3	2115.0	2148.8	54.0	1.4	1.2U	
	9400	NAG	1	2205.0	2206.0	6.0	11.0	3.0	r
	17000	TOK	1	2217.5	2217.8	2.0	16.0		r
	10700	PEN	3	2216.6	2217.5	12.2	19.6	9.8	
	17000	TOK	1	2226.0	2228.3	5.0	26.0		r
	10700	PEN	1	2231.0	2231.7	1.8	14.7	7.3	
	9400	NAG	3	2217.0	2228.2	25.0	22.0	7.0	0
	8800	SGM	3	2216.0	2228.4	30.0	20.7	5.0	
	10700	PEN	3	2250.2	2251.4	24.0	53.8	26.2	
	2800	OTT	3	2245.0	2300.0	100.0	2.6	1.5	
	10700	PEN	3	2324.6	2328.2	12.2	29.4	14.0	
07	17000	TOK	610	0026.0	0038.0U	114.0	8000.0		r
	9400	NAG	610	0018.0	0037.5	112.0	12750.0	765.0	r
	3750	NAG	610	0026.0	0037.5	114.0	4730.0	475.0	lr
	2800	OTT	610	0025.9	0038.0	90.0	2650.0		
	2000	NAG	610	0026.0	0037.8	129.0	2300.0	290.0	l
	1000	NAG	610	0026.0	0124.3	142.0	3890.0	390.0	lrLrlrL
	500	HIR	8	0029.0	0037.8	110.0	1435.0	155.0	
	200	HIR	8	0030.0	0038.3	95.0	810.0	95.0	
	9400	NAG	3	0340.0	0343.0	10.0	4.0	2.0	l
	9100	GOR	3	0342.0	0346.0	12.0	6.0	3.0	
	9400	NAG	3	0400.0	0404.0	10.0	5.0	2.0	0
	9100	GOR	3	0400.5	0404.5	10.0	7.0	3.5	
	9400	NAG	3	0429.0	0430.6	9.0	4.0	2.0	r
	9100	GOR	1	0429.0	0430.5	7.0	6.0	3.0	
	2000	NAG	3	0430.0	0432.4	10.0	2.0	1.0	l
	1000	NAG	7	0430.0	0433.0	20.0	2.0	1.0	0
	9400	NAG	1	0616.0	0618.0	4.0	4.0	2.0	r
	2000	HHI	3	0615.0	0620.0	40.0D	2.0		
	9400	NAG	7	0640.0	0646.0	66.0	11.0	5.0	r
	9400	HHI	3A7	0615.0E	0646.0	125.0D	17.0		
	9100	GOR	3	0641.5	0646.0	10.0	8.0	4.0	
	3750	NAG	3	0700.0	0723.0	40.0	2.0	1.0	0
	3000	HHI	3	0620.0	0647.0	121.0D	3.0	1.0	
	9400	HHI	1	0759.7	0800.0	7.3	11.0	4.0	
	9100	GOR	37	0800.0	0801.0	20.0	6.5	4.5	
	9100	GOR	11	0824.0		27.0	7.0		
	9100	GOR	3A	0854.0	0901.0	46.0	10.5	5.0	
	9400	HHI	1	0857.5	0859.0	7.3	18.0	5.5	
	9100	GOR	1	0857.5	0859.0	3.5	14.5	7.0	
	9400	HHI	3	0912.0U	0923.5	42.5	11.0		
	9100	GOR	3		0923.5	34.0D	10.0		
	3000	HHI	3	0919.0	0931.5	28.0	2.0	1.0	
	127	TOR	3	1005.0	1006.0	4.0	356.0	250.0	
	127	TOR	3	1041.0	1043.0	5.0	21.0D	17.0	
	3000	HHI	3A7	1145.0	1235.0	300.0	4.5	2.0	
	2880	OTT	3	1140.0	1240.0	120.0	3.0	1.5	
	2000	HHI	3A	1142.0	1230.0	183.0	2.0	1.0	
	1500	HHI	3	1140.0	1230.0	200.0	1.0		
	9400	HHI	37	1149.0	1152.0	6.0U	5.5	3.5	
	9400	HHI	3	1155.5	1200.0	7.5	4.0	2.0	
	9100	GOR	3A	1149.0	1152.0	11.0D	8.0	4.0	
			1	1149.0	1149.5	0.7	6.0	3.0	
			1	1151.0	1151.5	1.0	4.0	2.0	
	9400	HHI	3	1221.0	1228.0	31.0	12.0	5.5	
	9400	HHI	37	1252.0	1256.0	24.0	5.5	2.5	
	9100	GOR	37	1220.0U	1241.5	30.0	6.0	5.0	
	3000	HHI			1300.0				
	2000	HHI			1310.0				

(1)	(2)	(3)	(4)	(5)	(6)	(7)	(8)	(9)	(10)
07	9400	HHI	3A	1319.0	1319.5	9.0	11.0	3.5	
	9100	GOR	1	1319.0	1319.5	2.0	10.0	5.0	
	1500	HHI			1320.0				
	9400	HHI	1		1325.3		6.0		
	9100	GOR	1	1324.0	1325.0	3.0	4.0	2.0	
	9400	HHI	3	1349.0	1352.0	40.0	8.0	5.0	
	3000	HHI			1410.0				
	9400	HHI			1425.0				
	9400	HHI	3	1613.0	1615.8	12.0	12.0	5.0	
	9400	HHI	1	1626.5	1626.8	2.0	5.5	2.5	
	10700	PEN	7	1714.5	1716.3	9.4	10.0	5.0	
	10700	PEN	1	1725.3	1725.8	0.7	14.9		
	9400	HHI	2	1755.0	1756.8	2.5	28.0	11.0	
	8800	SGM	2	1755.0	1756.9	3.0	34.3	20.0	
	10700	PEN	1	1834.8	1835.4	1.8	10.1	5.1	
	10700	PEN	1	1856.5	1857.0	1.6	25.4	12.7	
	8800	SGM	3	1932.0	1937.0	8.0	5.0	3.0	
	2700	PEN	1	1941.9	1942.7	2.2	8.7	7.7	
	606	SGM	8	2142.6	2144.4	3.4	61.1	5.6	
08	17000	TOK	2	0031.0	0033.3	4.0	100.0		r
	9400	NAG	24		0033.2	25.0	225.0	45.0	r
			4			95.0	35.0	15.0	
	3750	NAG	274		0033.5	35.0	122.0	25.0	lr
			4			95.0	15.0	7.0	
	2800	OTT	3A		0050.0	115.0D	8.0		
			27	0025.0	0033.8	20.0	38.0	9.0	
	1000	NAG	27	0030.0	0031.4	10.0	18.0	2.0	0
	184	GOR	3	0446.7	0447.1	3.6	10.2	4.9	
	92	GOR	2	0445.0	0450.0	6.0	160.0U	6.0	
	9100	GOR	1	0512.0	0514.5	7.0	11.0	5.0	
	9100	GOR	3	0748.0	0803.0	33.0	6.0	4.0	
	9400	HHI	1	0830.0	0833.0	6.5	14.0	5.5	
	9100	GOR	1	0832.0	0833.0	8.0	13.0	4.0	
	260	AOO	1	0735.0	0905.5	155.0	20.0		
	127	TOR	3	0926.0	0928.0	3.0	40.0	27.0	
	127	TOR	3	0952.0	0952.0	4.0	38.0D	37.0	
	111	AOP	2	0952.6	0952.9	1.3	400.0	20.0	
	23	AOP	2	0952.7	0952.8	1.3	4000.0	800.0	
	9400	HHI	37	1120.0	1122.0	14.0	7.0	3.0	
	9400	HHI	1	1148.8	1150.3	6.0	12.0	5.5	
	8800	SGM	1	1149.5	1150.3	2.5	9.8	2.9	
	127	TOR	2	1127.0	1151.0	52.0	11.0		
	9400	HHI	3A	1200.0		250.0			
	9400	HHI	27	1212.0	1213.2	15.0	58.0	22.0	
					1214.5		50.0		
	8800	SGM	64	1212.5	1213.7	2.6	57.4	41.2	
			4			21.6	26.3	13.2	
	4995	SGM	14	1213.1	1214.6	2.2	9.7	5.0	
			4			21.5	3.6	1.8	
	9500	NERA	27	1237.0	1239.0	3.0	68.0	27.3	
	9400	HHI	274	1236.0	1239.0	47.0U	78.0	20.0	
	9100	GOR	274	1236.0	1238.8	5.0	74.0	36.0	
			4			50.0	44.0	22.0	
	8800	SGM	274	1236.7	1239.0	4.0	92.3	74.6	
			4			113.0	52.5	26.0	
	4995	SGM	24	1236.8	1239.1	4.0	37.2	30.5	
			4			110.0	25.0	12.5	
	3000	NERA	3	1238.0	1243.0	84.0	10.0	3.0	
	3000	HHI	3	1237.5	1245.0	224.0U	7.0	2.0	
	2800	OTT	3	1237.0	1244.0	155.0	8.6	4.3	
	2695	SGM	3	1237.1	1243.4	150.0	9.2	4.0	
	2000	HHI	3A	1237.0	1243.0	148.0	2.5	1.0	
			1	1242.5	1242.7	0.5	1.0	0.7	
	1500	HHI	3A	1242.0	1250.0	42.0	1.5	1.0	
			1	1242.0	1242.7	0.8	2.5	1.5	
	1415	SGM	1	1242.5	1242.7	0.3	1.5	0.6	
	606	SGM	8	1253.5	1256.6	3.2	2.0	0.6	
	10700	PEN	2	1312.4	1313.7	9.1U	68.5	28.4	
	10700	PEN	3	1337.0	1339.0	28.0D	83.2		
	10700	PEN	3	1337.5	1405.0U	28.0D			
	260	AOO	3	1338.0		0.5	15.0		
	260	AOO	3	1414.0		0.5	15.0		
	260	AOO	3	1444.0		0.5	20.0		
	10700	PEN	24	1706.8		6.2	254.0	64.0	
			4			48.0	54.0	27.0	
	9500	NERA	27	1708.5	1733.3	6.0	177.0	41.0	
	9400	HHI	274	1706.5	1711.5	50.0D	268.0		
	8800	SGM	U	1654.0		88.0	38.9D		
	4995	SGM	U	1654.0		64.0	23.9		
	3000	NERA	24	1709.5	1711.3	5.0	23.0	10.0	
			4			30.0	7.0	3.0	
	3000	HHI	24	1707.0	1711.5	23.0D	27.0		
	2800	OTT	24	1709.5	1711.5	4.5	14.4	7.2	
			4			109.0	4.8	2.4	
	2700	PEN	24	1709.0	1710.5	4.0	14.0	6.0	
			4			50.0	2.2	1.1	
	2695	SGM	U			31.0D	31.0D		
	2000	HHI	14	1710.0	1711.5	30.0	3.0	1.3	

(1)	(2)	(3)	(4)	(5)	(6)	(7)	(8)	(9)	(10)
08	8800	SGM	3	2100.0	2103.7	48.0	27.0	4.0	
	4995	SGM	3	2048.9	2103.5	42.0	17.8	3.0	
	2695	SGM	3	2047.0	2110.0	43.0	6.0	3.0	
	2800	OTT	37	2135.0	2145.0	40.0	1.6	0.8	
	200	HIR	8	2143.0	2143.8	5.0	310.0	25.0	
	9400	NAG	37	2227.0	2230.0	80.0	25.0	10.0	
	8800	SGM	2	2227.0	2230.5	5.0	23.7	4.0	
	4995	SGM	2	2227.0	2230.5	5.0	17.4	3.0	
	3750	NAG	3	2227.0	2252.0	120.0	10.0	5.0	
	2800	OTT	11	2220.0		20.0	5.6		
09	200	HIR	8	0037.0	0039.0	2.5	260.0	25.0	
	3750	NAG	3	0147.0	0157.0	30.0	6.0	3.0	0
	17000	TOK	6	0308.3	0308.9	114.0	195.0		r
	9400	NAG	6	0229.0	0316.3	170.0	385.0	75.0	r
	9100	GOR	6		0316.5	125.0D	204.0D		
	3750	NAG	6	0231.0	0414.0	160.0	200.0	57.0	lrlrlr
	3000	NERA	6	0410.0E		50.0D	150.0U		
	2000	NAG	6	0231.0	0356.1	150.0	515.0	70.0	lrlr
	1420	KIEL	6		0402.0	80.0	1110.0		
	1000	NAG	6	0308.0	0356.8	117.0	1865.0	180.0	L
	650	GOR	6		0357.0		698.0		
	612	TOK	6	0315.0	0411.3	100.0	265.0		l
	610	NERA	6	0328.0	0400.0	109.0D	400.0	40.0D	
	600	UCC	6	0339.0	0413.0U	190.0D	450.0U		
	500	HIR	8	0309.0	0402.0	111.0	200.0	50.0	
	460	KIEL	4		0330.0	80.0U	325.0		
	408	TOK	4	0313.0	0331.7	100.0	95.0	75.0	
	227.5	TOK	4	0317.0	0323.5	135.0	135.0		rl
	200	NERA	4	0328.0	0328.0	245.0D	150.0D	30.0D	l
	200	HIR	8	0315.0	0329.3	80.0	140.0	45.0	
	2000	NAG	37	0510.0	0513.4	20.0	16.0	4.0	0
	1000	NAG	37	0510.0	0522.0	20.0	17.0	10.0	l
	9100	GOR	1	0532.0	0534.0	4.0	4.0	2.0	
	9100	GOR	1	0541.0	0542.0	5.0	7.0	3.0	
	1000	NAG	6	0546.0	0551.0	12.0	55.0	12.0	l
	2000	NAG	6	0558.0	0607.0	22.0	13.0	5.0	0
	1000	NAG	6	0600.0	0605.0	21.0	9.0	5.0	0
	9400	HHI	U4	0620.0E		150.0D			
	3000	HHI	U4	0625.0E		350.0D			
	2000	HHI	U4	0615.0E		555.0D			
	1000	HHI	U4	0615.0E		585.0D			
	9400	HHI	3A7	0720.0	0725.0	55.0U	15.0	5.0	
	9100	GOR	3	0720.0	0724.0	21.0	15.0	6.0	
	6100	KIS	3	0713.0	0726.0	30.0	19.0	7.0	
	9400	HHI			0755.0		10.0		
	9100	GOR	3	0749.0	0755.0	15.0	5.0	2.0	
	9100	GOR	3	1140.0	1150.0	20.0D	7.0		
	2800	OTT	12	1100.0		220.0	−7.2		
	4995	SGM	3	1714.0	1723.5	22.0	7.7	2.5	
	2695	SGM	3	1714.0	1723.6	23.0	4.8	2.4	
	1415	SGM	3	1714.0	1728.0	44.0	3.2	1.5	
	606	SGM	3	1714.0	1757.0	186.0	1.2	0.6	
	127	TOR	9	all day		360.0D		4.0	
10	9400	NAG	3	0050.0	0110.0	40.0	7.0	3.0	r
	3750	NAG	3	0050.0	0110.0	60.0	9.0	4.0	r
	2800	OTT	3	0045.0	0110.0	70.0D	6.2		
	2000	NAG	3	0050.0	0110.0	40.0	2.0	1.0	0
	3750	NAG	1	0215.5	0216.1	1.0	3.0	1.0	0
	3750	NAG	1	0333.0	0333.3	1.0	3.0	1.0	0
	9400	NAG	37	0340.0	0340.9	10.0	25.0	4.0	r
	9400	HHI	3A	0709.0	0727.0	111.0	11.0	5.5	
	9400	HHI	1	0710.5	0711.2	1.5	17.0	8.0	
	9100	GOR	14	0710.5	0711.4	1.5	14.0	8.0	
			4			22.0	4.0	2.0	
	6100	KIS	37	0710.0	0711.0	11.0	14.0	4.0	
	3000	NERA	37	0709.2	0716.0	13.0	10.0	6.0	
	3000	HHI	374	0709.0	0716.0	96.0U	9.0	2.0	
	2000	HHI	374	0708.0	0716.0	172.0	6.0	2.3	
	1500	HHI	374	0708.0	0717.0	152.0	6.5	2.0	
	127	TOR	3	0924.0	0924.0	2.0	76.0D	68.0	
	111	AOP	2	0925.2	0925.4	0.5	350.0	20.0	
	23	AOP	2	0940.8	0941.7	1.1	2000.0	300.0	
	127	TOR	2	0953.0	0956.0	4.0	21.0	11.0	
	127	TOR	2	1105.0	1105.0	5.0	7.0	3.0	
	23	AOP	3	1128.9	1128.9	0.2	1000.0	300.0	
	9400	HHI	3A7	1142.0	1146.7	138.0	30.0	10.0	
			1	1216.0	1218.0	5.0	13.5	2.0	
	8800	SGM	3A7	1141.0	1218.0	121.0	14.8	7.0	
			1	1144.5	1148.5	3.5	18.5	6.2	
	4995	SGM	3A7	1142.0	1148.0	103.0	22.3	11.0	
			2	1145.0	1146.5	3.5	20.3	6.5	
	3000	NERA	37	1144.6	1149.0	60.0U	13.0	6.0	
	3000	HHI	37	1144.0	1146.5	136.0	11.0	3.0	
	2800	OTT	3	1144.0	1146.0	136.0	9.0	4.5	
	2695	SGM	3A7	1142.8	1151.0	126.0	8.5	4.5	
			17	1144.8	1146.5	5.2	6.7	3.0	
	2000	HHI	3	1145.0	1155.0	110.0	2.0	1.0	
	1500	HHI	3	1145.0	1200.0	55.0	0.7	0.2	

(1)	(2)	(3)	(4)	(5)	(6)	(7)	(8)	(9)	(10)
10	127	TOR	2	1152.0	1155.0	7.0	6.0	2.0	
	328	PEN	3	1342.0	1342.5	3.6	92.0	28.0	
	—10700	PEN	24	1620.0	1629.3	8.0	147.0	71.0	
			4			58.0	46.0	20.3	
	—9500	NERA	24	1628.0	1631.0	5.0	30%	10%	
			4			12.0	10%	8%	
	—9400	HHI	3A	1619.0		100.0			
			2	1627.5	1631.0	8.0U	142.0	47.0	
	—8800	SGM	U	1627.0U	1638.0U	175.0D	25.0D		
	—4995	SGM	U	1627.0U	1638.0U	124.0D	15.0D		
	—3000	NERA	24	1627.0	1631.0	11.0	17.0	8.0	
			4			70.0	8.0	5.0	
	—2800	OTT	3A	1627.0	1637.0	153.0	8.2	4.1	
			27	1630.0	1631.0	7.0	9.0	4.5	
	—2700	PEN	3	1625.0	1629.0	75.0	11.5	6.0	
	—2695	SGM	U	1627.0U	1638.0U	122.0D	10.0D		
	—2000	HHI	3	1629.5	1630.0	72.0	2.0	1.0	
	—1415	SGM	U	1627.0U	1638.0U	33.0D	2.0D		
	—8800	SGM	3	1936.0	2008.0	78.0	8.5	3.5	
	—4995	SGM	3	1939.0	2026.0	70.0	7.5	3.7	
	—2800	OTT	35	1930.0	1950.0	90.0	3.6	1.8	
	—2800	OTT	5	2100.0	2245.0	140.0	−3.2	−1.6	
11	—9400	HHI	1	0913.0	0913.6	2.5	5.0	2.5	
	—6100	KIS	2	0912.0	0913.0	5.0	20.0	5.7	
	—3100	SIM	2	0907.0			9.0		
	—3000	NERA	27	0914.0	0914.6	3.0	18.0	10.0	
	—3000	HHI	27	0912.5	0913.8	4.5U	19.0	5.0	
	—2000	HHI	17	0912.5	0913.8	4.0U	5.0	3.0	
	—1500	HHI	17	0912.5	0913.8	3.5U	4.5	2.5	
	—650	GOR	27	0912.5	0913.0U	3.2	8.0	2.5	
	—610	NERA	17	0914.0	0915.0	3.0	4.0	2.0	
	—600	UCC	27	0912.0	0914.0	4.0	9.0	5.0	
	—200	NERA	2	0908.0	0914.1	11.0	60.0		0
	—9400	HHI	1	0929.0	0930.0	3.5	11.0	3.5	
	—6100	KIS	2	0923.0	0925.0	7.0	42.0	12.0	
	—3000	NERA	27	0928.8	0930.5	5.0	30.0	15.0	
	—3000	HHI	27	0927.8	0930.0	5.2	25.0	10.0	
	—2000	HHI	6	0927.8	0928.0	4.5	3.5	1.5	
					0929.5		3.0		
	—1500	HHI	6	0927.8	0928.0	2.6	7.0	2.0	
					0929.5		6.0		
	—1420	KIEL	27	0913.0	0928.0	25.0	97.0		
	—808	AOO	2	0928.0	0929.5	2.0	20%		
	—650	GOR	6	0918.0	0929.0	19.5	48.0	26.0	
	—610	NERA	6	0928.8	0930.0	4.0	30.0	10.0	
	—606	SGM	27	0927.8	0929.3	4.0	28.1	6.2	
	—600	UCC	6	0922.0	0929.0	17.0	60.0	10.0	
	—536	AOO	8	0922.8	0929.5	7.0	100.0		
	—460	KIEL	8	0912.0	0929.0	26.0	103.0		
	—260	AOO	8	0907.0		26.0	60.0D		
	—234	AOP	3	0927.9	0928.1	0.3	400.0	50.0	
	—204	IZM	2	0925.7	0926.0	4.3	134.0		
	—200	NERA	2	0928.8	0929.0	5.0	170.0		0
	—127	TOR	3	0927.0	0927.0	2.0	76.0D	67.0	
	—9400	HHI	3A	0920.0U	1030.0		24.0		
	—3000	NERA	3A	0912.5	0935.0	40.0	15.0		
	—3000	HHI	3A	0912.5U	0933.0U		15.0		
			3		1030.0U		13.0		
					1035.0				
	—2000	HHI	3A	0912.5	0933.0U	332.0	4.5	1.5	
					0941.0				
					1115.0U		3.5		
	—1500	HHI	3A7	0912.5	0925.3	356.0	3.5	1.5	
			3		1140.0U		3.0		
	—234	AOP	0	0951.0	1016.0	39.0	20.0	3.0	
	—127	TOR	0	1011.0	1019.0	107.0	26.0D		
	—111	AOP	0	0951.0	1023.0	112.0	30.0	5.0	

Table 2 Comparison of Starting, Maximum and Ending Times of Radio Bursts and Flares in Hα

(1) Date July	(2) Start (UT)	(3) Max. (UT)	(4) End (UT)	(5) Frequency Range (MHz)	(6) Start (UT)	(7) Max. (UT)	(8) End (UT)	(9) McMath Plage Region	(10) Importance
03	0714	0716	0719	3000–1500	0713	0720	0740	8361	1N
		0725	0745			0730	0750	8361	1N
					0714		0745	8362	1N
06	0036	0040	0140	9400–3750	0031	0042	0130D	8362	SB
	0320	0400		9400–3750	0320	0338	0355	8358	SB
		0415	0515		0414		0500D	8362	SB
	0532	0535	0550	17000–9100	0533	0534			
						0540	0557	8362	1B
	0620	0620		17000–	0620E	0630			
		0630				0632	0700D	8362	SB
		0638	0700	–2000					
	1300	1304		9400–2695	1259	1305	1330	8362	SN
		1315			1318				
		1320	1335			1321	1337D	8382	SN
	1350	1351		10700–2000	1356				
		1355							
		1403				1403			
		1415	1420D				1440D	8362	SF
	2150	2150	2200	10700–2700	2149	2152	2215	8362	SN
	2215	2228	2240	17000–8800	2220	2230	2245	8362	SN
07	0025	0038	0220	17000– 227	0020	0040	0230	8362	2B 3B
	0630		1000	9400–2000	0613	0800	1000D	8362	1N 2N
	1140		1430	9400–1500	0420E		1310	8362	1B
					1319	1326	1337	8362	SN
08	0030	0033	0100	17000–1000	0025	0035	0050	8362	1N
	1120	1123		10700–1415	1116	1126	1140	8362	SN
		1150			1209				
		1215				1219			
		1237							
		1242				1248			
		1314	1330			1310	1330	8362	2N
	1700	1708	1730	10700–2000	1650	1700			
			1750			1715	1740	8362	2N
	2227	2230	2340	9400–3000	2226	2240	2340	8362	1N
09	0300	0308		17000– 200	0300			8362	2B
		0316				0310			
		0356				0313			
		0400				0346			
		0413	0500			0358	0500		
	1714	1723		4995– 606	1706		1738	8362	SN
		1757	1800		1750	1755	1800	8362	SN
10	0710	0711		9400–1500	0700		0710	8362	2N
		0716	0730		0710	0717	0750		
							0825		
	1142	1148	1200	9400–1500	1105		1140	8362	2N
		1218	1220						SF
	1620	1633		10700–1415	1612	1621		8379	SF
		1638	1740			1632			
						1648	1705		
					1653	1659	1825	8362	SF
11	0910	0913		9400– 127	0900E			8362	4N
		0928				0928			
		1000							
		1030	1200				1052		

18

Remarks on the Development and Activity of the Active Region during the Proton Flare Event of July 1966

L. Křivský

Astronomical Institute, Ondřejov, near Prague, Czechoslovakia

Abstract

By using the method of summation curves, some parameters of the development of the active region which produced the proton flare of July 1966 are derived. The method of summation curves demonstrates the main trends of the development of the active region, and with flares and sudden ionospheric disturbance effects gives a true picture of the dependence on time of the change of the energy loss.

It has been shown that in the period between 4 and 5 July, as a consequence of interaction between two spot groups in the photosphere a new configuration of magnetic fields and streams of large dimensions developed. This fact predetermined for several days a new development and trend, and also was the origin of the proton flare of 7 July. The proton flare is situated roughly in the region of the point of inflection of summation curves and coincides with the long-term change of magnetic fields of the spots (when one polarity decreases and the other increases to reach equilibrium), see Fig. 1.

It seems that this long-term change in the balance of polarities occurs very often during the period of the origin of proton flares.

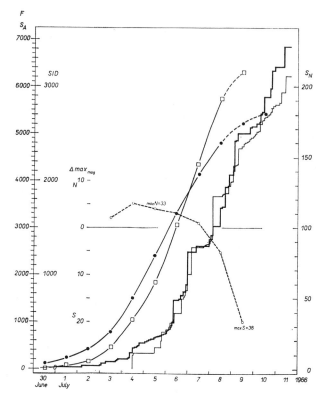

Fig. 1   The thin curve is a summation curve of the flare index F ($F = I \times D$), the heavy
curve shows the SID effects of all kinds caused by flares from the region investigated (SID $= I \times D$) where $I =$ importance, $D =$ duration. The curve with
squares is a summation curve of reduced areas of the whole group (S_A), the curve with
full circles is a summation curve of the number of spots (S_N). The curve Δmax$_{mag}$
(broken line) is obtained from the difference of the largest magnetic intensities of
spots with north and south polarity in the group. Points on the curve Δmax$_{mag}$
indicate the greatest measured values of magnetic field of spot intensities together
with their north and south polarity.

19

Ionospheric Effects of X-Ray Emission from an Active Region with a Proton Flare (30 June–11 July 1966)

L. Křivský* and G. Nestorov†

* Astronomical Institute, Ondřejov, near Prague, Czechoslovakia
† Geophysical Institute, Sofia, Bulgaria

Abstract

To illustrate the time distribution trend of the occurrence of sudden ionospheric disturbance (SID) effects of all kinds caused by flares in this active region, a summation curve was constructed from the values $I \times D$ (I = importance, D = duration), and, for comparison, also the summation curve of solar flares. The slope of the summation curve of flares and SID effects gives a characteristic of the time distribution in the "energy loss" of the active region. The change of the ionospheric absorption in the D region during daytime is characterized by other summation curves. These are constructed from the field intensity recordings of long-wave transmitters. This absorption can be considered as a criterion for a slowly varying X-emission of active regions on the sun in a wider spectral range. With the second extraordinary phenomenon, the flare from 11 July 1966 behind the limb (13–21°), an atypical ionospheric effect had been recorded at a number of stations. However, the main part of the X-emission flare source was hidden behind the disk, at least in this first phase of the flare development, since the usual typically rapid and intensive growth is absent in the sudden enhancement of atmospherics (SEA) effects and in the sudden cosmic noise absorption effect. The harder "impulse" emission < 1 Å, which in other cases causes a very rapid growth of the SEA effect and an initial maximum, did not penetrate in this case into the lowest levels of the D region. The first hard impulse X-emission must originate in similar cases from altitudes lower than 20,000 km and the later emission in a wider range of the harder and softer X-radiation originates in altitudes of 50,000–80,000 km.

137

A survey of all sudden ionospheric disturbance (SID) flare effects connected with the active region (34°N, CMP 3.3 July) where a proton flare and a powerful flare behind the limb occurred on 7 and 11 July 1966 respectively, is contained in the Compilation of Solar–Geophysical Data, Boulder (1966). To illustrate the time distribution trend of the occurrence of SID effects of all kinds caused by flares in this active region, a summation curve was constructed from the values $I \times D$ (where I is the "importance" of the effect, D its period in minutes). Original records of atmospherics and cosmic noise from European stations were also used to determine both the "mean" importance of effects and D. Figure 1 of the preceding paper (Křivský 1968) gives the summation curve of the SID effects thus processed, and, for comparison, the summation curve of solar flares ($I \times D$ is used again here) pertaining to the active region under investigation.

The slope of the summation curve of flares and SID effects gives the characteristic of the time distribution in the "energy loss" of the active region. From the summation curve of flares it is apparent that a change in the activity (as a result of the governing physical configuration of the active region) occurred on 5 and 6 July 1966 and that the new slope of the summation curve was then maintained until the setting of the group. The over-all slope of the SID curve was also steady roughly from 4 July 1966.

Copies of recordings in Sofia of the French long-wave transmitting station Allouis, 164 kHz, for the period 4–8 July 1966 and for 11 July 1966 are given in Figs. 1 and 3 to illustrate the X-emission effects of the active region on the lower ionosphere (D region) in the days before and after the proton flare of 7 July 1966, 0020. The only SFA (sudden field anomaly) effects marked are those caused by flares from the active region under investigation. From variations in the records it is evident that already before 7 July — on 5 July and especially on 6 July — the long-term conditions for the propagation of waves had substantially changed as a result of the fluctuation of the slowly varying X-emission in the active region. After the proton flare on 7 July the active region almost permanently emitted an ionizing X-emission (the signal level of the permanent variation is very low). Although other active regions had also been in action on the sun, it is possible to assume that this total, comparatively long change which became evident in the ionosphere under daytime conditions in Europe was primarily caused by the active region where the proton flare also occurred.

The change in ionospheric absorption in the D region during daytime is characterized by other summation curves in Fig. 2. These are constructed from the field intensity recordings in Sofia of the Priština (Yugoslavia) transmitting station (1412 kHz, $d = 170$ km). The absorption of the Athene 2761 kHz transmitting station was also measured in Sofia ($d = 850$ km). These two records can furnish the characteristics of the absorption conditions in the entire D region, since the rays of the transmitter travel through this entire region. Values $1/\rho$ (ρ = reflection coefficient) were taken and processed

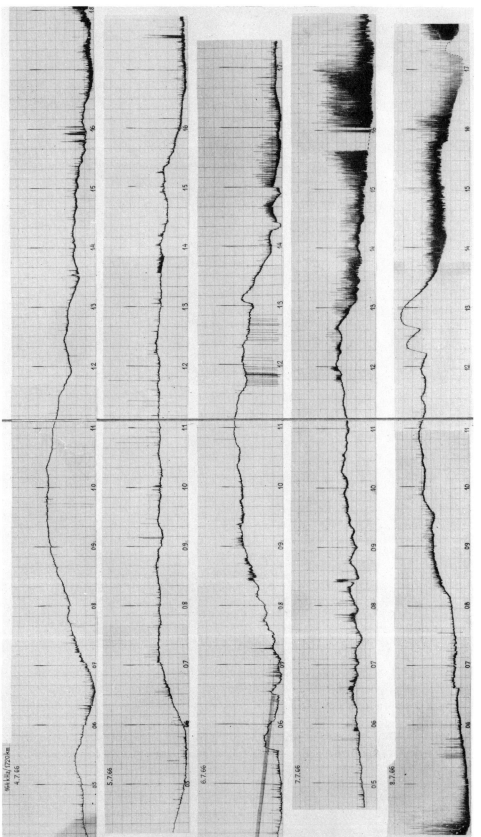

Fig. 1   Copies of recordings of the French long-wave transmitting station Allouis 164 kHz in Sofia.

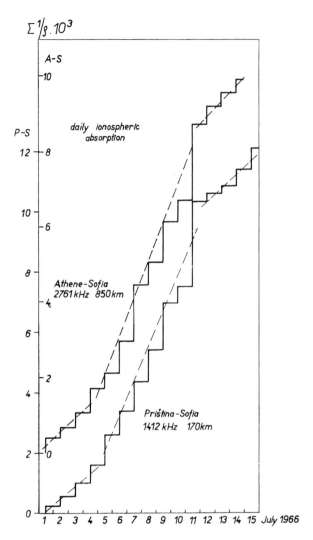

Fig. 2   The change of the values $1/\rho$ (ρ = reflection coefficient) in the D region during daytime is characterized by summation curves. These are constructed from the field intensity recordings of the Priština transmitting station (Yugoslavia) 1412 kHz in Sofia ($d = 170$ km), and from the Athene 2761 kHz transmitting station in Sofia ($d = 850$ km).

regularly for one hour at local noon, which is the most sensitive interval due to the minimum zenith distance of the sun. This absorption can be considered as a criterion for a slowly varying X-emission of the active regions on the sun over a wider spectral range. Although there had also been other active regions in the X-emission which had radiated more constantly, it is evident from the sharp turn on the curves following 11 July that when the active region and the coronal part had set, the $1/\rho$ curve abruptly began registering only very small contributions. The part played by the active region in the daytime ionospheric absorption was already marked by 4 and 5 July, when the slope of the summation curves was increasing. The highest absorption was registered on 11 July, when a powerful flare occurred behind the west limb. This could be explained by the fact that the spatial direction of the non-flare X-emission radiation in the active region was tangential to the limb.

The analysis of the ionospheric effects of the proton flare of 7 July 1966 contains data of the authors from Boulder, since this flare occurred in European night.

With the second extraordinary phenomenon, the flare of 11 July 1966 behind the limb (13–21°), an atypical ionospheric effect had been recorded at a number of stations, as evident from the copies of records in Fig. 3. From the SEA and SFA effects it is evident that the X-emission of the limb phenomenon consisted of two bursts, the first at 0912 to 0913 with the maximum at 0919 to 0920, and the second, more powerful, which began at 0920 and reached peak value at 0944 to 0945, which is in compliance with the two phases of the radio bursts in the centimetre, decimetre, and metre ranges (according to the measurements by the radiotelescope at Ondřejov). The cosmic noise recording shows clearly the superposition of the actual radio emission of the flare and of the absorption effect SCNA (a fall). The first burst of the X-emission had its origin clearly in the very bright part protruding above the solar limb at 0910 to 0920, which represented nothing else than the appearance of the top parts of the flare filament above the limb of the disk. However, the main part of the X-emission flare source was hidden behind the disk, at least in this first phase of the flare development, since the usual typically rapid and intensive growth is absent in the SEA and SCNA effects. The second X-emission burst, which is also occasionally present in some flares, and is associated with the origin of the eruptive dark filament on the disk, corresponds with the appearance of the entire flare filament, with its lowest very bright part above the limb of the disk, and simultaneously with the exposive disintegration process and transformation of the upper part of this emission filament into the shape of a distorted loop.

Due to the usual recurrence of flares with outflow of particles in individual active regions, we can assume that the flare behind the limb of the disk on 11 July was also a "proton" flare, although all its characteristic effects could not be observed on the earth. Let us assume that with the appearance of this flare on the disk the ionospheric effects of the X-emission would have the same character and course as usual, i.e. with SEA effects a rapid initial growth and, after the maximum is attained, a slower fall with possible fluctuations. It seems very probable that the flare space which, before the maximum optical brightness was radiating a harder X-emission impulse character (Valníček 1967) and linked with the development phase of an Y-type flare (Křivský published in Švestka 1966), was located in the lower

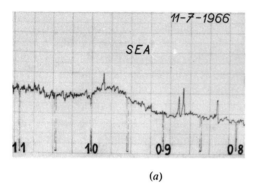

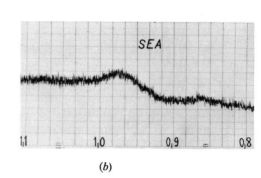

(a)   (b)

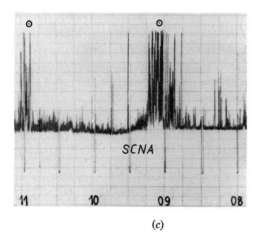

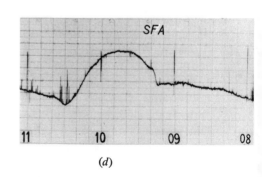

(c)   (d)

Fig. 3   Copies of recordings of SID effects of 11 July 1966: *a.* atmospherics 27 kHz
Ondřejov-Úpice; *b.* atmospherics 29 kHz Sofia; *c.* cosmic noise 29 MHz
Ondřejov-Úpice; *d.* field intensity of the transmitter Allouis 164 kHz in Sofia.

chromosphere and was therefore hidden behind the disk. These parts of the flare shone brightly at the beginning of its development (from minimum altitudes of 20,000–25,000 km above the photosphere) in a range that was somewhat softer due to the fact they had already caused a deployment of the SFA effect. The emission involved was about 2.3 Å, which penetrated to an altitude of 75 km above the earth (Nicolet 1961, Nestorov 1964). The still harder "impulse" emission, less than 1 Å, which in other cases causes a very rapid growth of the SEA effect and an initial maximum, did not penetrate in this case into the lowest levels of the D region.

It is thus possible to derive from this analysis a rough estimate of the distribution of the X-emission sources within the flare: the first hard impulse X-emission must originate in similar cases from altitudes lower than 20,000–25,000 km and the later emission in a wider range of the harder and softer X-radiation originates at altitudes of 50,000–80,000 km (the altitudes of the bright knots of the flare filament above the limb). These results proceed from the undoubted assumption that the "base" of the flare was located in the active region 13–21° behind the west limb of the disk. It is also evident that by means of ionospheric methods it is also possible to follow the process of the slowly varying X-emission of the active region over the course of days. The large daytime absorption at a time when the group was located behind the limb of the disk can be explained by the existence of the tangential nature of the emitting space of the flare, which was directed towards the earth.

References

KŘIVSKÝ, L., 1968, Remarks on the development and activity of the active region during the proton flare event of July 1966, *Ann. IQSY*, this volume, Paper 18.

NESTOROV, G., 1964, *C. R. Acad. Bulg. Sci.*, **17**, 893–896.

NICOLET, M., 1961, Aeronomy, *Handb. Phys.*, Ed. S. Flügge (Springer-Verlag, Berlin).

Solar–Geophysical Data, 1966, FB-264–265, U.S. Department of Commerce, ESSA, Environmental Data Service (Government Publishing Office, Washington, D.C.).

ŠVESTKA, Z., 1966, *Space Sci. Rev.*, **5**, 388–418.

VALNÍČEK, B., 1967, *Bull. Astr. Insts Czech.*, **18**, 249–251.

20

X-Ray Emission Events preceding the Proton Flare of 7 July 1966

H. Friedman and R. W. Kreplin
E. O. Hulburt Center for Space Research, Naval Research Laboratory, Washington, D.C., USA

Abstract

Solar X-ray emission on 6 July was characterized by a "storminess" in the 0–8 and 8–20 Å bands with 0–3 Å flux present above background levels on almost all telemetry records. This variable emission is found to originate from subflare activity in the plage region which produced the polar-cap absorption flare of 7 July.

The NRL Solar X-ray Monitoring Satellite (1965–93A) has been described briefly in a preceding paper (Friedman and Kreplin 1968). In this paper a description of the X-ray emission history of the sun will be presented for the 24-hour period preceding the flare of 7 July 1966.

The data presented here have been obtained from data acquisition stations operated by the U.S. Navy, from the complex of stations of the NASA STADAN network, and from records kindly donated by Arcetri Observatory, Florence, the French CNES stations in Africa, the Radio Research Laboratories, Tokyo, Kyoto University, and the Physical Research Laboratories, Ahmedabad, India.

The X-ray flux in the 24 hours preceding the flare of 7 July is extremely variable. On ten passes the X-ray intensity was observed to change within a period of 5 to 15 minutes, in some cases dramatically. In most cases it will be seen that these rapid variations are associated with solar flares from the active region (McMath 8362) which produced the proton flare of 7 July.

In the following series of figures we shall examine the records for 6 July in detail. Figure 1 covers the period from 0000 to 0425 UT. The flux levels from

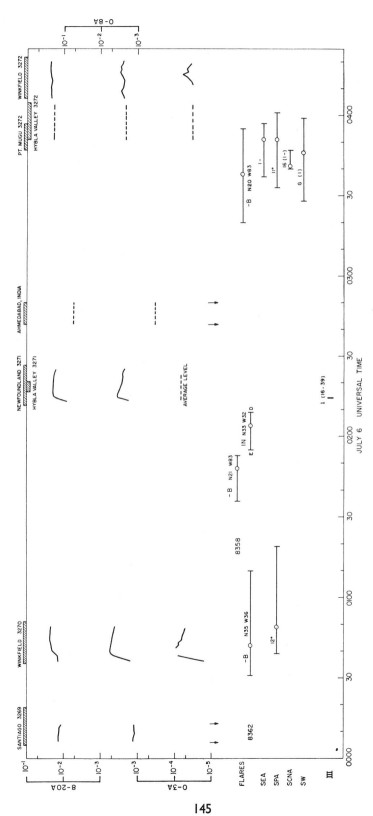

Fig. 1 Solar X-ray activity between 0000 and 0425 UT on 6 July 1966. Hα solar flare observations, ionospheric disturbances, and solar radio emission are plotted in the lower half of the figure. The description notation is the same as that used in the IER–FB series publications of *Solar–Geophysical Data.*

145

the 8–20, 1–8, and 0.5–3 Å photometers are shown near the top of the figure, and the associated solar flares, solar radio emission, and ionospheric effects are shown at the bottom. Note that the emission history is not the same in each of these bands. Consider for instance the pass starting at 0036 UT. The 0–3 Å flux is estimated to have reached maximum at about 0039.30 and the 0–8 Å flux at 0040.20, but the 8–20 Å signal does not reach its peak until 0044.00, almost five minutes after the 0–3 Å maximum.

The solar flare associated with this X-ray enhancement was observed to begin at 0031, the maximum at 0042. It ended at about 0110. Haleakala classified it as − B and Manila as 1N. Comparing the optical observation with the X-ray emission indicates that the 0–3 and 0–8 Å emission peaked 2.5 and 1.5 minutes respectively prior to the recorded peak of the Hα flare.

The only recorded ionospheric disturbance was a sudden phase anomaly (SPA) which was observed by Manila monitoring the NPG transmitter near Seattle. The maximum phase advance measured was 12 degrees. Starting time was given as 0039 with maximum at 0049 and ending time about 0119 UT. Thus the SPA begins about the time of maximum in the 0–3 Å emission but the peak occurs well after the maximum in the 8–20 Å X-ray emission.

Prior to this flare the flux levels were 1.4×10^{-2} erg cm^{-2} s^{-1} in the 8–20 Å band, 1.2×10^{-3} erg cm^{-2} s^{-1} in the 0–8 Å band and below threshold (1×10^{-5} erg cm^{-2} s^{-1}) in the 0–3 Å band. The increases during the flare were about 65 per cent for 8–20 Å, a factor of 3.5 in 0–8 Å and a factor of more than 10 in the 0–3 Å band.

The next pass which showed some variation was recorded between 0211.40 and 0225.50 UT. The 0.5–3 Å photometer signal is less than 0.2 volt on the telemetry record which means that it cannot be reduced by the process of digitization and machine computation. For this reason only an average level represented by a dashed line is illustrated. This has been obtained by hand reduction and computation. No flares were recorded during this interval. There were, however, two flares observed prior to the pass. The first occurred in region 8358 (21°N 83°W) and was classified as a brilliant subflare. The flare most closely associated with this time interval was observed by Manila to start before 0155, and end after 0209 UT. It was classified as 1N and occurred in region 8362 at 33°N 32°W.

There were no ionospheric effects associated with the flare, but a Type III radio burst was observed at about 0214.

On the next telemetry record available the flux values had decreased by a considerable amount. This record was made at the Physical Research Laboratory at Ahmedabad, India, between 0242 and 0250 UT and was reduced by hand at NRL to ensure consistency in the data reading between this record and others taken during the day.

Probably some X-ray emission was associated with one or the other of the preceding flares and we observe in these two telemetry records a slow decay of the X-ray emission with time. Such a decaying flux has been observed numbers of times in the telemetry records obtained from the SOLRAD 8 Satellite.

In orbit 3272 telemetry records were acquired covering the time intervals 0347.00–0356.45 UT, 0351.20–0404.50 UT, and 0406.30–0421.50 UT. These three passes provide a period of continuous monitoring from 0347 to 0422 with only a two-minute gap between 0404 and 0406, showing that in this interval the X-ray emission from the sun is slowly increasing and that the general levels are only slightly lower than during the small flare observed at 0036 UT. Two flares occurred in this general period. Only the first, observed by Haleakala, is shown in Fig. 1. It began at 0320 and ended about 0355. This flare occurred in region 8358 near the west limb and was classified as − B. The second, observed by Manila, is shown in Fig. 2. It started before 0414 and ended after 0500. Its maximum occurred at 0429. It was classified as − B and occurred in region 8362. Both of these flares were geophysically significant. Short-wave fadeouts (SWF), SPA's, and sudden cosmic noise absorption (SCNA) were observed associated with both flares.

Recall that the satellite X-ray data were acquired between 0347 and 0422. The first flare had reached maximum nine minutes earlier and had almost ended by the time of the first telemetry record. The third flare began in Hα one minute before the end of the last pass and did not reach maximum until seven minutes later. Thus the telemetry records were very neatly placed where they would yield the least information about these two very interesting events.

We were somewhat more fortunate during the next series of passes, which occurred in orbit 3273. The time period covered by these records and the reduced X-ray fluxes are shown in Fig. 2. It is seen that the sun was under observation from 0537 to 0630. All passes but the last were digitized and machine-reduced. Two data points were read from the Madagascar record by hand. From 0538 until 0539 the 0.5–3 Å photometer is saturated by an X-ray flux of greater than 1.8×10^{-4} erg cm^{-2} s^{-1}. After this time the flux decreases quite rapidly and reaches values below 10^{-5} erg cm^{-2} s^{-1} in about seven minutes. The 1–8 Å photometer experiment also remains saturated from 0538 to about 0539 with 0–8 Å flux values in excess of 1.5×10^{-2} erg cm^{-2} s^{-1}. The decay rate in this case is somewhat slower than in the 0–3 Å band, about ten minutes being required for a change of a factor of 10. (Since machine processing could not be used on the 0.5–3 Å photometer data, the comparison should be made with some caution.) The 8–20 Å flux recovers even more slowly. It remains saturated at levels greater than 6×10^{-2} erg cm^{-2} s^{-1} from 0538 until 0541, then decreases to a steady level of 1.4×10^{-2} erg cm^{-2} s^{-1} in about fifteen minutes. During the Madagascar pass which was noisy an increase in flux levels was observed on all bands, the largest being in the 0–3 Å band and the smallest in the 8–20 Å band.

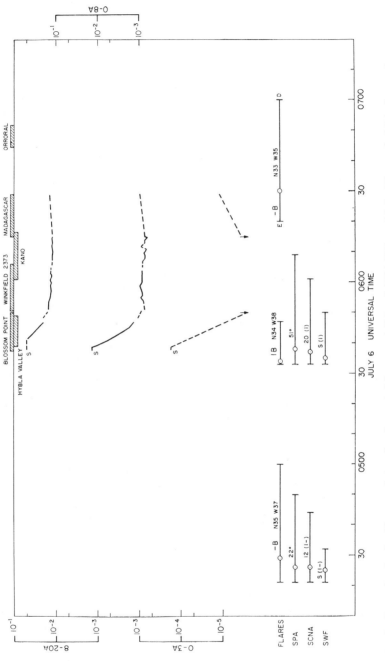

Fig. 2   Records of solar X-ray emission for the period between 0425 and 0720 UT on 6 July. The symbol S indicates that the X-ray photometers were saturated at the beginning of the Blossom Point and Hybla Valley passes in orbit 3273.

The ionospheric and radio observations associated with these records are plotted in the lower part of Fig. 2. We find two flares both occurring in the region which produced the polar-cap absorption (PCA) flare of 7 July (McMath 8362). The first of these was observed by Tashkent and Manila. The starting time was given as 0533 with maximum at 0534 and ending at 0548. Manila gave the time of maximum as 0540 and the end about 0557. The difference in judgment of flare maximum by the two observatories of six minutes is not unusual. Both observatories, however, agreed that the flare classification was 1B. The "explosive" rise to maximum of about one minute is quite significant since this property seems to be characteristic of flares which produce sudden ionospheric disturbances (SID's) through emission of hard X-rays, i.e. in the region below 3 Å. This flare was accompanied by an SPA of 51°, a sudden frequency deviation (SFD) in high-frequency radio transmission, a sudden SWF of importance 1 and an SCNA of 20 dB. The maximum phase in the ionospheric disturbances fell within a few minutes of Hα maximum. The short-wave radio fadeout associated with this flare started at 0533 with maximum at 0535 and ended at 0550.

The second flare in this period began before 0620 and ended about 0708. Its maximum phase occurred at 0632 as observed at Bucharest and it was classified at − B. No associated ionospheric effects were observed, and only a modest increase in X-ray emission was indicated on the Madagascar record.

In the period from 0730 to 1120 the X-ray measurements show relatively low values with little change observed from pass to pass. The data for this period have been plotted in Fig. 2 of Friedman and Kreplin 1968 (this volume, Paper 11).

It is of great interest to note that the sun was not reported to be quiet in this period, in fact a limb flare in region 8358 was observed by Arcetri and by Kharkov Observatories and classified at 2B and 2N, respectively. That this flare produced no unusual X-ray emission is remarkable. However, no ionospheric effects were recorded, which means that either this flare produced no significant X-ray emission capable of producing excess D-region ionization or that its importance was greatly overestimated.

At 0911 the satellite transmission was recorded by Hybla Valley and three minutes later by Newfoundland. On this pass another X-ray flare was observed. Because of heavy Van Allen belt particle interference, the recordings could not be machine-reduced and, therefore, only a hand-reduced plot has been prepared and included in Fig. 2 of Paper 11. The approximate time of maximum for the 0–3 Å emission is 0913, for the 0–8 Å emission 0916, and for the 8–20 Å flux sometime after 0923.

The X-ray levels are relatively low when compared with those representative of periods in which flares occurred, so perhaps it is not surprising that this event does not correlate well with observed Hα flares. Although beginning at about 0914, subflare activity consisting of several eruptive centers and intensity maxima continued until about 1330 UT in region

8362. No ionospheric or outstanding solar radio emission was listed for this interval.

In the period from 1230 to 1625 (refer to Fig. 2 of Paper 11) two X-ray emission events were observed but were of only minor significance. Between 1241 and 1249 a flux increase was observed in the 0–3, 0–8, and 8–20 Å bands. Between 1253 and 1308 a recording was made which showed relatively steady levels in all bands. In all, the increases observed were no greater than a factor of 3 in the 0–3 Å band, 2 in the 0–8 Å band and only 50 per cent in the 8–20 Å band.

Passes recorded at Point Mugu and Santiago between 1418 and 1456 indicate X-ray emission decreasing in intensity from a previously higher level. This event can be associated with a − B flare in region 8362 which began at 1355 and reached maximum at about 1404. The end time was listed as occurring after 1409. This flare was located in region 8362.

The pass recorded on orbit 3279 between 1604 and 1618 covered the maximum phase of a brilliant flare which occurred near the west limb in region 8361. Haleakala Observatory listed the beginning time as about 1600 with maximum phase at 1610. No flare classification other than B was given. Although the X-ray flux during the flare was relatively high there was no indication of any variability such as was seen during other small flares on this day from region 8362.

The period between about 1650 and 2000 UT was not covered too well, only three telemetry records showing generally decreasing flux levels were obtained. The records were made by the CNES Pretoria Station in South Africa (1658–1704 UT), Maui, Hawaii (1747–1800 UT), and by the Radio Research Laboratories of the Japanese Ministry of Posts and Telecommunications (1955–1956 UT). These data are also shown in Fig. 2 of Paper 11.

The last period in the day is the most interesting: three of the four passes observed between 2000 and 2400 UT showed varying X-ray flux levels. These data are illustrated in Fig. 3. The first pass of the period recorded by Arcetri Observatory contained only about two minutes of usable data and for this reason nothing can be said concerning the time variation of the solar X-ray emission. The next pass recorded by Kyoto University in Japan was quite noisy but did indeed indicate decreasing flux levels. It was reduced at only two points. The last two passes provided somewhat cleaner data. The first of these was recorded at Santiago, Chile, and the second at Winkfield, England, and simultaneously at Arcetri. Both passes coincide with the maximum phase of an X-ray flare.

From the Santiago pass which began at 2151, we see the rise of the X-ray flux to maximum levels of 3×10^{-2} erg cm^{-2} s^{-1} in the 8–20 Å band at 2156 and 1.4×10^{-2} erg cm^{-2} s^{-1} in the 0–8 Å band just before 2153 UT. In the 0–3 Å band the flux is greater than 2.8×10^{-4} erg cm^{-2} s^{-1} but due to saturation of the amplifier the time of maximum cannot be accurately determined. It probably occurs between 2152 and 2153 UT.

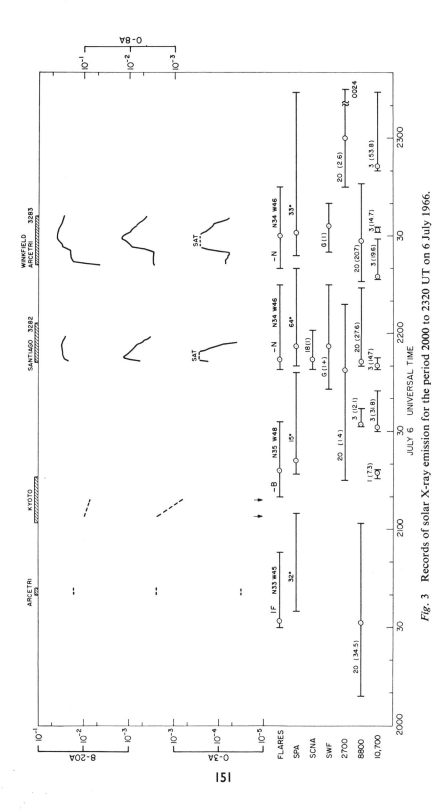

Fig. 3   Records of solar X-ray emission for the period 2000 to 2320 UT on 6 July 1966.

151

At the start of the Winkfield pass in orbit 3283 the X-ray flare has not yet started. The rapid rise in the 8–16 Å photometer signal in the first minute of the pass is probably due to atmospheric absorption since, at this time of day (2330 UT) and year, the satellite orbit would be in sunlight only because of its high inclination and altitude. The increase in X-ray flux begins at 2225.30 in the 8–20 Å region, and at 2225.00 in both the 0–8 and 0–3 Å bands. In the 8–20 Å band a maximum flux level of 4×10^{-2} erg cm^{-2} s^{-1} is reached at 2230. In the 0–8 Å band the maximum occurs one-half minute earlier at a level of 1.5×10^{-2} erg cm^{-2} s^{-1}. As in the previous record the time of maximum can only be estimated because of saturation indicating a flux level in excess of 2.8×10^{-4} erg cm^{-2} s^{-1} for the 0–3 Å band. The peak probably occurs between 2227.30 and 2229.00 UT.

The first record of the period made by Arcetri occurred eight minutes after maximum phase of a 1F flare which occurred in region 8362; while the record indicates relatively high flux levels the pass was not long enough to observe any change in the solar X-ray emission as a function of time. This flare was accompanied by an SPA and a radio noise burst at 8800 MHz.

The second record of the interval was made after the 1F flare of 2030 and before a $-$B flare which began at 2110 UT. The flux levels are low, as would be expected, the 0.5–3 Å photometer current being below the electrometer noise level.

The Santiago record made in orbit 3282 spans a period in which a normal subflare occurred in region 8362. In this case the Hα flare apparently rises to peak intensity slightly before the 0–8 Å emission. The associated SCNA follows the Hα history quite closely, but the SPA and the gradual short-wave fadeout more closely match the emission maximum in the 8–20 Å band. Solar radio outbursts on 2700, 8800, and 10,700 MHz are also seen to accompany this flare. Their times of maximum phase are, however, earlier than the Hα peak and the X-ray peaks.

The last flare of the period began at 2220, reached maximum phase at 2230 and ended about 2245. The time of maximum closely matches the peak in the 8–20 Å band, while both the 0–8 Å and 0–3 Å bands reach maximum perhaps a minute earlier. An SPA and gradual SWF are associated with this flare as well as 8800 MHz radio noise burst.

In summary then, the 24-hour period preceding the proton flare of 7 July 1966 was characterized by generally high levels of X-ray emission showing considerable variability. The X-ray emission can be best correlated with small flares which occurred in McMath region 8362, the same region in which the flare of 7 July occurred. The active region on the west limb produced little or no enhancement of the solar X-ray flux.

Four real-time telemetry records coincided with flares or subflares. These records showed that the rise to maximum flux values and later decay was most rapid in the 0–3 Å band and slowest in the 8–20 Å band when compared with the time rate of change of flux levels in the 0–8 Å band. The rise to maximum requires from 2 to 5 minutes in the 0–8 Å band and the decay takes place in 10 to 30 minutes. The enhancement in flux levels during these flares is approximately a factor of 2 in the 8–20 Å band, 5 in the 0–8 Å band and more than 10 in the 0–3 Å band. The times required to reach maximum intensity are different in the different bands. The 0–3 Å peak occurs from $\frac{1}{2}$ to 2 minutes earlier than the 0–8 Å maximum and the 8–20 Å peak 3 to 10 minutes later.

References

FRIEDMAN, H., and R. W. KREPLIN, 1968, The slowly varying component of solar X-ray emission in the period 1–15 July 1966, *Ann. IQSY*, this volume, Paper 11.

Solar–Geophysical Data, IER–FB Series, U.S. Department of Commerce, ESSA, Environmental Data Service (Government Printing Office, Washington, D. C.).

21

The Behavior of the Active Region prior to the Proton Flare 7 July 1966, based on λ-Sweep Records

H. W. Dodson

McMath–Hulbert Observatory, The University of Michigan, Pontiac, Michigan, USA

Abstract

The eighteen λ-sweeps secured between 1330 and 2232 UT on 6 July 1966 provided no evidence of Hα flares with unusually wide emission or great intensity. Only for the three subflares that began at about 2116, 2149, and 2222 UT respectively, was the onset of flare emission sufficiently sudden to lead to reasonably close agreement in reports from optical observers. No other flares were observed after these events and before the onset of the proton flare at 7 July 0025 UT. Heavy absorption characterized the region. Rising and falling prominences were observed. Spectroheliograms made in K_{1-2} emission indicated interesting phenomena in the lower levels of the chromosphere. The necessary circumstances for the occurrence of a proton flare apparently do not include a large number of impulsive, high-level, major flare phenomena during the preceding twelve hours. The role of absorption and the absence of detectable emission at 10-cm and meter wavelengths with the flares and subflares that did occur seem worthy of consideration.

I Introduction

The term "λ-sweep" is used in this report to describe a series of seventeen spectroheliograms made with systematic changes of wavelength through a range of 6 ångströms centered on Hα, or 3 ångströms centered on the K-line of Ca$^+$. On 6 July 1966 eighteen λ-sweeps were made at the McMath–Hulbert Observatory between 1330 and 2232 UT with the Solar Tower Telescope and spectroheliograph, using a focal length of 40 ft and slit widths

154

that transmitted approximately 0.1 Å. The proton flare began at about 0025 on 7 July and after the sun had passed below the horizon at Lake Angelus.

The eighteen λ-sweeps of 6 July comprise 300 spectroheliograms. Each "sweep" across Hα was completed in approximately 2 minutes, and across the K-line in 4–5 minutes. Atmospheric circumstances sometimes modified this time interval. The λ-sweeps of 6 July 1966 are listed in Table 1 which contains also a brief summary of the concomitant solar circumstances.

If the solar situation is not too complicated, spectroheliograms in a λ-sweep permit (*a*) close comparison of the positions of chromospheric and photospheric features, (*b*) detection of moving material through Doppler shifts, within the velocity limitations of the λ-sweep, (*c*) identification of the portions of flares with wide emission, and (*d*) comparison of high-level and low-level chromospheric phenomena.

2   Characteristics of the Proton Region 1330–2232 UT, 6 July 1966

The region that produced the proton flare on 7 July 1966 was the site of almost continual, minor flare activity during the twelve hours that preceded the proton event, but there were no major impulsive flares or widespread shortwave fades. Furthermore from 1400 to 2245 there was a conspicuous absence of events at radio frequencies below 8000 MHz. The large preceding umbra of V polarity was covered by relatively bright Hα and calcium plage; the large preceding umbra of R polarity was either "exposed" or covered by absorption (see Figs. 1 and 2). The positions of these two major umbrae are indicated on Figs. 1–4 by the large letters V and R, respectively.

3   Absorption

The most obvious characteristic of the region according to the λ-sweeps was the abundance of what seems to have been absorbing material at both high and low levels in the solar atmosphere, observed in the form of filaments, active dark flocculi, and large "pools" or regions of structureless dark material. The absorbing material occurred over both the plage and the surrounding region and extended as far from the plage as the limits marked by the filaments at the preceding and following extremities of the region (see Figs. 1, 2, and 3). The large amorphous absorption ring probably constituted an Hα aspect of the K_3 "circumfacule" described by Deslandres and d'Azambuja (d'Azambuja 1930).

Absorbing material was especially abundant at position A, (Fig. 3) north of the large preceding umbra of V polarity. Center-of-the-line spectroheliograms showed this concentration of absorption, high in the solar atmosphere, to be close to, but *not* coincident in position with, the large umbra. Because this absorption resembles a "spot" on small-scale spectroheliograms, it can lead to false superposition of records if so interpreted.

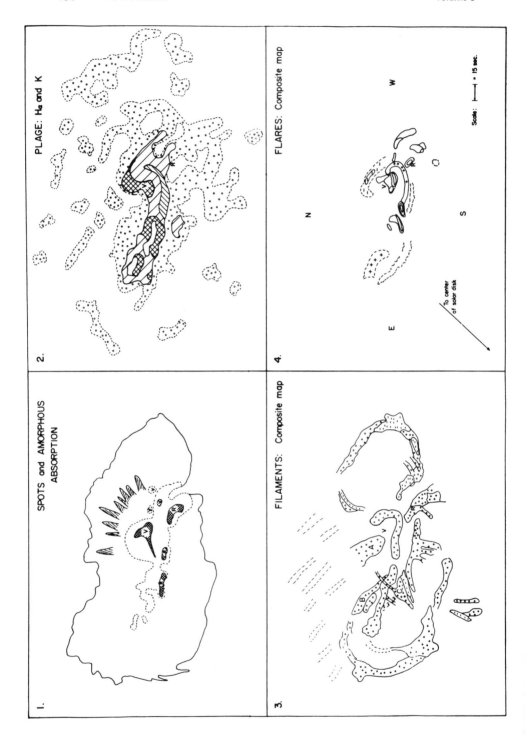

1. SPOTS and AMORPHOUS ABSORPTION

2. PLAGE: Hα and K

3. FILAMENTS: Composite map

4. FLARES: Composite map

Scale: ⊢⊣ = 15 sec.

To center of solar disk

The absorption within the interior portions of the plage appeared to form a filament running more or less between the spots (Figs. 1, 3, 5B). Throughout the interval here studied this absorption track was interrupted by at least one "SE to NW" traversal which followed the general direction of the slender SE extension of the large northern umbra. The filamentary material occurred between spots of the same as well as of opposite polarity.

4 Moving Material

Doppler-shifted radiation on the λ-sweep spectroheliograms shows that there was moving material throughout the entire observing interval. To the north and west of the center of the region the gases often had a net Doppler shift to the violet. This can be interpreted to mean that the gases were rising from the solar disk, or that they were traveling parallel to the solar surface toward the center of activity, or a mixture of the two. In the southern and eastern half of the scene, net Doppler shifts were primarily to the red, and the gases were either descending or moving toward the active center parallel to the surface of the sun.

Well-defined individual streamers or knots, shifted by as much as 1.5 Å, were observed for short intervals of time. It must be borne in mind constantly that the phenomena observed are taking place in three dimensions and are seen in projection against the solar surface in a region around 50° from the center of the disk.

Five observations that seem to involve some aspect of moving material are as follows:

Figs. 1–4   Composite maps of various aspects of the center of activity 33°N 40°W, 6 July 1966, during approximately 11 hours prior to the production of a proton flare 7 July 0025.

   1   Spots and amorphous absorption. Polarities of the spots are indicated by the letters V and R. Dotted lines show the general outline of the penumbra. The feature in north-west crossed by diagonal lines is an absorption phenomenon at −0.5 Å.

   2   Plage Hα and K. The Hα plage is indicated by full lines and has been cross-hatched to indicate relative intensity. The limit of the calcium plage is indicated by a dotted line.

   3   Filaments. Absorption features with apparent Doppler shifts to the violet are indicated by − signs; shifts to the red are shown by +. Dotted lines indicate poorly defined features.

   4   Flares. Well-defined flaring regions are drawn in full outline. Less well-defined regions of transient brightening are shown by broken lines; + and − signs indicate apparent Doppler shifts.

   All of these maps can be superposed using the frames of the respective drawings as the guide for superposition. In all cases, the large letters V and R should coincide exactly.

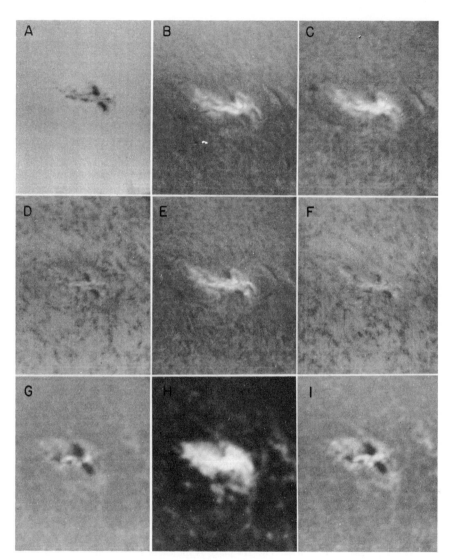

a. All of the λ-sweeps from 1620 UT to the end of the observations at 2232 UT show that hydrogen gases were slowly descending (Doppler shifts of the order of + 1.0 Å) along the filament-like feature B that extended from the eastward extremity of the region toward the center of the plage (Fig. 3).

b. Between 1838 and 2006 UT descending gases were abundant in the southeast in location C, in line with the slender umbral extension from the large spot of V polarity. During the next two hours descending material occurred with greater frequency and abundance along the southern border of the plage and moved closer and closer to the large "exposed" southern umbra (Fig. 3).

c. "Ascending gases" (Doppler shift ~ −0.50 to −0.75 Å) in the form of a fan-like fringe of slender dark structures along the northwestern boundary of the Hα plage were visible on spectroheliograms made with radiation on the violet side of Hα. This feature was conspicuous as early as 1947 and could still be seen at the close of observations at 2232 UT. It did not appear on spectroheliograms made with radiation to the redward of Hα (see Fig. 5D, E, F).

d. Another distinct phenomenon reached maximum development between 2039 and 2045 UT. Large numbers of small, dark, curved structures were photographed in both the center and wings of the Hα line (Fig. 5C). These little dark arcs or "stripes" divided the flare then in progress and the bright parts of the plage into numerous bright segments. The small absorption features tended to be parallel to each other like the elements of cirrus clouds. Many of them occurred beyond the limits of the Hα plage, and seemed to lie along the boundary of the much larger calcium plage.

e. Between 2040 and 2101 UT the large preceding filament was apparently rising and showed Doppler shifts of the order of 1.5 Å. This filament seemed to be connected with the preceding portion of the plage.

5 Flares

λ-sweeps were obtained during all but one of the five flare events that took place between 1740 and 2300 UT on 6 July. No subsequent flares or subflares

---

Fig. 5 Spectroheliograms illustrating various phenomena in the center of activity, 33°N 40°W, 6 July 1966, during approximately 11 hours prior to the proton flare. (North at top, west at right.)

A. Spots: (Hα − 3 Å), 1838.
B. Hα plage and filament (center of Hα), 1852.
C. Hα plage, small flare, and "stripes" (centre of Hα), 2039.
D. Absorption "fringe" present (Hα − 0.5 Å), 1947–1949.
E. Hα plage and small flare (center of Hα), 1947–1949.
F. Absorption "fringe" not present (Hα + 0.5 Å), 1947–1949.
G. Calcium spectroheliogram (K − 0.5 Å), 1812–1816.
H. Calcium spectroheliogram (center of K line), 1812–1816.
I. Calcium spectroheliogram (K + 0.5 Å), 1812–1816.

were reported between this latter time and the onset of the proton flare (see Table 1). The areas of the flaring regions as photographed in the center of Hα were not great and observers, world-wide, agreed in evaluating the events as subflares or as flares with importance no greater than 1. The λ-sweeps show no case of wide Hα flare emission within the observing interval.

Flaring occurred repeatedly in the same location. Figure 4 is a composite map showing the positions of the flaring regions. Flare emission occurred on the borders of absorption features. It occurred over some umbrae and avoided others.

Early in the observing period flare emission took place in small isolated segments. With successive rises to maximum, the flare segments appeared to become larger, until by 2116 a continuous flare arc could be traced between the large leading umbra in the north (polarity V) and the umbra in the middle of the chain of southern spots (polarity R). Because of Doppler shifts this arc does not show in its entirety on any one spectroheliogram made with slits transmitting only 0.1 Å. The greatest Doppler shift in the arc was of the order of $+2$ Å and occurred near the eastern edge of one of the small leading spots (V polarity). Some of the flare-arcs, concave, towards the large northern umbra, changed their relative positions with successive flarings. They appeared to be extending "outward" from this spot, i.e. toward the southwest (see Fig. 4).

The observations as a whole give the impression of a slow increase in area from subflare to subflare of the portion of the region that produced bright Hα emission. The "growth" appeared first in observations made on the redward side of the Hα line. From as early as 1838 UT flare emission had occurred over the large umbra (V polarity) in the northern part of the spot group. Successive flare brightenings produced more and more flare segments in close proximity to the large umbra of R polarity in the southern part of the plage. In the last observation, 2232, flare emission appeared to have impinged upon this umbra. Flare emission was not wide on any of the λ-sweeps.

6 The Calcium λ-Sweeps

Two calcium λ-sweeps were obtained between 1742 and 1816 UT. The observations covered the rise and post-maximum phase of a small flare with a "sudden frequency deviation" (SFD), a small fade on the WWV recorders at Lake Angelus, and emission at 8000 MHz. In general, flares appear very similar on Hα and K spectroheliograms provided the records have been made with narrow slits centered on the respective spectrum lines. Furthermore, in Hα, the portion of the flare with the widest emission is generally a very bright part of the flare as recorded on center-of-the-line spectroheliograms. In calcium the situation is often quite different. Conspicuous bright features are frequently visible 0.50 to 1.0 Å on either side of K_3 that do not correspond to the brightest part of the flare in K_3 or Hα. These bright K_{1-2} features have

Table I List of Times (UT) of λ-Sweeps, 6 July 1966, and Summary of Concomitant Flare, Ionospheric, and Radio-Frequency Phenomena*

λ-Sweep UT	Flares	Ionospheric Disturbances	Radio Frequency Events
1330–1332	SN just ended	—	4995 and 8000 MHz events, ending.
1620–1622			
1742–1747† 1811–1816† 1838–1845 1852–1854	<u>SN</u> 1747–1900 (4 stations) Max.: 1801, 1803, 1840, and ?	<u>SFD</u> 1758–1807	Events at 8000 MHz 1755–1859 UT No events at other frequencies.
1947–1950 1952–2002 2003–2006	<u>SN to IN</u> 1936–2100 (4 stations) Max.: 1942, 1947, 2032, and ?	<u>SFD</u> 2030–2037	Two events at 8000 MHz between 1937 and 2102 UT with max. at 1939.5 and 2031 respectively.
2039–2041 2043–2045 2046–2049 2059–2101		<u>SPA</u> 2035–2105	No events at other frequencies.
2110–2112 2116–2118 2121–2123	<u>SN</u> 2116–2139 (4 stations) Max.: 2118, 2118, 2118, 2120	<u>SFD</u> 2117–2120 <u>SPA</u> 2117–2148	Events reported at 8000 and 10,700 MHz but at no other frequencies.
No observations	<u>SN</u> 2149–2215 Max.: 2152	<u>SWF</u> 2143–2215 Also SFD & SPA	Events reported at 8000, 9400, and 10,700 MHz but at no other frequencies.
2224–2226 2230–2232	<u>SN</u> 2222–2250 (4 stations) Max.: 2229, 2230, 2230, 2231	<u>SWF</u> 2225–2240 <u>SPA</u> 2230–0300	Events reported at 8000, 9400, and 10,700 MHz but at no other frequencies.
No observations	No other flares or subflares reported prior to start of proton flare, 7 July at 0025 ± UT.	SPA in progress	Two events at 10,700 MHz between 2231 and 2340 UT; 2800 MHz shows small increase starting at 2245 UT.

* Data as available on 1 April 1967.
† Calcium records.

some of the characteristics of giant "points" (the source of the spectroscopic feature called Ellerman bomb or "moustache") which are at times shown to be associated with subsequently moving material (McMath *et al.* 1960).

On 6 July, the calcium λ-sweeps revealed the existence of several of these large, bright K_{1-2} features during the aforementioned flare. They increased in size and brightness as the Hα flare rose to maximum (Fig. 5G, H, I). Their position did not correspond to the brightest features on spectroheliograms recorded in K_3. The brightest portions of the K_3 spectroheliograms resembled closely the total Hα plage.

References

D'AZAMBUJA, L., 1930, Recherche sur la structure de la chromosphère solaire, *Annls Obs. Paris*, **8**, 1–120.
McMATH, R., O. MOHLER, and H. DODSON, 1960, Solar features associated with Ellerman's "Solar hydrogen bombs", *Proc. Natn. Acad. Sci., USA*, **46**, 165.

22

Variations in the Active Region, McMath #8362 prior to the Proton Flare of 7 July 1966

R. R. Fisher and G. R. Mann

Institute for Astronomy, University of Hawaii, Honolulu, Hawaii, USA

Abstract

The active region around McMath plage #8362 was extensively observed by several observatories prior to the proton flare of 7 July 1966. This plage was associated with a Mount Wilson γ-type spot region. Nine subflares were observed before the event, starting about $7\frac{1}{2}$ hours before the proton event. There was some modification of the disk structure and of a prominence to the east of the active region. Line-of-sight velocity fields were detected in this same region with an average of $+1.8$ km s^{-1} (toward the observer) for an extensive portion of the region. One subflare apparently produced a small surge of dark material, and this material's motion was strictly governed, presumably by complex magnetic fields.

The region around McMath plage #8362, the active region that produced the proton flare of 7 July 1966, was observed before the flare by several different stations. The observations used in this study are from Culgoora, Haleakala, Lockheed, and Sacramento Peak. On-band filtergrams of the entire disk were supplemented by off-band and broad-band observations from Sacramento Peak, and larger scale filtergrams from Haleakala. These films were studied from their beginnings up to the time of the flare.

The plage was observed for about 8 hours before the flare, and nine subflares were observed in the active plage area, associated with a complex γ-type spot group, before the proton flare. The first subflare observed occurred at 1640 UT on 6 July, and the last one at 2318 UT on 6 July. At this time there was a cessation of activity until the proton flare occurred at approximately 0030 UT. The plage brightenings were produced by three separate regions, one of which is close to the origin of the proton flare at 35°N and 47°W of CM. Latitude and longitude west of CM are given for the events to the nearest degree, although there is considerable dispersion in the estimated B and $L-L_0$, amounting to almost $\pm 1°$.

Table 1   Times, Position and Area Estimates for Pre-Flare Subflares

| Time (UT) | | | Position, $\pm 1°$ | | Area |
| | | | B(N) | $L-L_0$ | $(10^{-6} \times$ Area of |
Begin	Max.	End	(°)	CMD (°)	Disk)
1640	1643	1700	36	47	20
1730		1800	36	45	20
1827	1834	1852	35	45	40
1940	1944	1958	36	45	30
2033	2034	2053	36	47	30
2117	2120	2141	36	47	60
2152	2154	2206	36	47	15
2225	2227	2246	36	47	30
2318	2320	2326	35	45	30

Isophotal contours have been drawn for the plage and subflares from the 50 mm image filtergrams taken at Haleakala and are presented in Figs. 1 and 2. The contours are drawn at approximately two and four times the background disk brightness. The activity seen in these drawings is similar to later activity in the plage. At 1640 UT there was a small brightening at 35°N 46°W, close to the region that later produced the proton flare. There was a slow brightening of the area just between the two major spots at 34°N 44°W at the same time; these two areas subsided over the next hour. At 1730 UT there was another subflare at 35°N 44°W. These active parts of the plage produced the other subflares and increased in area and brightness until the largest pre-flare event at 2117 UT. The average duration of these events was 20 minutes; the average area in terms of millionths of the disk was about 30×10^{-6}. (Figures 1, 2, and 3 appear on pp. 166–168.)

There were some perturbations of disk features during the pre-flare period. The filament just east of the plage was strongly controlled by the activity in the plage. The greatest activation of this filament took place after the 1730 UT event, at which time there was a considerable change in the morphology of the filament. This seems to be the filament most strongly coupled to the active region; the filaments just to the west of the plage, between the plage and the limb, were never greatly affected by the pre-flare activity. One other feature deserves mention. A dark structure superimposed over the bright plage was observed in association with the subflare at 2225 UT. The feature appeared as a dark area curving around the northern sunspot; the material then reversed its direction of growth and traveled south and east parallel to the major axis of the plage. This feature was apparently a small surge emitted from the subflare and the material went into absorption over the plage.

An attempt was made to define the line-of-sight velocity field structure around the plage. The Sacramento Peak record has two pairs of off-band filtergrams, one of the pair from the blue wing and the other from the red wing, and these pairs were taken 10 and 20 minutes before the proton flare. One pair, 0020.05 UT and 0020.10 UT was found suitable for a photographic difference analysis of the line-of-sight velocity fields (Fig. 3). This technique has been used extensively to study velocity and magnetic fields (Leighton 1959, Noyes and Leighton 1963). The equatorial rotation may be used directly to calibrate the density variations of the difference plate over a ± 2 km s^{-1} range, since for this day the coordinates of the center of the disk almost coincided with the equatorial circle. The line-of-sight velocities may be associated with density variations by a microdensitometer trace across the equator:

$$D(B, L - L_0) = D(0, L_0) + \gamma f\{v(B, L - L_0)\} \tag{1}$$

and

$$v(B_0, L - L_0) \simeq v(0, L - L_0) = \omega R_{\odot} \cos(L - L_0) \tag{2}$$

where $\omega = 2.91$ rad s^{-1} (Ward 1966), $D(0, L_0)$ is the density at the center of the disk, and γ is the effective gamma for the difference plate. In the case $D_0 = 2.4$ and $\gamma = 4.8$, a check for self-consistency was made by comparing the measured density of the area around the active region with the background density calculated from

$$v(B, L - L_0) = \omega(B)R_{\odot} \sin(B) \cos(L - L_0) \cos(B_0) \tag{3}$$

and Eqs. (1) and (2).

The expected density of the plate was 2.5 associated with a line-of-sight velocity of -0.7 km s^{-1}. The measured density was 2.55 associated with a line-of-sight velocity of -0.8 km s^{-1}. The only significant area that is of interest is the region to the east of the plage. The area between the plage and the region of the active prominence shows a $+1.8$ km s^{-1} line-of-sight velocity. The sunspots may still be seen in relation to this area, since the exposure for the sunspots in the positive print is in the nonlinear portion of the (H, D) curve.

Acknowledgments

We would like to acknowledge the help of the directors of the Culgoora Observatory, The Lockheed Solar Observatory, and Sacramento Peak Observatory who kindly supplied film records used in this work.

The support for this work was provided in part by NASA under Contract number NGR 12-001-011 and in part by ESSA under Contract number 21-F-66-222-F-310-239.

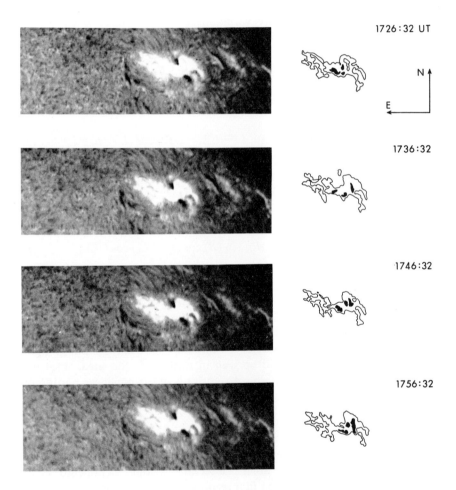

Figs. 1–2   Time evolution of the active region and isophotal contours of the plage. After the third observation, the image size was reduced to 46 mm, from 51 mm, so that a shorter exposure time could be used. The contours are for approximately 2 and 4 times the background intensity of the disk.

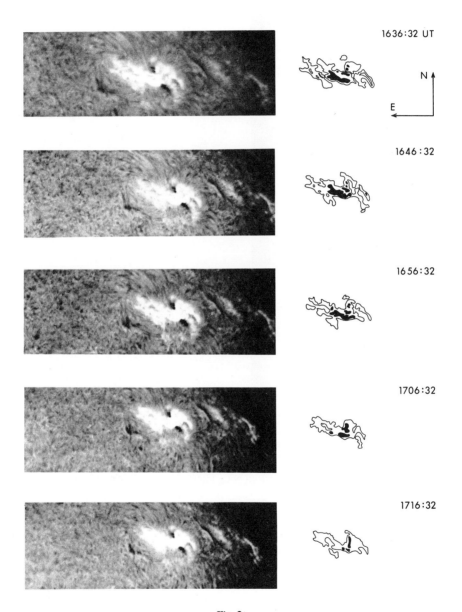

Fig. 2

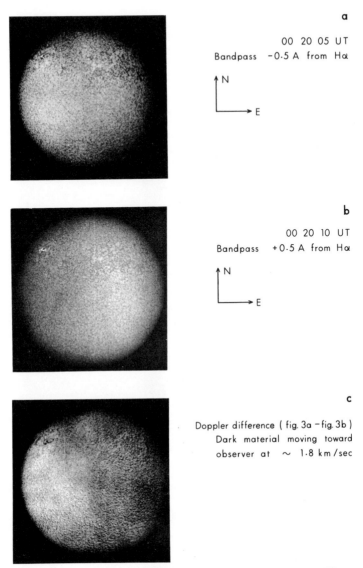

a

00 20 05 UT
Bandpass   −0·5 A from Hα

↑N
└──→ E

b

00 20 10 UT
Bandpass   +0·5 A from Hα

↑N
└──→ E

c

Doppler difference (fig. 3a − fig. 3b)
Dark material moving toward
observer at ∼ 1·8 km/sec

Fig. 3   (*a*) Blue wing filtergram, (*b*) Red wing filtergram, (*c*) Doppler difference of (*a*) and (*b*).

References

LEIGHTON, R. B., 1959, Observations of solar magnetic fields in plage regions, *Astrophys. J.*, **130**, 366–380.

NOYES, R. W., and R. B. LEIGHTON, 1963, Velocity fields in the solar atmosphere, II. The oscillatory field, *Astrophys. J.*, **138**, 631–647.

WARD, F., 1966, Determination of the solar rotation rate from the motion of identifiable features, *Astrophys. J.*, **145**, 416–425.

23

Evolution of the Sunspot Group after the Proton Flare of 7 July 1966

P. S. McIntosh and C. Sawyer

Environmental Research Laboratories, Environmental Science Services Administration, Boulder, Colorado, USA

Abstract

The total area of the sunspot group continues to increase for at least two days following the proton flare. However, the large umbrae near the center begin to decay, even as rapid growth continues at both the leading and following ends of the group. The decline of the central umbrae, which underlie the brightest parts of the flare, begins within half a day of the time of the flare, and is probably related to its occurrence.

Howard (1963) noted that a major flare has the effect of rapidly ageing the sunspot group in which it occurs. He cited five examples in which, during the day after a cosmic-ray flare, the area of the sunspot group decreased by an amount varying from 3 per cent to 75 per cent. Antalová (1965) found that sunspots over which ribbonlike flares began showed decreased area and large changes in motion after the flare. Spots toward which the flare advanced during its development showed stabler motions, and sometimes grew larger after the flare. We shall show that, after the proton flare of 7 July 1966, the total area of the sunspot group continued to increase for about two days. Although the central umbrae, which dominated the group when the flare began and over which the brightest parts of the flare were located, declined during this period, continued growth at both the leading and following edges of the group overwhelmed the central decay and resulted in an over-all increase in area.

According to daily measures made routinely at various observatories and quoted in Table 1, the area of the sunspot group continued to increase after

Table I   Area of Sunspot Group before and after Flare of
           7 July 1966

Source	Date	Apparent Area, A_D
Solnechnye Dannye	06.2 July	1134
	07.2	1282
Rome	06.3 July	1082
	07.3	1400
U.S. Naval Observatory	06.4 July	1151
	07.4	1175

the flare, *even in projection*, although the group was well past central meridian. Each of the three sets of measurements shows the apparent area to be larger after the flare than before the flare.

We supplemented the daily values from these three sources by measuring the sunspot-group area on white-light patrol films. At Sacramento Peak Observatory a 6-inch (15-cm) refractor forms a 21-mm image of the sun that is photographed once a minute on extremely fine-grain 35-mm film. This film was projected into a camera and the portion including the sunspot group copied on color transparency film, with enlargement by a factor of 7 to 19. This enlarged negative image of the sunspot group was projected on to a screen, where the penumbral outline was traced. The areas actually measured were of the order of 5000 mm², so that the accuracy of the estimated area values is limited by uncertainties in the location of the penumbral border rather than by errors of area measurement.

The values of whole-spot area plotted in Fig. 1 have been corrected for foreshortening by multiplying by the secant of the angular distance from the center of the disk. (Corrected area is expressed in units of millionths of the hemisphere, each unit twice as large as a millionth of the disk.) The size and uncertainty of the secant correction near the limb magnifies the disagreement among individual measures. Nevertheless, it seems clear that area growth continued through 8 July, but at a slower rate after the time of the flare early on 7 July. Throughout the period from 4.5 July to 9.5 July, while the apparent area of the group was at least 500 millionths of the disk, deviations of individual measurements from the smooth curve were no greater than 15 per cent of the smoothed value, and these small deviations showed no clear relation to the proton flare of 7 July, or to other optically important flares that occurred in the region (Fig. 2).

The total area, however, does not describe the actual development of the whole group. Figure 3*b* shows that on 6 July two large umbrae (which were of opposite magnetic polarity) dominated the region. The penumbra between them was uncommonly dark and had thick, short, dark filaments aligned perpendicular to the line joining the umbrae. These umbrae attained their

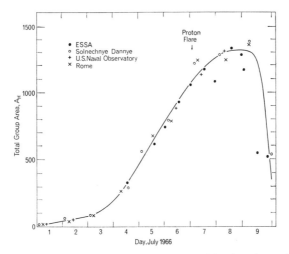

Fig. 1   Area of the sunspot group, corrected for foreshortening.

maximum area sometime during the 6-hour interval that preceded the flare. In the hours after the flare the northern member became lighter and fractured by light bridges. As both spots grew smaller, the separation of their neighboring borders increased. The penumbra between them lost its unusually dark character and became broken with light patches. This decay continued at a steady rate until a day after the flare (Fig. 3*d*). At that time the rate of separation decreased and may have ceased altogether by west-limb passage (Fig. 3*e*). The penumbra just to the east of the central pair of umbrae also became more fragmented and less dark and decreased in area after the flare.

An umbra that lay to the west of the central pair grew rapidly right through the time of the flare and as long as it could be seen on the disk (see especially Figs. 3*c* and *d*). The areas (corrected for foreshortening) of the northernmost decaying central umbra and of the growing umbra in the leading part of the group are shown for the days around the flare day in Fig. 4, which shows that

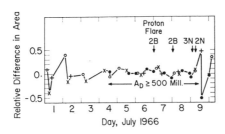

Fig. 2   Deviations from the smoothed curve of individual measures of area of the sun-spot group. Values from each observatory have been corrected for small systematic errors, not exceeding 5 per cent.

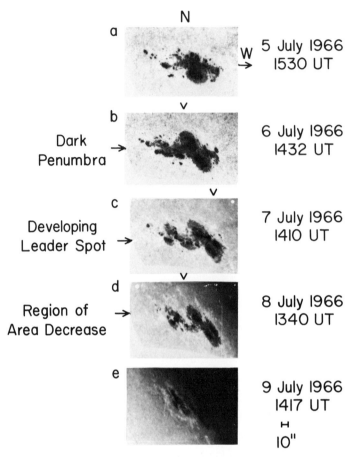

N

a   5 July 1966
                 W→ 1530 UT

Dark   b   6 July 1966
Penumbra →   1432 UT

Developing   c   7 July 1966
Leader Spot →   1410 UT

Region of   d   8 July 1966
Area Decrease →   1340 UT

e   9 July 1966
                     1417 UT

                     ⊢⊣
                     10"

Fig. 3   Enlarged portions of photographs from the Sacramento Peak Observatory
white-light patrol, showing the development of the sunspot group before and
after the proton flare. The features listed to the left of the pictures are located by
pairs of fiducial marks at the top and left side of each picture. The curved border
on the left of most of the pictures is the edge of the aperture on the copying
camera. (Original negatives courtesy of Sacramento Peak Observatory, Air
Force Cambridge Research Laboratories.)

a substantial decrease in area took place in some parts of the group even as
its total area increased.

The flare as seen in the center of the Hα line (Fig. 5A) appeared to spread
over almost the whole spot group. Light from the wings of Hα (Fig. 5B)
revealed the brightest parts of the flare along with the underlying sunspots.
The flare first appeared, and was most brilliant, close to the northernmost
central spot. The southern member of the central pair formed a second
emission center from which the bright filament extended toward the following
part of the group. The off-band pictures show that the flare never covered the

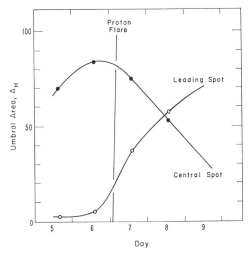

Fig. 4 Corrected areas of separate umbrae around the flare day. The flare began, and was most intense, over the central spot, but the brightest part of the flare never covered the leading spot.

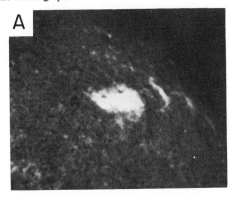

Fig. 5 The proton flare as seen in light from: A, the center of the Hα line; B, ±1Å from the center of the Hα line. 7 July 1966, 0046 UT. (Courtesy of Sacramento Peak Observatory, Air Force Cambridge Research Laboratories.)

leading umbra that grew so large in the days following the flare, nor did it reach the spots in the following end of the group, which also continued to develop after the flare.

We find, then, that only the parts of the sunspot group that lay directly under the brightest part of the flare declined after the flare. The deterioration began no more than 6 hours before the flare, and appeared to abate about a day after the flare. The close relation in both space and time leads us to believe that the partial decay of the sunspot group was physically related to the flare.

Acknowledgments

We are grateful to Howard DeMastus and to John W. Evans of Sacramento Peak Observatory for making available to us films from both the white-light and Hα patrols. We thank Robert Howard for sending patrol magnetograms and sunspot drawings from Mount Wilson Observatory, and thank the other observatories that share their observations and measurements through the World Data Centers.

This work was partially supported by NASA Contract R-102.

References

ANTALOVÁ, A., 1965, Interdependence of sunspot proper motions and chromospheric flares, *Bull. Astr. Insts Czech.*, **16**, 32–38.
HOWARD, R., 1963, On the relation of major solar flares with changes in sunspot areas, *Astrophys. J.*, **138**, 1312–1313.

24

Optical Observations of the Proton Flare of 7 July 1966

M. K. McCabe* and P. A. Caldwell†

* Institute for Astronomy, University of Hawaii, Honolulu, Hawaii, USA
†Culgoora Solar Observatory, Physics Division, C.S.I.R.O., Narrabri, Australia

Abstract

The proton flare of 7 July was not a spectacular event from the optical point of view, but it showed several characteristics that have been previously observed in relation to flares which produce high-energy particles.

The flare occurred in a magnetically complex sunspot group — Mount Wilson type γ. It showed a flash phase lasting about two minutes during the rise of intensity to a maximum. The flare had a Y-shaped phase with the long flare filament developing in a region between sunspots of opposite polarities and it covered several of the sunspot umbrae. The quality of the photographs obtained was not such as to make it possible to detect a flare nimbus after maximum, nor to identify any loop prominences in the region. A neighboring filament disappeared, but the process was not at all sudden, and any changes in the fine chromospheric structure surrounding the region were not detectable.

1   Introduction

In this paper we discuss the Hα optical observations of the proton flare of 7 July 1966. The flare occurred between 0020 and 0237 UT, and photographs were taken during flare patrol programs at several observatories. In the course of the investigation we have examined films from Culgoora, Haleakala, Lockheed, and Sacramento Peak Observatories and a set of prints from Manila Observatory patrol. The coverage of the flare was not complete from Sacramento Peak and Lockheed due to the time of sunset and clouds;

however, the film from the former observatory was particularly useful on account of the increase in the normal rate of exposure to one every five seconds from 0037 UT and the programmed sequence which included off-band, wide-band, and short exposures.

The coverage by Culgoora and Haleakala Observatories was complete, the rate for the former being two frames per minute, and for the latter one per minute before 0030 UT and subsequently one every ten seconds. However, the seeing quality at Haleakala was not good due to the unfavorable time of day for that site.

2 Flare Development

On 7 July 1966, a flare of importance 2B occurred in McMath plage region 8362; the heliographic coordinates of the center of gravity of the flare were 35°N 209°W and its position on the disk 47° west of the central merdian. The intensity increased rapidly between 0026 and 0036 UT after which the shape of the flare changed; the maximum intensity shown by density measurements occurred at 0052. There was a correspondingly sharp increase in the flare area which by 0036 reached a maximum of the order of 12 square degrees after correction for foreshortening; it fluctuated about this level between 0038 and 0053 after which it slowly decreased and by 0130 had dropped to half the maximum value. A series of photographs from the Haleakala Hα flare patrol film shows the development of the flare (Fig. 1).

Details of the sunspot configuration are discussed elsewhere in this series of papers, but Fig. 2a shows a sketch of the spot group for reference during the discussion of the relative positions of spots and flares. In general, the upper spots of the group have south polarities and the lower ones north.

The flare commenced at 0026 as two small bright areas adjacent to the larger spots, although there had been a plage brightening next to spot X from as far back in time as 0007. These areas expanded rapidly within the plage during a flash phase and formed a bright region to the west of the spots partly covering the umbrae by 0027. Examination of photographs taken with a shorter than normal exposure shows that the region has two bright centers corresponding to the starting points of the flare.

The structure of the flare and its relationship to the sunspots is seen more clearly in sketches made from off-band pictures (Fig. 2a). Region A contributed mainly to the initial development and the flash phase of the flare. After maximum brightness its shape changed significantly by a fading of the northern part and an extension to the east from south of X, while it covered more than half the umbra of that spot by 0037, and then some light plage formed north of the spot. During its decay period its form changed little except for some increased brightness in the NW between 0206 and 0237, by which time the whole flare had died down.

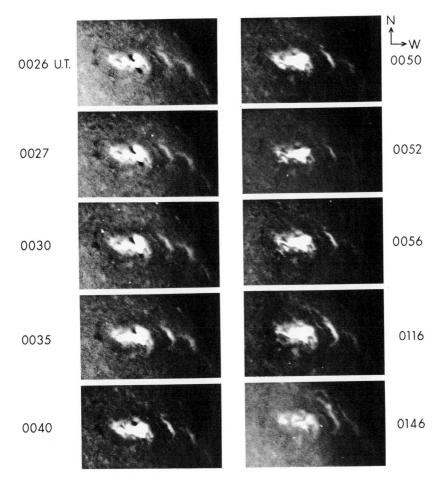

Fig. 1   The flare of 7 July 1966.
(Hα filtergrams from Haleakala Observatory.)

While region A was changing slowly there were developments taking place east of the large spots until the whole flare took on the characteristic appearance of a horizontal Y-shape by about 0046. The long filament (C in Fig. 2a) grew from the early brightening near sunspot Z. By 0030 there was a bright region forming to the east of X and Z (Fig. 2a); at first it covered only one of the small spots but later moved slightly further south, covering all three spots and coalescing with B, by which time the umbra of spot Z was almost completely obscured. The flare filament extended to the east also, following the line of sunspots to form the feature D by 0040 (Fig. 2a). D expanded and a portion became detached to the south; at 0051 a small finger extended to the east of this and from it again another fainter portion appeared to move to the

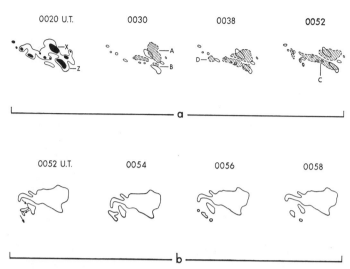

Fig. 2   The structure of the flare.
    a.   Relationship of flare filaments to sunspot umbrae. The first sketch shows the
        sunspot group configuration, the other three the flare regions (hatched) and
        sunspot umbrae.
    b.   Moving flare material south-east of the plage, 0052–0058 UT. Arrows
        indicate direction of motion.
    (Sketches from Sacramento Peak Hα filtergrams: *a*, off-band; *b*, line center.)

south-west at 0054 before disappearing at 0059. The directions of these
motions, or successive brightenings, are shown in Fig. 2*b*.

    The off-band photographs during the period 0040–0059 were carefully
examined to detect line-of-sight movements of flare material, but there were
no significant differences between the pictures on either side of the line.

3   Isophotal Contours

    In Fig. 3 we show a series of contour maps which demonstrate the bright-
ness levels of the plage and flare regions and their relative changes with time.
The contours were drawn on isodensitracer records made from Hα filtergrams
of resolution about 3″ of arc, magnified 100 times. Traces were made in the
N–S direction with a stepping distance equivalent to 12.4 μm on the film, or
every 1.5″ arc; the scanning spot measured 25 μm in the N–S and 13.9 μm in
the E–W direction. Density differences between adjacent contours were 0.12,
but in most cases only every third contour has been reproduced representing
density changes of 0.36; extra ones have been included where they show
special features. The shaded areas indicate the visible portions of sunspot
umbrae.

    Figures 3*a*, *b*, and *c* show the plage before the flare, the first plage brighten-
ing near umbra X and the first flare centers respectively. The breaking-up of

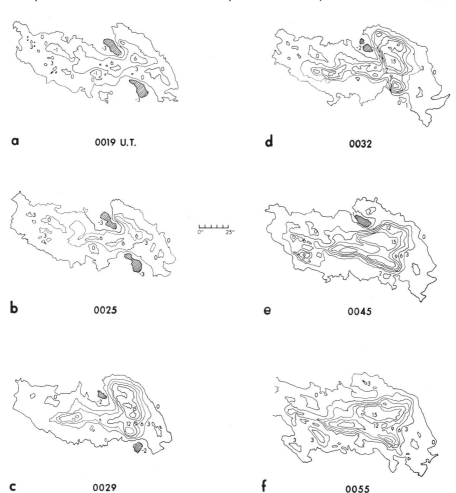

Fig. 3   Isophotal contour maps. The zero contour on each map is drawn at the first indication of plage brightening above the background level. The contour numbers represent multiples of density increments of 0.12. Negative contours are at levels darker than the background and the shaded areas correspond to sunspot umbrae.

(Maps prepared from Hα filtergrams from Culgoora Observatory.)

the flaring region and the brightening over umbra Z can be seen in Fig. 3*d*, while Fig. 3*e* shows the formation of the parallel bright filaments, the development of the eastern region, and the continued presence of bright points near umbra Z and at the northernmost part of the plage (brightness level 2). In Fig. 3*f* the flare shows three bright centers and further development at the east where there was the apparent motion of bright material to the south.

4 Associated Activity

During the lifetime of the proton flare there were two subflares in neighboring regions. One of these, at 35°N 62°W, commenced at 0031 in the plage (Fig. 1) directly west of the sunspot group. It reached maximum brightness at 0034 and faded by 0050, by which time the plage was larger and brighter than in the pre-flare state. The second flare, a faint one at 35°N 56°W (Fig. 1) showed at the north end of the filament west of the spot region; it lasted from 0050 to 0055 with a maximum at 0053. It was visible as an absorption feature between 0050 and 0100 on the photographs taken with the band-pass of the filter displaced 0.5 Å to the blue side of the Hα line, but it was not recorded on the red side of the line.

The dark filament to the east of the active region showed a distinct formation before the flare; there were no sudden changes as a result of the flare but a gradual disappearance with the northernmost curved structure being unidentifiable by 0040 and the rest completely lost by 0145. It had formed again by 1240 when the first photographs were obtained after a break in observations of six hours.

5 Post-Flare Appearance

As the flare regions faded, there were small brightness fluctuations along the line of spots and a clear impression of parallel bright filaments. The two faint plages west of the flare lengthened and showed changes in brightness. By 0500 they had both faded and the main plage region had an appearance similar to what it was before the start of the flare.

Acknowledgments

We wish to thank the Directors of Sacramento Peak, Lockheed, and Manila Observatories for supplying photographic records of the flare event; also G. Richard Mann and Miss Peggy Beswick who were responsible for obtaining the films at Haleakala and Culgoora Observatories and who assisted in the analysis. The work at Culgoora was done with the guidance of G. E. Moreton. The equal-density traces were made at the Weapons Research Establishment, Salisbury, South Australia. The work at Haleakala was supported in part by ESSA Contract E 22-25-67(N) and by NASA Contract NGR 12-001-011, and at Culgoora by ESSA Contract CST-7537.

25

The Dynamic Spectrum of the Proton Event of 7 July 1966

R. T. Stewart

CSIRO Solar Observatory, Culgoora, N.S.W., Australia

Abstract

The main features of the dynamic spectrum are a short-wave fade-out at 0027 UT and an intense burst of spectral Type II from 0038 to 0047 UT. No Type III bursts accompany the flash phase, but "herring-bone" structure is present between 0039 and 0045.5 UT. A second portion of Type III burst occurs from 0112 to 0113 UT. There is a suggestion of some weak continuum following the events described above, but its intensity is too low for positive identification.

A description of the dynamic spectrum of the proton event of 7 July 1966 is given below. The observations were recorded at the CSIRO Solar Observatory, Culgoora, N.S.W., Australia, on low sensitivity equipment and cover the frequency range 10 to 200 MHz. The main features of the spectrum are shown in Fig. 1, viz. a short-wave fade-out (SWF) commencing at 0027 UT and an intense burst of spectral Type II (Wild and McCready 1950) from 0038 to 0047 UT followed by a short intense portion of Type II burst from 0112 to 0113 UT. It can be seen from Fig. 1 that the Type II burst has both fundamental and second harmonic components of strong intensity with the fundamental drifting from a starting frequency near 70 MHz down to at least 15 MHz where it is partly obscured by the fade-out. The frequency drift of the Type II burst cannot be estimated with any degree of certainty, owing to the diffuse broad-banded nature of the burst. No Type III bursts accompany the flash phase (at the time of the fade-out) (Wild *et al.* 1954) but

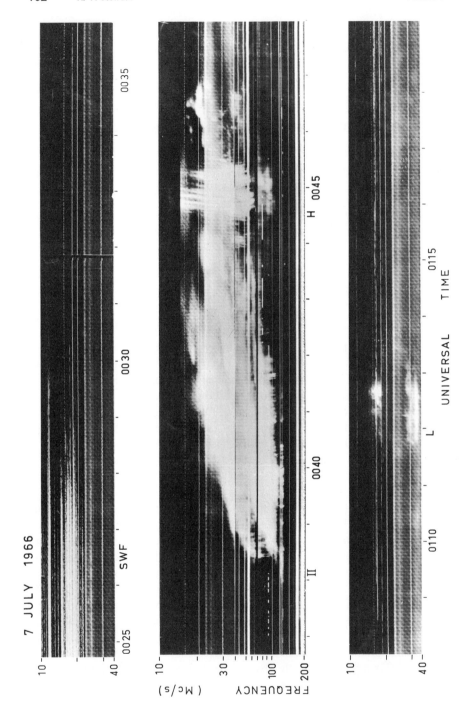

"herring-bone" structure (Roberts 1959) is present between 0039 and 0045.5 UT. The portion of Type II burst from 0112 and 0113 UT appears to be harmonic with the fundamental component partly obscured by the fade-out. There is a suggestion of some weak continuum following the events described above but its intensity is too low for positive identification on the low sensitivity record.

References

ROBERTS, J. A., 1959, Solar radio bursts of spectral type II, *Aust. J. Phys.*, **12**, 327–356.
WILD, J. P., and L. L. McCREADY, 1950, Observations of the spectrum of high-intensity solar radiation at metre wavelengths, *Aust. J. Scient. Res.*, A3, 387–408.
WILD, J. P., J. A. ROBERTS, and J. D. MURRAY, 1954, Radio evidence of the ejection of very fast particles from the sun, *Nature, Lond.*, **173**, 532–534.

Fig. 1   Reproduction of the main features of the dynamic spectrum of the proton event of 7 July 1966. Each minute of Universal Time is marked along the bottom of the record with time increasing from left to right. Frequency is marked on the left-hand side of the record in steps of ten from 10 MHz to 100 MHz and another mark is given at 200 MHz. The main features are a short-wave fade-out (SWF) commencing at 0027 UT followed by an intense Type II burst (II) from 0038 to 0047 UT with a second intense portion (L) from 0112 to 0113 UT. Intense "herring-bone" structure (H) can be seen in the Type II burst from 0044 to 0045.5 UT.

26

Decametric Radio Spectra and Positions during the Flare of 7 July 1966, 0041 UT

J. W. Warwick

Department of Astro-Geophysics, University of Colorado, Boulder, Colorado, USA

Abstract

Boulder decametric spectra for this event exist only from 0053 UT to about 0200 UT and do not include the phases of premaximum or maximum emission. The data from the Type IV phase appear like those from other large events observed here and elsewhere.

The flare of 7 July 1966 which reached maximum at 0041 UT (the time reported by Manila Observatory) produced strong Type IV emission in the range of decametric frequencies, while late in the observing day at Boulder this emission produced meaningful fringes that indicate true solar source positions without significant contamination by ionospheric refraction. The Boulder data extend from about 0053 UT until after 0200 UT, but unfortunately do not include the maximum or premaximum phase of radio emission. During the Boulder observations, the Type IV emission begins near the center of the sun close to the flare in the sun's north-west quadrant and moves (on the assumption of radial velocity) at a speed of 380 km s^{-1} outward from the flare to a distance 1.3 $R_\odot$ from the sun's center at 0130 UT. After 0130 UT, the emission drifts slowly back towards the flare and fades from our view at 0200 UT.

Bursts appear superposed on the Type IV continuum at 0056.6–0057.2 UT, 0101.6–0102.2 UT, and 0110.2–0110.4 UT. These are probably all Type III bursts, that lie close to the center of the sun, not far from the Type IV emission occurring simultaneously. However, the Type IV burst moves outward throughout the time interval of these Type III bursts; a strong Type III burst at 0111.7–0113.1 UT lies farther from the Type IV burst centroid than the earlier Type III's. Its position is, like theirs, close to the sun's center.

This Type III, at *low* frequencies, lies at the same position as the concurrent Type IV burst. We infer that the shift at higher frequencies is solar in origin and not a result of ionospheric refraction. (Refraction produces shifts that increase sharply toward low frequencies.) This strong Type III burst extends down to about 16 MHz on our records; the Type IV emission extends only to about 20.5 MHz. The altitude of the sun is about 14° at 0110 UT; $20.5 \times \sin 14° = 5.3$ MHz, which ought to be close to $foF2$ at the penetration point of the solar emission through the ionosphere. The actual measured $foF2$ value in Boulder is 5.9 MHz. Note however that the low-frequency part of the Type III burst at 0112 UT arrives at our receivers despite this apparent cutoff.

Measurable ionospheric absorption occurs on our 18 MHz fixed-frequency receiver during the entire event, and also is recognizable on the spectrographic record. At 0047.3 UT the cosmic noise level at 18 MHz along a vertical path through the ionosphere is about 49 per cent of the pre-burst value. The fixed frequency receivers (at 9, 18, and 36 MHz), all of which have vertically beamed antennas, show no trace of the solar emission. Ionospheric refraction at 20 to 40 MHz should be large for a solar altitude of only 14°. Two effects reduce its importance: the low value of $foF2$ (both observed by vertical soundings in Boulder and deduced from the spectrograph record) and the fact that the interferometer fringes during this event lie within 3° of perpendicularity to the sun's almucantar.

In summary, this Type IV burst, and the superposed Type III's, behave much like those observed on other occasions here and elsewhere: the Type IV moves outwards away from the flare, and returns only in the final phase, while sub-bursts (probably Type III's) during the Type IV lie close to the sun's center. Unfortunately, we have no measurements during the maximum of this interesting event.

27

Single-Frequency Bursts observed in Japan during the Proton Event of 7 July 1966

S. Enome

The Research Institute of Atmospherics, Nagoya University, Nagoya, Japan

Abstract

A table and figures give the characteristics of the Type IV solar radio burst which started at 0018 UT on 7 July 1966, as observed in Japan at Mitaka, Hiraiso, and Toyokawa observing stations.

The Type IV burst which started at 0018 UT on 7 July 1966 is one of the most intense solar radio bursts ever observed since the routine observations of solar radio emission were started.

Table I

Frequency (MHz)	Observatory	Starting Time (UT)	Time of Maximum (UT)	Duration (min.)	Type	Maximum Flux Density $(10^{-22}$ W m^{-2} Hz$^{-1})$ Peak	Maximum Flux Density $(10^{-22}$ W m^{-2} Hz$^{-1})$ Mean	Polarization (0, l, r, L, R.)
17000	Mitaka	0026	0038*	56	C	8000		r
9400	Toyokawa	0018	0037.5	112	C	12750	765	r
3750	Toyokawa	0026	0037.5	114	C	4730	475	l–r
2000	Toyokawa	0026	0037.8	129	C	2300	290	l
1000	Toyokawa	0026	0124.3	142	C	3890	390	l–r–L–r–l–r–L
612	Mitaka	0030	0120*	95	C	1500*		r
500	Hiraiso	0029	0037.8	110	C	1435	155	
408	Mitaka	0031	0037.1	105	C	420*		
227.5	Mitaka	0035	0039	84	C	950		l–r–l
200	Hiraiso	0030	0038.3	96	C	810	95	

* Uncertain

In Japan this was observed at Tokyo Astronomical Observatory, Mitaka, the Radio Research Laboratory, Hiraiso, and the Research Institute of Atmospherics, Toyokawa.

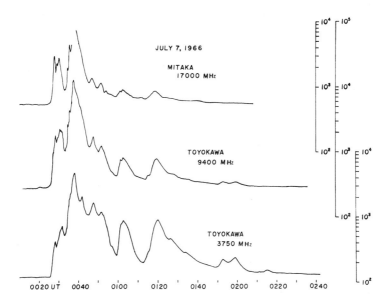

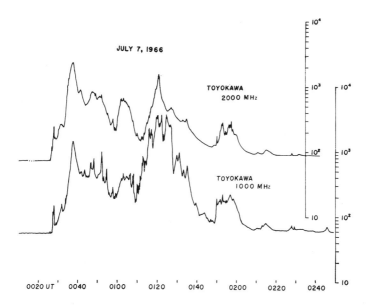

Fig. 1   Development of flux density of solar radio burst of 7 July 1966.

Characteristics of the burst are given in Table 1 and include starting time of the burst, time of maximum flux density, duration, type, maximum flux density, and polarization at various frequencies. Figures 1 and 2 show the complex development of flux density and polarization.

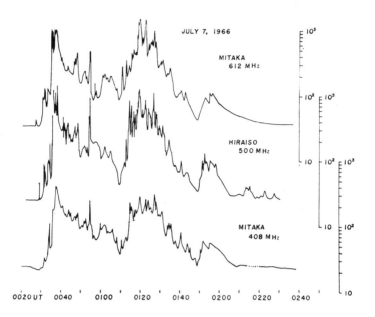

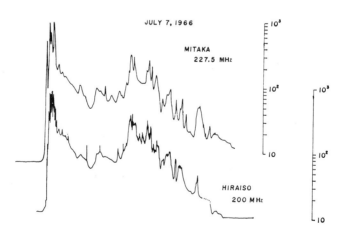

Fig. 1 (*continued*)

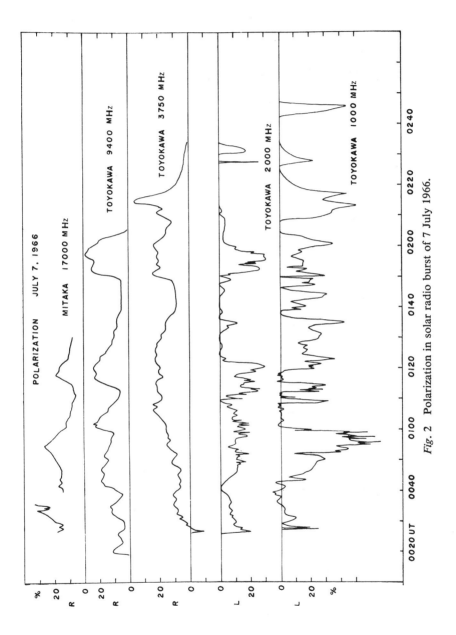

Fig. 2   Polarization in solar radio burst of 7 July 1966.

28

The Complete Type IV Burst associated with the 7 July 1966 Proton Event

K. Kai*

The Tokyo Astronomical Observatory, University of Tokyo, Tokyo, Japan

Abstract

It is aimed to provide all available data of the solar radio burst associated with the 7 July 1966 proton flare and to describe the characteristics of the burst as completely as possible. The combined dynamic spectrum is presented, drawn on the basis of both single-frequency and spectral observations.

The burst is clearly of Type IV, but it is characterized by the metre wave component which is much weaker than the high-frequency components and less persistent than usual. This may be attributed to the limb effect.

The purpose of this short paper is to provide all the available data of the solar radio burst associated with the 7 July 1966 proton event and to describe a picture of the burst as completely as possible since this may be useful for future discussions on the nature of the burst itself and on its relation to different phenomena such as optical flare, magnetic storm, emission of energetic particles, and so on. A detailed discussion on these problems, however, is beyond the scope of the present paper.

Single-frequency observations were made for the 7 July burst at various stations in the world. The range of observing frequency is from 18 MHz to 17 GHz. Dynamic spectra, on the other hand, were obtained with the aid of spectrometers both at the Culgoora Observatory, Australia, (10–250 MHz) and at the High Altitude Observatory, Boulder, Colorado, USA,

---

* Now at Division of Radiophysics, C.S.I.R.O., Epping, Sydney, N.S.W., Australia.

(7.8–40.3 MHz). Detailed features of spectrometric observations are given by Stewart (1968) and of single-frequency observations by Enome (1968). We attempt here to combine these two features to obtain a "complete picture" of the burst.

A combined dynamic spectrum is shown in Fig. 1. For frequencies above 200 MHz this figure is drawn on the basis of single-frequency records while for frequencies below 200 MHz it is drawn schematically from the dynamic spectra obtained at both the Culgoora Observatory and the High

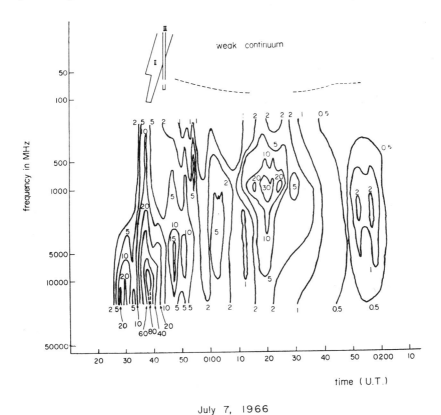

July 7, 1966

Fig. 1   Combined dynamic spectrum. For description see text.

Altitude Observatory. Numerals written on equi-flux density curves show the value of flux density given in units of 10^{-20} W m^{-2} Hz^{-1}.

Some characteristic features of this event may be obtained from the combined dynamic spectrum:

(i) The burst is considered to be of Type IV because it covers a fairly wide range of frequencies, it is sufficiently strong, and it has a long duration of the order of two hours.

(ii) This Type IV burst may morphologically consist of three components; the first component covers the centimetre wavelength range, the second the decimetre wavelength range and the third one the metre wavelength range. For simplicity, the nomenclatures IV μ, IV dm, and IV m, which are most commonly used, are tentatively assigned to these three components, respectively.

(iii) IV μ is fairly strong and IV dm is considerably stronger, but IV m is rather weak and is of shorter duration. Its duration is of the same order as those of high-frequency components.

(iv) A reversal of the sense of polarization is found between 2000 and 3750 MHz.

(v) After about 0100 UT, IV dm shows considerable circular polarization. The degree of polarization, however, is 50 to 60 per cent at most.

(vi) It may be possible that there is a clear gap between IV dm and IV m.

(vii) A Type II burst preceding a weak continuum starts almost simultaneously with the high-frequency component extending to 200 MHz. Type III bursts occur near the end of the Type II burst.

It should be noted that this Type IV burst seems slightly different in some respects ((ii)–(v)) from the fully developed Type IV burst. This may be due to the fact that the present burst occurs near the limb. If this is so, it may be concluded that the 7 July burst is a normal Type IV burst, although slightly modified by the limb effect. Nevertheless this event may have great importance in the sense that simultaneous observations were undertaken in almost complete form for various kinds of phenomena.

Acknowledgments

The author would like to express his appreciation to all the observatories which have contributed useful material. The present work is entirely due to their kind cooperation.

References

ENOME, S., 1968, Single frequency bursts observed in Japan during the proton event of 7 July 1966, *Ann. IQS Y*, this volume, Paper 27.

STEWART, R. T., 1968, The dynamic spectrum of the proton event of 7 July 1966, *Ann. IQS Y*, this volume, Paper 25.

29

Very High Energy Solar X-Rays observed during the Proton Event of 7 July 1966

T. L. Cline*, S. S. Holt*, and E. W. Hones, Jr.†
* NASA–Goddard Space Flight Center, Greenbelt, Maryland, USA
† Los Alamos Scientific Laboratories, Los Alamos, New Mexico, USA

Abstract

The time history and spectral intensity of solar X-rays of energies from 80 to more than 500 keV were observed during the flare event of 7 July 1966. These measurements, made with the satellite OGO-3, cover the highest energy range available thus far and show this event to have the greatest measured hard X-ray intensity of any solar event studied in detail to date. Three intensity peaks at about 0027, 0029, and 0037 UT coincide with the times of microwave intensity maxima. A study of the spectral and temporal features of the X-ray emission, and comparison with the radio data, indicate a nonthermal bremsstrahlung origin for the X-rays.

Solar bursts of X-rays with energy *below* 150 keV have been observed from balloons and satellites for nearly a decade, with the consensus of opinion attributing the hard X-radiation to nonthermal bremsstrahlung processes in the flare region (de Jager 1964), as first proposed by Peterson and Winckler (1959). It was recently suggested that all of the observations of energetic flare X-rays to date may instead be explained in terms of the bremsstrahlung of thermal electrons (Chubb *et al.* 1966). The measurements presented here were made over a somewhat higher energy interval, 80 to 800 keV, during the first high-intensity X-ray flare of the new solar cycle, that of 7 July 1966. They appear to be much more easily reconciled to the nonthermal bremsstrahlung hypothesis.

The data were obtained with an X-ray spectrometer incorporated in a low-energy positron detector (Cline and Hones 1968). This detector, shown schematically in Fig. 1, was designed primarily to search for interplanetary positrons by looking for 511 keV annihilation quanta coincident with stopping particles. In an alternate mode of data acquisition, single X-rays are monitored using one of the CsI crystals with its plastic anticoincidence shield. Once each 18.5 seconds integral intensity measurements are made using each of 16 energy levels equally spaced between 80 keV and 1 MeV for 1.15 seconds, allowing for both temporal and spectral analysis of the X-ray data. The detector was mounted on one of the solar panels of OGO-3. During the 7 July event it was continuously pointed at the sun and enjoyed uninterrupted data recovery. The spectrometer was calibrated by monitoring the annihilation line before and after the flare.

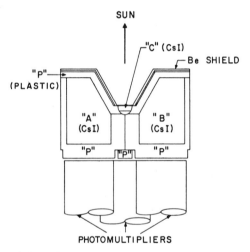

Fig. 1   Schematic representation of the X-ray spectrometer.

The 7 July 1966 event was not only unusually intense in hard X-rays but was also found to be the first event in which a detectable intensity of relativistic solar electrons was observed in interplanetary space (Cline and McDonald 1968). The solar Hα flare of importance 3 was observed at 35°N 48°W in McMath plage region 8362 starting at 0025 UT, and is described in other papers in this volume. The dynamic radio spectrum (Hakura 1968) has intense microwave bursts at about 0027, 0030, and 0038 UT ascribed to the synchrotron radiation of electrons in the sunspot field, followed by radiation peaking in intensity at longer wavelengths from about 0100 to 0200 UT which is related to electrons in the higher corona.

The time history of X-rays of energy greater than 80 keV is shown in Fig. 2. The intensity maxima at about 0027, 0029, and 0037 UT correlate well with the microwave bursts at 17,000 MHz. The third maximum corresponds to more than 300 photons cm^{-2} s^{-1} above 80 keV at its peak. The excellent correlation between X-ray and microwave data in similar events has been pointed out previously by Kundu (1961) at somewhat lower X-ray energies. The spectrum of detectable X-rays extends in this case up to several hundred keV, exhibiting the same three maxima at the same times. This intense emission over such a large range of energies, from microwave radiation to quanta of nearly an MeV, with repetitive bursts exhibiting excellent temporal correlation, seems indicative of a nonthermal model for the X-ray generation.

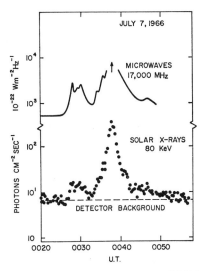

Fig. 2   Time history of X-rays above 80 keV for event of 7 July 1966. For purposes of time correlation, the 17,000 MHz data of T. Takakura (private communication, 1966) are also displayed on the same time base.

The integral X-ray energy spectrum, derived by averaging all the data taken during the 5.5 minutes of greatest intensity is shown in Fig. 3, corrected for background effects and detector inefficiencies. This correction is negligible at 80 keV, but the detector is only about 25 per cent efficient at 500 keV. The spectrum is shown compared with that computed for a variety of isothermal origins and is seen to be incompatible with bremsstrahlung generation from an optically thin isothermal region. It may be fitted, of course, to a superposition of multiple isothermal spectra having temperatures up to more than a billion degrees, but this procedure is too arbitrary to be definitive. Both the extremely high temperatures required by any multithermal model to match the experimental spectrum, and the rapid heating and cooling demanded by the time characteristics would seem to argue against a thermal mechanism.

As a measure of the relative shape of the spectrum in time, we have calculated the best power-law fit to the first three integral levels (80, 136, and

203 keV) as a function of time after background is subtracted out. This is shown in Fig. 4. The suggestion of a gradual flattening of the spectrum in time is also consistent with a nonthermal bremsstrahlung origin, in agreement with the above considerations. In contradistinction, Chubb *et al.* (1966) find a steepening of the spectral shape in time for the flares of 31 August 1959 and 1 September 1959, which they attribute to the cooling of an isothermal plasma. It is possible, of course, that the X-ray production in different flares may be governed by different mechanisms. The suggestion of Chubb *et al.* (1966) that the observations of Peterson and Winckler (1959) and Anderson

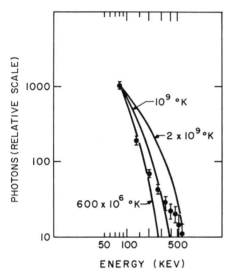

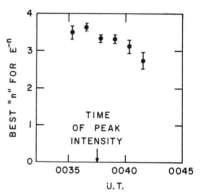

Fig. 3   Integral spectrum of solar X-rays of 7 July 1966. The solid lines represent the emission expected from isothermal sources, normalized so that they coincide with the 80 keV point on the experimental spectrum.

Fig. 4   Best power-law fit to the lowest three points on the experimental integral X-ray spectrum (80, 136, and 203 keV) as a function of time for 7 July 1966. The power law is calculated for the large maximum for times when the counting rate is larger than that observed in the two smaller maxima. Each point represents the average for four consecutive readouts.

and Winckler (1962), originally attributed to nonthermal bremsstrahlung emission, be reinterpreted in terms of a thermal mechanism is well taken, since a thermal hypothesis can account for the observations (although a multiple-temperature analysis is required). In the light of the present study, however, the attribution of hard flare X-rays to a thermal model in general would not be justified.

The detailed X-ray spectrum presented here affords the opportunity of studying the generating electron spectrum. Preliminary calculations have yielded an excellent fit to the X-ray generation with an input electron spectrum having a power law in kinetic energy above 80 keV. The implications of such an electron spectrum, with particular regard to the attendant synchrotron radio emission, are presently under investigation.

Acknowledgments

We wish to acknowledge the contributions of many persons to the success of the OGO-3 satellite; in particular, G. Porreca provided a great deal of assistance in the preparation of the detector package and electronics. We also thank S. Hayakawa for communicating the radio time history obtained by T. Takakura.

References

ANDERSON, D. A., and J. R. WINCKLER, 1962, Solar flare X-ray burst on September 28, 1961, *J. Geophys. Res.*, **67**, 4103–4117.

CHUBB, T. A., R. W. KREPLIN, and H. FRIEDMAN, 1966, Observations of hard X-ray emissions from solar flares, *J. Geophys. Res.*, **71**, 3611–3622.

CLINE, T. L., and E. W. HONES, JR.,1968, Search for low-energy interplanetary positrons, *Proc. 10th Int. Conf. on Cosmic Rays, Calgary 1967, Can. J. Phys.*, **46**, S527–S529.

CLINE, T. L., and F. B. McDONALD, 1968, Relativistic solar electrons observed during the 7 July 1966 proton flare event, *Ann. IQSY*, this volume, Paper 41.

HAKURA, Y., 1968, The polar cap absorption on 7–10 July 1966, *Ann. IQSY*, this volume, Paper 45.

DE JAGER, C., 1964, *Research in Geophysics*, Ed. H. Odishaw (The M.I.T. Press, Cambridge, Mass.), **1**, 1–42.

KUNDU, M. R., 1961, Bursts of centimeter-wave emission and the region of origin of X-rays from solar flares, *J. Geophys. Res.*, **66**, 4308–4312.

PETERSON, L. E., and J. R. WINCKLER, 1959, Gamma-ray burst from a solar flare, *J. Geophys. Res.*, **64**, 697–707.

30

The Solar X-Ray Flare of 7 July 1966

J. A. Van Allen

Department of Physics and Astronomy, University of Iowa, Iowa City, Iowa, USA

Abstract

A major solar X-ray flare was observed on 7 July 1966 by University of Iowa equipment on the spinning satellite Explorer 33. Details of the detector are given. The maximum intensity of the X-ray flare occurred at 0042 UT and reached a value 28 times that of the pre-flare ambient value. The X-ray flare is attributed to the McMath plage region 8362.

There is general overall resemblance to solar radio noise at 2700 MHz and detailed resemblance to ionospheric D-layer absorption of cosmic radio noise at 22 MHz.

A more detailed account is published in *J. Geophys. Res.*, 1967, **72**, 5903–5911.

A major solar X-ray flare was observed on 7 July 1966 by University of Iowa equipment on the spinning satellite Explorer 33 of the Goddard Space Flight Center/National Aeronautics and Space Administration. The principal detector is an EON 6213 Geiger–Müller tube having a 1.7 mg cm^{-2} thickness mica window and a fan-shaped collimator whose central axis is orthogonal to the spin axis of the satellite. The tube is a self-quenching one filled to a total nominal pressure of 429 mmHg (at 0°C) with neon (410 mm), argon (7 mm), and chlorine (12 mm), and its effective volume is a cylinder 0.7 cm in length and 0.24 cm in diameter. The absolute photon efficiency $\epsilon(\lambda)$ is shown as a function of λ in Fig. 1. For any reasonable solar X-ray spectrum, the absolute energy flux $F(\lambda)$ in erg cm^{-2} s^{-1} of monochromatic radiation of wavelength λ required to produce a counting rate R is approximated by a constant ratio $F/R = 1.8 \times 10^{-6}$ erg cm^{-2} count^{-1} for $2 < \lambda < 12$ Å and infinity elsewhere. The foregoing value is for a beam of X-rays striking the detector parallel to its cylindrical axis (i.e. normal to its window). The sensitivity is diminished by a geometric obliquity factor $f(\alpha)$ whose value ranges from 4.85 for the angle α between the spin axis and the spacecraft-sun line equal to 90° to a value of 81 for $\alpha = 124.1$, the latter being appropriate to 7 July 1966. The dynamic range of the detector extends typically over a factor of about 10^4. A 6.39-second observation of the whole sun is made each 81.8 seconds.

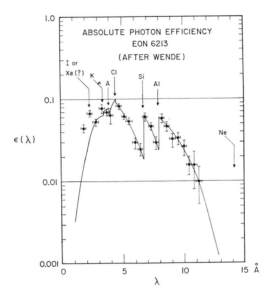

Fig. 1   Absolute photon efficiency of EON 6213 Geiger–Müller tube for a soft X-ray beam parallel to the axis of the tube. $\epsilon(\lambda)$ is the number of counts per photon of wavelength λ incident within the effective diameter of the tube (0.24 mm).

The observed time history of the intensity of soft solar X-rays on 6–7 July 1966 is shown in Fig. 2. Two minor X-ray flares had their maxima at 2153 and 2229 UT on 6 July. The major flare during the period shown had its onset at 0023 and its maximum intensity at 0042 UT on 7 July. The increase during the period 0026 to 0035 is well represented by $1 - \exp(-\Delta t/3.8 \text{ min})$ where $\Delta t = 0$ at 0026 and the asymptotic value of the counting rate for this phase is taken to be 150 counts/sec. There is a significant change of form at 0035.

The decline of intensity (ambient pre-flare intensity subtracted) from 0042 to 0200 is accurately exponential in form with an e-folding time of 36 minutes. The further decline after 0217 (no data between 0200 and 0217) is complex and/or less trustworthy but has a similar e-folding time.

The ratio of maximum X-ray intensity to the pre-flare ambient value is 28, in the pass band of the detector, $2 < \lambda < 12$ Å.

On the right-hand side of Fig. 2 is an approximate scale of absolute energy flux taking $F(2\text{--}12 \text{ Å})/R = 1.8 \times 10^{-6}$ erg cm^{-2} count^{-1} and $f(\alpha) = 81$. The maximum value of the flux is 3×10^{-2} and the ambient quiescent value 1.1×10^{-3} erg cm^{-2} s^{-1}. The time integral

$$\int_{0023}^{0345} F' \, dt = 97 \text{ erg cm}^{-2} \text{ at 1 AU,}$$

where F' is the difference between the total energy flux and the pre-flare or "quiet sun" flux. Assuming equal flux over 2π steradians at the sun, the total emission was 1.4×10^{29} ergs $(2 < \lambda < 12$ Å). Particles from the sun were first detected at 0058 UT, 35 minutes after detection of the X-rays. The X-ray flare is attributed to McMath plage region 8362 at a position on the sun of 34°N 48°W.

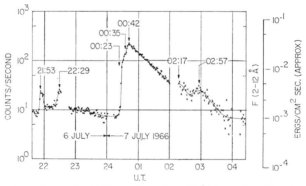

Fig. 2   Time dependence of soft X-ray $(2 < \lambda < 12$ Å) intensity. Absolute energy flux is given by the scale on the right, accurate to about 30 per cent.

In addition to enhanced X-ray and optical emission and noteworthy acceleration and emission of energetic particles (Krimigis, Van Allen, and Armstrong 1967), there was a wide variety of enhanced radio emission (see compilation of Hakura 1967). A sample of such observations is the recording of solar radio noise at 2700 MHz by the Dominion Radio Astrophysical Observatory at Penticton, B.C. It is reproduced in Fig. 3 from ESSA/CRPL-FB-264 of August 1966. There is a general resemblance between this complex curve and the X-ray flux curve but the two are quite different in detail. The physical association between the two phenomena appears to be of a general rather than an intimate nature.

The most relevant terrestrial observation is that of the ionospheric (D-layer) absorption of cosmic radio noise (Friedman 1964). Such a curve, also from Penticton, at 22 MHz is reproduced from Hakura's paper (1967) in Fig. 3. The detailed resemblance to the soft X-ray curve (including the pause in the leading side at 0035) is striking.

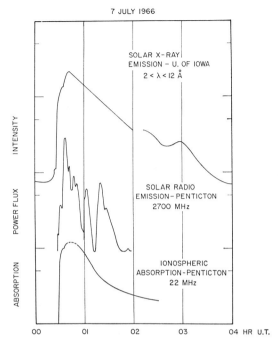

Fig. 3 Comparison of the intensity–time curve for soft solar X-rays with those for solar radio noise at 2700 MHz and ionospheric absorption of cosmic radio noise at 22 MHz (ESSA 1966, Hakura 1967). All three curves are semilogarithmic with a factor of 10 between major divisions on the vertical scale.

No further interpretation is undertaken herein, but it is hoped that the detailed, quantitative record of the 7 July 1966 X-ray flare will be of value to other workers in the fields of solar and ionospheric physics.

A more detailed account is published in the *Journal of Geophysical Research*, 1967, **72**, 5903–5911.

Acknowledgment

This work was supported in part by National Aeronautics and Space Administration Contract NAS5-9076 and by Office of Naval Research Contract Nonr 1509(06).

References

FRIEDMAN, H., 1964, Ionospheric constitution and solar control, *Research in Geophysics*, Ed. H. Odishaw (The M.I.T. Press, Cambridge, Mass.), **1**, 197–241.
HAKURA, Y., 1967, The polar cap absorption of July 7–10, 1966, Goddard Space Flight Center Report X-641-67-116, March 1967 (NASA, Washington D.C.).
KRIMIGIS, S. M., J. A. VAN ALLEN, and T. P. ARMSTRONG, 1967, Simultaneous observations of solar protons inside and outside the magnetosphere, *Phys. Rev. Lett.*, **18**, 1204–1207.

31

X-Ray Emission from the Proton Flare of 7 July 1966

H. Friedman and R. W. Kreplin

E. O. Hulburt Center for Space Research, Naval Research Laboratory, Washington, D.C., USA

Abstract

Although the start of the polar-cap absorption flare did not coincide with a ground-station telemetry recording, the levels were far above saturation values one and one-half hours after the flare began. The decay of X-ray emission was very slow; about six hours elapsed before the X-ray emission returned to pre-flare levels.

The NRL SOLRAD 8 Satellite (1965–93A) has been briefly described by Friedman and Kreplin (1968). Since all data transmission occurred in real time, solar X-ray flux measurements were obtained only when the satellite was in range of a telemetry ground station. On 7 July the first telemetry record was obtained by the Newfoundland station of the NASA STADAN system at 0141 UT and so, unfortunately, no record is available showing the rise to maximum of X-ray emission produced by this proton flare. Since all of the photometer amplifiers were heavily saturated from 0141 to 0157, the maximum flux levels during the flare are also unknown. We can only state that the fluxes were certainly much greater than 5×10^{-2} erg cm^{-2} s^{-1} in the 8–20 Å band, 1.4×10^{-2} erg cm^{-2} s^{-1} in the 0–8 Å band, and 2.3×10^{-4} erg cm^{-2} s^{-1} in the band below 3 Å.

In Fig. 2 of Paper 11, we have plotted all of the X-ray data obtained on the 7 July. None of the records for the period 0000 to 1045 UT show significant variation in flux levels on a short time scale, but there is a general decrease from the maximum levels obtained in the record acquired by Point Mugu at 0330 until about 0900. The flare X-ray emission decay required 4 hours

15 minutes to decrease by an order of magnitude in the band below 3 Å, 5 hours 15 minutes in the band below 8 Å, and 3 hours 15 minutes to decrease by a factor of 2 in the 8–20 Å band. During the remainder of the day there is considerable variability with levels about the same as those observed on 6 July prior to the proton flare.

References

FRIEDMAN, H., and R. W. KREPLIN, 1968, The slowly varying component of solar X-ray emission in the period 1–15 July 1966, *Ann. IQSY*, this volume, Paper 11.

32

The X-Ray and Extreme Ultraviolet Radiation of the 7 July 1966 Proton Flare as deduced from Sudden Ionospheric Disturbance Data

R. F. Donnelly

Institute for Telecommunication Sciences and Aeronomy, Environmental Science Services Administration, Boulder, Colorado, USA

Abstract

The X-ray and extreme ultraviolet radiation deduced from sudden ionospheric disturbances are discussed for the solar flare of 0026 UT, 7 July 1966. Estimates are given as a function of time for the flare radiation in the 0.3–1, 0.2–2, 0.2–5, 0.2–10, and 10–1030 Å wavelength ranges. The time dependence of these radiations are compared with solar radio emission.

I Introduction

Sudden ionospheric disturbances (SID) associated with the solar flare of 0026 UT 7 July 1966 have been analyzed to deduce the flare enhancements of X-ray and extreme ultraviolet radiation. The analysis of the ionospheric data has been discussed in detail elsewhere (Donnelly 1968). The results relevant to solar physics are presented here.

The height profile of the photo-ionization rate in the ionosphere due to solar radiation varies considerably with the photon wavelength λ. Roughly speaking, radiation at $\lambda < 5$ Å produces ionization in the D region (60–90 km) of the ionosphere; 5–100 Å radiation produces ionization in the E region (90–140 km); 100–800 Å produces ionization primarily in the F1 region (140–200 km); and 800–1030 Å produces ionization in the E and F1 regions. Ground-based measurements of flare-induced deviations in the amplitude, time of propagation, phase, or frequency of radio waves reflected from the ionosphere are made over a wide range of frequencies (16 kHz–30 MHz). These SID measurements may be used to try to deduce first the increase in ionization as a function of height and time, then the corresponding photo-ionization rate, and finally the enhancement of solar radiation. A unique solution for the wavelength dependence of the flare radiation cannot be obtained for wavelengths longer than 10 Å because a variety of wavelengths produce ionization at the same heights. Also, our lack of accurate knowledge of the radio propagation paths and of various ionospheric parameters at the time of the flare further limit the precision with which the X-ray and ultraviolet radiation can be deduced. Nevertheless, SID data may be used to make reasonable estimates of an upper limit of the flare radiation enhancements in wavelength ranges grouped according to the ionospheric heights where they produce ionization.

2 Upper Limits of X-Ray and Ultraviolet Radiation

Table 1 gives estimates of the upper limits for the flare radiation enhancements in several wavelength bands. These estimates, which depend upon the models assumed (Donnelly 1968) for various ionospheric parameters, are probably accurate to within an order of magnitude. No estimates are given for wavelengths less than 0.2 Å because SID data are relatively insensitive to flare enhancements at such short wavelengths.

A particular type of SID called "sudden frequency deviation" (SFD) shows that an enhancement of radiation must have occurred at wavelengths somewhere in the 10–1030 Å range. Donnelly (1967) has shown that flare enhancements at $\lambda > 100$ Å must contribute to most SFD's observed at Boulder. However, during the 7 July proton flare, the propagation paths used to observe SFD's were distributed in height in such a manner that the SFD data do not prove that some enhancement occurred at $\lambda > 100$ Å during this event.

3 Sufficient X-Ray and Ultraviolet Enhancements

A variety of spectra for the flare X-ray and ultraviolet radiation can satisfactorily explain the SID observations. Each of these spectra must include appreciable radiation in the 0.5–5 Å range to explain the observed sudden phase anomalies (SPA), shortwave fadeouts (SWF), and sudden cosmic noise absorption (SCNA). They must also include some radiation in the 10–1030 Å range to explain SFD's observed on radio waves reflected from the F region in the ionosphere. An example of a spectrum that is sufficient to explain the SID observations studied is one where the X-ray enhancement is zero at wavelengths below 0.7 Å, rises sharply to a maximum with respect to wavelength at 1.5 Å of about 0.1 erg cm^{-2} s^{-1} Å^{-1} at about 0039 UT, drops

Table I   Estimates of Upper Bounds* of the Flare Enhancement of Radiation deduced from SID's

| Time (UT) | Wavelength Ranges (Å) | | | | |
	0.3–1	0.2–2	0.2–5	0.2–10	10–1030
0027	0.01	0.02	0.04	0.05	0.6
0028	0.015	0.03	0.07	0.09	1.3
0029	0.022	0.05	0.10	0.14	1.6
0030	0.023	0.06	0.12	0.17	1.7
0031	0.022	0.06	0.13	0.20	1.7
0032	0.022	0.07	0.17	0.26	1.7
0033	0.023	0.07	0.22	0.33	1.6
0034	0.024	0.08	0.29	0.44	1.9
0035	0.025	0.08	0.41	0.60	2.2
0036	0.030	0.09	0.58	0.81	2.9
0037	0.040	0.12	0.80	1.10	3.6
0038	0.052	0.15	0.94	1.4	3.9
0039	0.066	0.20	1.13	1.7	3.9
0040	0.065	0.21	1.3	1.9	4.1
0041	0.065	0.21	1.4	2.1	4.5
0042	0.062	0.21	1.4	2.0	4.7
0043	0.057	0.19	1.3	2.0	5.0
0044	0.053	0.18	1.2	1.8	5.2
0045	0.051	0.17	1.13	1.7	5.3
0050	0.030	0.11	0.83	1.3	5.0
0055	0.027	0.086	0.61	1.0	4.5
0100	0.017	0.081	0.39	0.64	4.0
Type of SID	SWF SCNA	SWF SCNA	SWF SCNA	SFD	SFD

* In units of erg cm^{-2} s^{-1} above the earth's atmosphere. These values are for the flare *enhancement* of radiation alone ($\Delta\Phi$) and do not give the total flux density ($\Phi = \Delta\Phi + \Phi_0$). The pre-flare or background flux density (Φ_0) is not included. The type of SID which most influenced the results is listed below the column of each wavelength range, where SFD denotes sudden frequency deviation, SWF denotes shortwave fadeout, and SCNA denotes sudden cosmic noise absorption.

to half the maximum at 3 Å, and gradually decreases at longer wavelengths to 10 per cent of the maximum at 10 Å. An enhancement in the 10–50 Å range with a peak of about 1 erg cm^{-2} s^{-1} at 0041 UT and an enhancement near 300 Å with peaks of about 0.5 erg cm^{-2} s^{-1} at 0038 and 0044 UT completes the example. The total X-ray and extreme ultraviolet enhancement for this example has a peak flux density of less than 2 erg cm^{-2} s^{-1}. Hence, radiation enhancements sufficient to explain the SID observations may be much smaller than the upper limits given in Table 1.

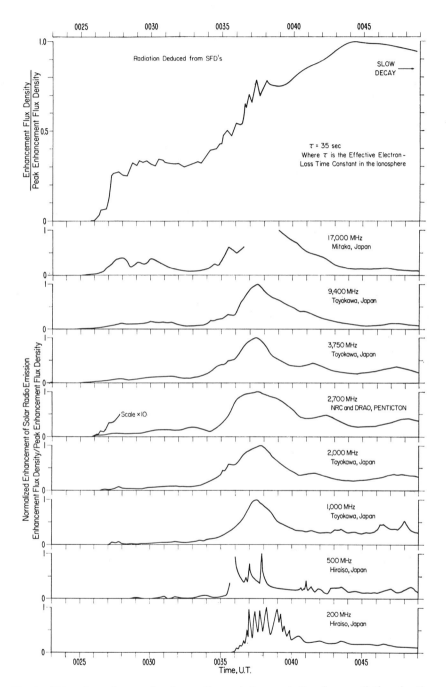

Fig. 1   Time dependence of solar radio emission and the flare radiation in the 10–1030 Å range deduced from SFD data.

4 Time Dependence

The SID data indicate that the X-ray and extreme ultraviolet enhancement started at about 0026 UT. The SFD's observed on radio waves reflected near the bottom of the E layer, the SPA data, and the SWF data indicate that the X-ray enhancement in the 0.2–10 Å range increased rapidly until about 0029 UT, remained relatively constant until 0035 UT, then again increased rapidly until about 0038 UT. A fairly flat peak was reached somewhere between 0039 and 0042 UT, and was followed by a slow decay. The time dependence of the X-ray enhancement deduced from SID data is in fair agreement with the centimeter-wavelength radio emission shown in Fig. 1, except that the X-ray peak apparently occurred several minutes after the peak radio emission. Major peaks not accompanied by any significant ionospheric effects occurred in the solar radio emission at frequencies less than 2700 MHz at about 0120 UT.

The SFD observations on radio waves reflected from the F region showed that this SFD was the longest ($\simeq 1$ hr) of all SFD's observed at Boulder since observations began in October 1960. It lasted more than twice as long as the second longest and more than 10 times longer than the average SFD's. Figure 1 shows the time dependence of the radiation enhancement deduced from these SFD data. It is in fair agreement with the time dependence of the centimeter-wavelength radio emission except that the peak lags even further behind the peak radio emission.

Acknowledgments

I am thankful to those scientists who generously shared their solar radio data, in particular the following: Dr. T. Takakura, Tokyo Astronomical Observatory; Professor H. Tanaka, Nagoya University; Mr. Arthur Covington, National Research Council, Ottawa; and Mr. Noboru Wakai, Hiraiso Radio Wave Observatory.

References

DONNELLY, R. F., 1967, An investigation of sudden frequency deviations due to the immediate ionospheric effects of solar flares, *ESSA Tech. Rep.* IER 19-ITSA 19 (ESSA, Boulder, Colorado).
——— 1968, An analysis of sudden ionospheric disturbances associated with the proton flare of 0026 UT, 7 July 1966 (to be published as an *ESSA Technical Report*).

33

The Geomagnetic Crochet of 7 July 1966

S. Pintér

Geomagnetic Observatory of the Slovak Academy of Sciences, Hurbanovo, Czechoslovakia

Abstract

The geomagnetic crochet began at 0026 UT with a sudden short impulse. It then expanded more slowly, as is characteristic for a crochet associated with the proton flares. The geomagnetic crochet reached its maximum about 0046 UT and was over at about 0230 UT. During the period of increase of the crochet to its maximum value, geomagnetic pulsations occurred. The pulsations are characterized by their irregular form with a variable period from 40 to 100 seconds.

The geomagnetic crochet is detectable not only in the sunlit hemisphere but also in the dark hemisphere. The time of maximum of the crochet is not simultaneous all over the world, but shows a systematic time lag in the sunlit hemisphere, i.e. the maximum stage at each station takes place later with increasing distance from the sub-solar point on the earth.

The value of the product of the recombination coefficient and the electron density of the D region of the ionosphere $(\alpha N)_D$ was determined on the basis of the duration of the decrease of the horizontal component of the geomagnetic crochet from maximum to normal value. The value of $(\alpha N)_D$ is then about $1.8 \times 10^{-4}\,\mathrm{s}^{-1}$.

During solar flares the intensity of the X-radiation suddenly increases; this is in the spectral range 0.1–10 Å and causes an increase in the ionization within the D layer of the ionosphere (Hakura 1966). As a consequence of this increased ionization there are sudden ionospheric disturbances (SID). To these ionospheric disturbances also belong the solar flare effects (SFE) with which this work deals.

On 7 July 1966 a proton flare accompanied by a solar flare effect was observed. Its position on the solar disk was 35°N and 47°W and its importance was 2B. The optical flare began at 0022 UT, its maximum was observed at 0041 UT and it ended at 0238 UT.

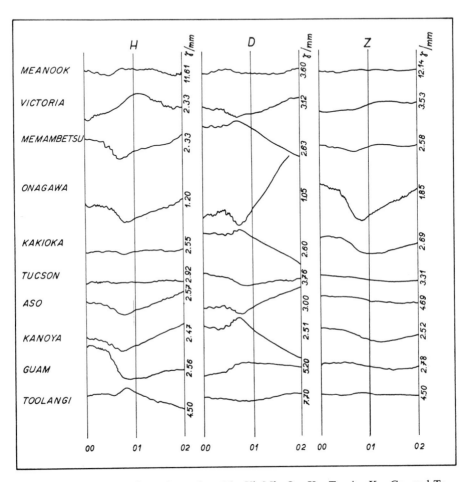

Fig. 1   Magnetogram from the stations Me, Vi, Mb, On, Ka, Tu, As, Ky, Gu, and To in the northern and southern hemisphere, showing the geomagnetic crochet of 7 July 1966.

The geomagnetic crochet began at 0026 UT with a sudden short impulse which lasted for about 1 minute. Then the crochet expanded more slowly as is characteristic for crochets associated with proton flares (Pintér 1967a). The geomagnetic crochet reached its maximum about 0046 UT and was over at about 0230 UT. Typical examples of geomagnetic crochet records from various observatories are illustrated in Fig. 1. During the increase of the geomagnetic crochet to its maximum value geomagnetic pulsations occurred. In Fig. 2 are illustrated the geomagnetic pulsations obtained from the Japan geomagnetic observatories at Memambetsu and Kanoya. The pulsations are characterized by their irregular form and they begin with an impulse. According to international classification these pulsations are irregular ones of type Pi 2 with a variable period from 40 to 100 seconds. The maximum amplitude was observed at 0027 UT.

From the above-mentioned data it is apparent that the geomagnetic crochet began 4 minutes after the beginning of the optically observed flare; thus the start of the crochet is within the interval during which the intensity

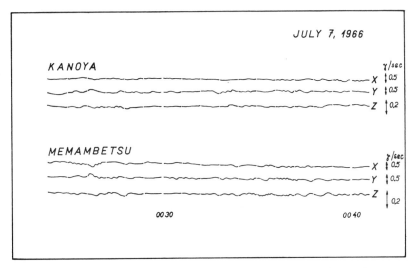

Fig. 2   Examples of geomagnetic pulsations accompanying the crochet.

of the flare is increasing to the maximum in Hα. The maximum of the crochet is about 5 minutes behind the maximum of the solar flare as measured by the horizontal component of the geomagnetic field of the crochet. This retardation of the maximum of the crochet in relation to the maximum of the flare Δt_{gc} can be explained by the reaction of the D region of the ionosphere on the impulsive rise of the intensity of the hard X-ray.

Ohshio (1964) showed, according to the analysis of 15 geomagnetic crochets during the IGY, that the crochets were detectable not only in the sunlit hemisphere but also in the polar region and often even in the dark hemisphere. This is the reason why $|\Delta H_{max}|$ of the geomagnetic crochet observed on 7 July 1966, which was associated with the solar proton flare, was investigated in relation to the solar zenith angle on the ground. Dependence between $|\Delta H_{max}|$ and the solar zenith angle found in this way is showed in Fig. 3

where the abscissa gives the solar zenith angle on the earth. It is seen from Fig. 3 that the absolute values of the amplitude ΔH_{max} are largest near the sub-solar point and that they decrease with the solar zenith angle x. Geographical coordinates of the sub-solar point at the time of maximum of geomagnetic crochet were $\phi = 22.7°N$, $\lambda = 168.7°E$. In the Fig. 3 there is shown the boundary between day and night which corresponds to the solar zenith angle 100.5°. It is seen that the crochets also occur behind this line on the dark part of the earth. Their amplitude is small (about 0.5–2γ) and their

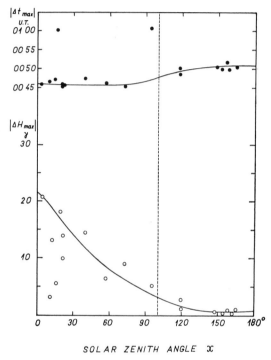

Fig. 3   Dependence on the solar zenith angle of the maximum geomagnetic crochet, and its time of occurrence.

form indistinct. Examples of magnetograms with crochets recorded in the dark hemisphere of the earth are shown in Fig. 4.

In the upper part of Fig. 3 are drawn the time maxima of the geomagnetic crochets observed at the various observatories as a function of the angle x. The maximum time does not occur simultaneously at the various stations on the earth, but a time lag is determined as a function of the solar zenith angle x. The microcrochets observed on the dark hemisphere of the earth are 5–7 minutes behind the beginning of the crochet on the sunlit hemisphere of the earth.

As the geomagnetic crochets begin at the time of the sudden increase in ionization produced by the intensive influx of solar X-rays and the increase of the crochet to maximum is accompanied by the intensive influx of the X-ray, it is apparent that the time of decrease of the crochet from maximum to normal value is linked with the cessation of the influx of X-rays into the ionospheric D region where the crochet was produced. After the influence of the ionization stops, recombination begins within the corresponding region of the ionosphere. The value of the product of the recombination coefficient and the electron density of the D region of the ionosphere $(\alpha N)_D$ was determined on the basis of the duration of the decrease of the horizontal component ΔH of the geomagnetic crochet from maximum to normal value. The value of $(\alpha N)_D$ is then about $1.8 \times 10^{-4}\,\mathrm{s}^{-1}$ (Pintér 1967a, b).

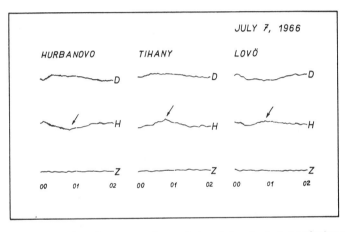

Fig. 4   Examples of geomagnetic crochet variation in dark hemisphere.

On the basis of the observed data it is possible to conclude that during the development of the solar proton flare to the hard X-ray in the range 0.1–10 Å there is generated a radiation in the range of about tens of ångströms which is able to produce the increase of ionization within the D region.

Acknowledgments

The author wishes to express his thanks to the directors of the following observatories for magnetograms received: Abisko, Sodankylö, Nurmijärvi, Meanook, Lovö, Wingst, Witteveen, Wien–Kobenzl, Tihany, Boulder, Grocko, Memambetsu, Tortosa, Onagawa, Kakioka, Simosato, Aso, Tucson, Kanoya, Honolulu, San Juan, M'Bour, Guam, Kodaikanal, Ibadan, Apia, La Quiaca, Watheroo, Pilar Hermanus, Toolangi, Amberley.

References

HAKURA, Y., 1966, Time variations in the solar X-rays producing SID's, *Rep. Ionosph. Space Res. Japan*, **20**, 30–32.

OHSHIO, M., 1964, Solar flare effect on geomagnetic variation, *J. Radio Res. Labs. Japan*, **11**, 377–490.

PINTÉR, S., 1967a, Geomagnetic crochets of solar flares observed in Hurbanovo, *Bull. Astr. Insts Czech.*, **18**, 274–281.

—— 1967b, Geomagnetic crochets associated with proton flares, *Bull. Astr. Insts Czech.*, **18**, 282–286.

34

Later Development of the Center of Activity of the Proton Flare, 7 July 1966: Optical Observations

H. W. Dodson and E. R. Hedeman

McMath–Hulbert Observatory, The University of Michigan, Pontiac, Michigan, USA

Abstract

The center of activity that was the site of a proton flare on 7 July 1966 continued through at least two subsequent rotations. In the first of these, in late July, spot area and radio emission were greatly diminished, but the calcium plage had increased in area by 50 per cent. Flares continued to occur in the region, and the major flare of 28 July is of special interest. In the August rotation, the post-proton region of July at latitude 33°N through differential rotation became co-longitudinal at 182° with a previously following region in latitude 22°N. This region at lower latitude produced major proton flares on 28 August and 2 September.

I Introduction

The center of activity that was the site of the proton flare on 7 July 1966 could be recognized as an entity for at least two subsequent rotations (see Figs. 1 and 2). In its passage across the solar disk in the rotation following that of the proton event, the spot (CMP 31 July) was reduced in area to less than 100 millionths of the hemisphere and was classified on seven days as a simple α_p of Brunner Type J. On six days during its transit, small ephemeral spots of R polarity were observed following the stable V spot making the spot group on those days of magnetic class β_p. The Stanford measurements of 9.1-cm emission for this region showed a greatly diminished radio temperature. In spite of these circumstances, the associated calcium plage was still large and relatively bright. Though somewhat fragmented and divided by a filament, the plage had increased in area by 50 per cent between 7 July and the

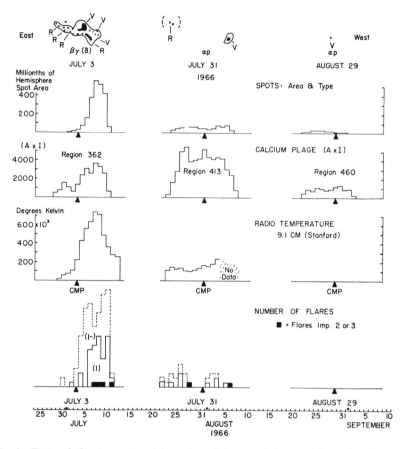

Fig. 1   Data relating to spots, calcium plage, 9.1-cm emission, and flares for the center
          of activity associated with the proton flare of 7 July 1966.
          The parentheses around the "R" spots on 31 July indicate that the spots were
          ephemeral.

re-appearance of the region at the end of the month (see Figs. 1 and 2).
Magnetographic measurements at Mount Wilson showed that it was a
bipolar plage.

2   Flare of 28 July 1966

The region in late July continued to produce flares but at a lower rate than
in the preceding rotation (see Fig. 1). The flare of 28 July, 2216 UT, importance 2B or greater, is worthy of special comment. The flare was centered
at 36°N 33°E. It began to brighten at least as early as 2216 UT and had two
intensity maxima in Hα at approximately 2240 and 2330 UT, respectively.
Only during the initial 15 minutes of the slow rise to the first maximum did

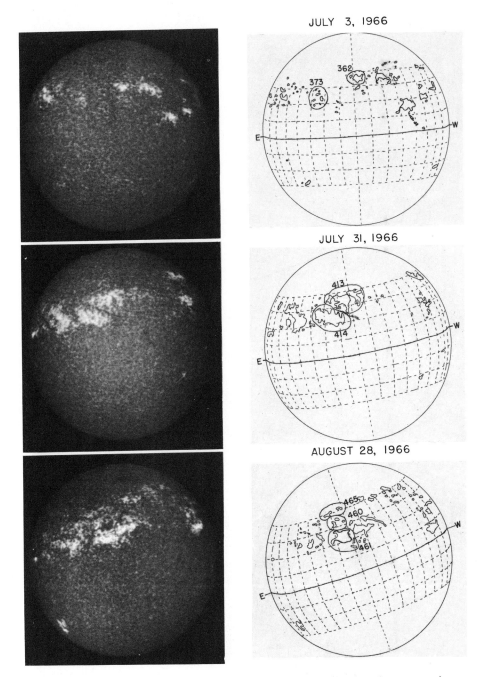

Fig. 2   Calcium spectroheliograms and heliographic maps showing three successive transits of the central meridian by the region associated with the proton flare of 7 July 1966.

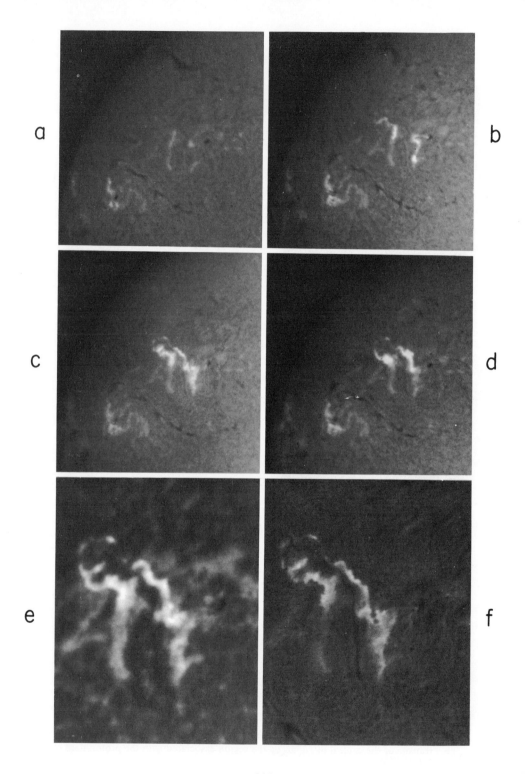

the Hα flare emission occur close to the simple α-type spot then present in the region. After 2235 the Hα flare, emission was far from all spots (see Figs. 3 and 4).

Emission at radio frequencies was enhanced for more than two hours after the start of this flare. Peak flux occurred during the rise to the first Hα maximum, and the flux increased markedly with decreasing frequency, over a range from 2400 to 1000 MHz.

According to Dr. Van Allen's "Preliminary Catalogue of Solar X-Ray Events, $2 < \lambda < 12$ Å for Explorer 33", this flare on 28 July 1966 produced strong X-ray emission. The peak ratio of the flare-associated X-ray emission to that of the quiet sun was 13. For the flare of 7 July 1966 the corresponding value was 28. The X-ray maximum took place at 2330 UT during the second increase in Hα intensity and when the large Hα flare consisted primarily of two bright filaments on the borders of a large absorption feature far from the spot[1] (see Fig. 4A).

The flare was accompanied by the disintegration of a large filament far to the north of the region. The filament ceased to be visible in the center of Hα at approximately 2230, and from 2310 to 2320 erupting prominence material was observed at the northeast limb (see Fig. 4A). Small, transient, bright and dark features apparently emanating from the disintegrating filament also appeared directed towards the flare. It is clear that in late July, the region that was the site of the proton flare of 7 July was still capable of producing a major flare.

3   Relationships between 7 July and 28 August Proton Regions

The third and last distinct rotation of the July proton region (CMP ~ 29 August) presented interesting circumstances. In late August the region was not detectable as a separate source of enhanced 9.1 cm radiation and no flares were reported as taking place within its bounds. A small α-type spot without penumbra was present from east limb passage to CMD west 32°. The calcium plage, though greatly fragmented and reduced in intensity, was still a detectable feature. Because of its high latitude (35°N) and differential

---

Fig. 3   Hα and K records of the flare of 28 July 1966, 2216 UT.
   Hα filtroheliograms: Flare patrol telescope
      a.   Prior to outbreak of flare, 1805 UT.
      b.   Initial phase of flare, 2218 UT.
      c.   Flare near first intensity maximum, 2245 UT.
      d.   Flare near second intensity maximum, 2332 UT.
   Spectroheliograms: Telescope, 40 ft focal length
      e.   K₃, 2300 UT.
      f.   Hα, 2300 UT.

---

[1] It should be noted that a subflare occurred in a neighboring plage, 25°N 78°E from 2323 to 2340 UT.

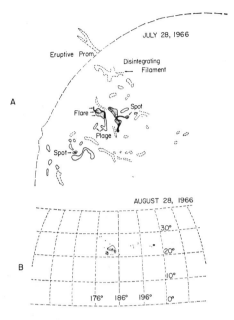

Fig. 4   A.   Composite drawing of flare showing change in location with time.
              Black, flare at about 2218 UT.
              Crosshatched, flare at about 2241 UT.
              Dotted, flare at about 2330 UT.
         B.   Spot map, 28 August 1966.

rotation, the 7 July proton region had drifted with time closer and closer
to a "following" region at latitude 24°N with which it had been co-existent
since early July. At that time, the two regions had been separated by about
27° of longitude. In late August the spots in the two regions became co-
longitudinal at about 180° Carrington longitude (see Figs. 2 and 4B). On
28 August the region with the lower latitude (24°N) became the site of another
proton flare. To assist in recognition of the proton regions of 7 July and
28 August in Fig. 2, information relating to them is presented in Table 1.

Table I   Data relating to the Proton Regions of 7 July and 28 August 1966

	7 July Region			28 August Region		
Date of CMP	3 July	31 July	30 Aug.	5 July	2 Aug.	30 Aug.
McMath Plage No.	8362	8413	{8460 8465	8373	8414	8461
Latitude	33°N	35°N	33°N	24°N	25°N	22°N
Longitude	209°	198°	182°	182°	178°	182°

The two proton regions here described were in the "following" (eastern) part of a persistent zone of activity which in 1966 extended across about 100° of solar longitude ($\sim 270° \rightarrow 170°$). In early August in the preceding part of this zone, a large spot appeared at the low latitude of 07°N. It persisted for at least six rotations. Phenomena within this zone, of which the 7 July proton region was a part, dominated solar activity during the entire second half of 1966.

35

Magnetic Field Decay in the Group 21034 during the Proton Flare Period of July 1966

E. I. Mogilevsky, L. B. Demkina, Yu. N. Dolginova, B. A. Ioshpa, V. N. Obridko, B. D. Shelting, and I. A. Zhulin

Institute of Terrestrial Magnetism, Ionosphere, and Radio-Wave Propagation of the USSR Academy of Sciences, Moscow, USSR

Abstract

It has been noted that while considering magnetic field decay after the flare, one can make only detailed photographic measurements of the spot-group field because the region of Hα radiation in the proton flare is closely connected with the distribution of the magnetic field of the spot group. For two groups of spots (No. 21034 and 18521) of the Proton Flare Project programme, in which proton flares were observed, a similarity of magnetic field structure has been emphasized. After the proton event of 7 July in the group 21034 a sudden growth of S-polarity magnetic flux and considerable decrease of N-polarity flux have been observed. During the next rotation of the sun the group 21034 was observed continuously as a slowly decaying unipolar spot of S-polarity with the magnetic class "αp".

Chromospheric flares in general, and proton flares especially, are directly associated with the variations of the sunspot magnetic field. This is well seen in the isodensitogram of the great chromospheric flare of 7 July 1966 obtained at Culgoora observatory in Australia on the Hα filtergram of the flare ($T = 0040$ UT); one can see that the isolines of the brightest places in the flare are located almost completely over the group of spots, roughly repeating the isolines of its magnetic field.[1] Therefore, we considered it possible in the

---

[1] But it is necessary to say that the large umbrae of the spots, where the intensity of magnetic field had the largest value, are not the places of flare brightness.

examination of the problem of the decay of the magnetic field group 21034 of the proton flare to utilize only the data on the magnetic field of the group of spots which have been obtained photographically with sufficient detail. We used the observations from the solar tower telescope IZMIRAN during the period 3–9 July and at the subsequent appearance of the group (26 July–3 August), as well as the observations of these groups obtained at the observatory Monte Maric. In order to obtain a sufficiently full idea of the magnetic field distribution in the groups observed, we have received 15–30 twin polarization spectrograms in the region of the line Fe I 6302.5 Å. Simultaneously with this a sequence filming of the sun at the spectrograph entrance slit was carried out. This made it possible to obtain magnetic field measurements at 20–30 points in the slit height, and to relate them to the group picture.[2] Thus, it became possible to obtain from 150 to 300 field values, which might partly serve also for mutual control. The charts of magnetic field in the group were built up from these data. Figure 1 helps to trace the course of the group 21034 development within the two rotations 1509–1510, as well as the evolution of the second group of the proton flare programme No. 18521 within the rotations 1510–1511. One must pay attention to the definite similarity of the groups 21034 and 18521 in their maximum (proton) phase of development. From the more detailed charts of Fig. 2 one can judge more about the character of the similarity of these groups in this period. Both these groups had two characteristic parallel chains of umbrae with opposite polarity of magnetic field, which were generally maintained at the period of greatest development, in spite of other essential changes. In one complex penumbra both groups had umbrae with opposite polarity of magnetic field and belonged to the typical δ class, where both usual and proton flares may most probably be observed (Warwick 1966). However, the first (the high-latitude group 21034) had already attained the maximum development at the first rotation, and decayed in the next. Before the proton phase (in August–September) the second proton flare low-latitude group 18521 had been observed as a small group from May onwards and only at the fifth (last) rotation did it reach maximum development.

Table 1 and the magnetic charts (Fig. 2) present the sequence of magnetic flux variations in the group 21034 on some days for which there were some data of detailed measurements. In the absence of detailed measurements the magnetic flux estimation was made conventionally from the equation

$$\phi = H_{\max} \times S_{\mathrm{u}} + \tfrac{1}{3} H_{\max} \times S_{\mathrm{p}}$$

where $H_{\max}$ is the maximum field strength in the umbrae according to the routine observational data (*Solnechnye Dannye* 1966), S_{u} is the umbral area, and S_{p} the penumbral area. Flux values obtained in such a way are given in

---

[2] Observations were carried out in Cassegrain focus of the tower telescope (F_{eff} 27 metres).

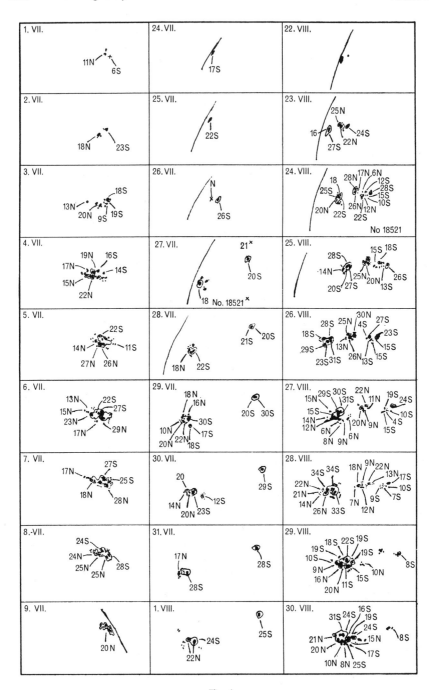

Fig. 1

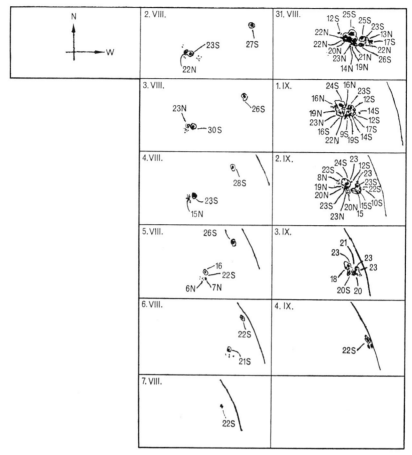

Fig. 1   Development of the group No. 21034 in rotations 1509, 1510, and of the group No. 18521 in rotations 1510, 1511. Magnetic fields in umbrae of spots are given in hundreds of oersteds.

brackets in Table 1. The magnetic class was determined mainly from the data (*Solar–Geophysical Data* 1966).

Most significant is the fact that, despite some significant changes in the group before the flare of 7 July, an approximate equality of magnetic fluxes was maintained, while after the flare (8 July) a sharp increase in the magnetic flux of S-polarity took place at nearly negligible growth of ϕ_N. On the following days (9 and 10 July), decay of the group was noticed; this was mainly due to the decrease of umbrae and penumbrae of N-polarity. Assuming that a similar course of development took place in the group at the opposite, invisible, side of the solar disk, one can realize why in the next rotation the group appeared as a relatively stable unipolar spot of S-polarity. One may assume that of all the umbrae of S-polarity in rotation 1509 only one umbra

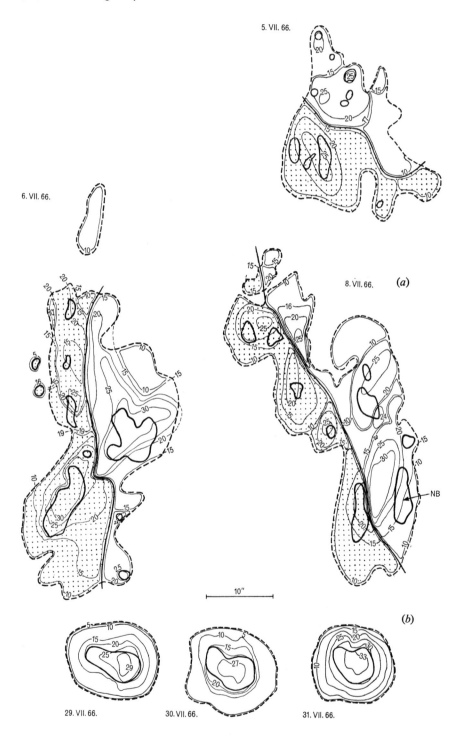

5. VII. 66.

6. VII. 66.

8. VII. 66.   (a)

NB

10"

(b)

29. VII. 66.   30. VII. 66.   31. VII. 66.

Table I   Magnetic Characteristics of the Group 21034

Date and Time of Observations	Area of the Spot (in 10^{-6} parts of hemisphere)		Magnetic Flux of the Spot (maxwells $\times 10^{22}$)		Magnetic Flux of the Marked Spot Umbra
	N-polarity	S-polarity	N	S	S
1.14 July 1966	(15)		(no observation)		
2.14	(32)	(32)			
3.13	46	35	—	—	
4.60	228	41	—	—	
5.21	255	200	1.01	0.95	
6.38	470	355	2.37	2.16	(a) 0.40
7.28	(580)	(550)	(3.04)	(3.0)	(—)
8.35	500	800	2.53	4.89	(a) 0.15*
			—	—	(b) 0.27
9.26	1394		—	—	
24.15 July 1966	—	(68)	—	(0.14)	
25.15	—	116	—	(0.30)	
26.16	—	173	—	(0.52)	
27.33	—	185	—	(0.43)	
28.19	—	165	—	(0.40)	
29.18	—	171	—	0.73(0.6)	0.26
30.21	—	168	—	0.63(0.56)	0.22
31.24	—	136	—	0.87(0.45)	0.31
1.16 August 1966	—	156	—	(0.46)	
2.21	—	131	—	(0.42)	
3.15	—	169	—	(0.52)	
4.32	—	171	—	(56)	
5.15	—	156	—	(0.47)	
6.16	—	(168)	—	(0.43)	

* (a), (b) Calculation of S-polarity magnetic flux for 8 July was made by two methods: (a) the core marked NB in Fig. 2a had N-polarity according to our insufficiently reliable data. Therefore, the first flux values, marked (a), appeared to be an insertion of the core magnetic field NB into N-polarity; (b) corresponds to the polarity distribution shown in Fig. 2a as follows from the data published in Solnechnȳe Dannȳe 1966, Solar–Geophysical Data 1966, Monthly Bulletin (Solar Phenomena) 1966.

remained in the next rotation; this umbra is marked by an arrow in Fig. 2a. This statement is supported to some extent by consideration of the group evolution and close values of the magnetic fluxes of corresponding spot umbrae.

From Table 1 and Figs. 1 and 2b we can see that in rotation 1510 the unipolar group was gradually decreasing in area, maintaining the field

Fig. 2   Magnetic chart of the group No. 21034 for 5, 6, and 8 July (a), and for 29–31 July (b). N-polarity regions are marked with dots. The field is given in hundreds of oersteds.

distribution within the spot nearly unchanged (magnetic class was preferably "αp").[3] But in the floccule surrounding this group significant changes were observed: weak flares, changing sources of radio noise component S_a.

These phenomena were observed in the tail part of the active region, situated close to the neighbouring active region of the second group 18521 of the proton flare programme, which achieved the proton phase at the next rotation of the sun. It seems important to emphasize this last point due to the assumption that the subsequent rapid development of the group 18521 (which was a non-effective small group during the three previous revolutions of the sun) might be stimulated by the magnetic field of the decaying high-latitude group 21034. It is possible that such an influence on the group 18521 might also be caused by the group 16111 (according to Mount Wilson), rapidly developing at the same latitude (22°N). No magnetograph charts were available within the region of the group 21034 for the solar rotations 1510 and 1511. As judged by the character of the decay of calcium floccule around the group 21034, the floccule and its magnetic field were gradually decaying into supergranulation cells with subsequent decrease of the intensity.

Acknowledgments

We thank Professor M. Cimino, Dr. V. Croce and Dr. Caldwell for observational material received.

References

Monthly Bulletin (Solar Phenomena), 1966, Nos 103, 104.
Solar–Geophysical Data, 1966, FB-264-265, US Department of Commerce, ESSA, Environmental Data Service (Government Printing Office, Washington D.C.).
Solnechnÿe Dannÿe (Sunspots magnetic fields), 1966, *Bull. Soln. Dann.*, Nos. 7–9.
WARWICK, C. S., 1966, Sunspot configurations and proton flares, *Astrophys. J.*, **145**, 215–223.

---

[3] It is interesting to note that at this time the area of the spot is nearly equal to the area of the supergranule.

B

On the Development and Activity of the Active Region associated with the Proton Flare Event of July 1966: Summary of Observations and Conclusions

V. Banin*, L. D. de Feiter†, A. D. Fokker†, M. J. Martres‡, and M. Pick‡

* SibIZMIR, Irkutsk, USSR
† Sterrewacht "Sonnenborgh", Utrecht, Netherlands
‡ Observatoire de Paris, Meudon, France

Abstract

The solar active region respectively named by Mount Wilson, McMath, and Meudon observatories as 16067, 8362 and 150915 was located at 210° and 34°N. In the first part of this paper the most important observations as derived from the different contributions are discussed and compared. The second part deals with the specific features of the proton flare. To conclude we discuss some properties of the active region which could appear as conditions that are necessary for the preparation and production of proton flares.

I Birth of the Active Region

On 28 and 29 June, the formation of a dark oval bordered by bright features appeared in the K_3 network. This new formation took place among the patches of an old expanding region (Fortini and Torelli, Paper 4).[1]

Figure 1 summarizes the development of the active centre. The building up was marked by the successive formation of three pairs of spot clusters, on 30.5 June, 1.5 July, and 3.1 July respectively (McIntosh, Paper 5). Each pair is displaced eastward from the former by a few degrees in longitude.

In each pair the leading spots were farther away from the equator than the following ones, contrary to the normal occurrence (McIntosh, Paper 5). *So*

---

[1] Paper numbers refer to articles in this volume.

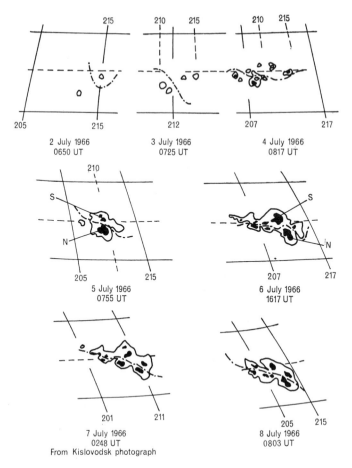

Fig. 1   Drawings of spots: approximate position in longitude and magnetic polarities.
Spectroheliograms K IV Meudon.   Magnetic maps Crimea and Meudon.

the general inversion line is roughly parallel to the equator and the western
following spot is close to the eastern leading spot of another pair.

1.1   Early Development, from 3 July to 6 July

The evolution of these spots, growing and merging together, leads to the
classical δ configuration, characterized by spots of inverse polarities in the
same penumbra (Künzel 1960). During the same period an enhancement of
the brightness and the area of the faculae was observed in the K_3 line (Fortini
and Torelli, Paper 4). The corrected area of the Hα plage increased rapidly
and reached its maximum on 6 July. Figure 2 shows that the sunspot area had
not yet reached its maximum by that time (Popovici and Dimitriu, Paper 3).
The flare activity started on 3 July just after the appearance of the third pair

of sunspots (Bruzek, Paper 12, Křivský, Paper 18, Kai, Paper 28) but the importance of the flares was small. X-ray emission was observed by the NRL solar X-ray monitoring satellite (1965–93A) (Friedman and Kreplin, Paper 11). The flux levels were recorded by photometers and ion chambers whose energy ranges are respectively 0.5–3, 1–8, 8–20, and 44–60 Å. An increase in X-ray emission began on 4 July and continued through 5 July with considerable variability from pass to pass. Radio emission of the active centre at centimetric and decimetric wavelengths was first noticed on 2 or 3 July (Tanaka, Kakinuma, and Enome, Paper 9).

For each radio frequency the general evolution of the radio flux was the same as the evolution of the sunspot area.

Figure 3 shows that the flux, like the total spot area, continued to increase up to 8 July and thereafter rapidly decreased.

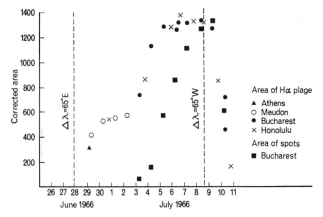

Fig. 2   Variation of sunspot area and Hα plage area (from C. Popovici and A. Dimitriu, Paper 3).

There is, however, a shift in the radio spectrum towards higher frequencies during the life of the active centre. Figure 4 shows that until 4.5 July the flux density decreased with increasing frequency between 4 and 9.4 GHz. This corresponds to the kind of spectrum exhibited by the majority of the active centres (Avignon *et al.* 1963). A sudden rise of the flux, which is especially marked at about 9.4 GHz, occurred between 4.5 and 5.0 July. So in the 4–9 GHz frequency interval, the spectrum became relatively flat (Tanaka *et al.*, Paper 9). This feature has been reported by Tanaka and Kakinuma (1964) as being typical for the active centres that produce proton emissions or Type IV bursts. Other characteristic features of such active centres are

a. the presence of a strong horizontal gradient of the longitudinal magnetic field;

b. a greater-than-normal ratio of the 3 cm flux density to the total sunspot area (Avignon *et al.* 1966).

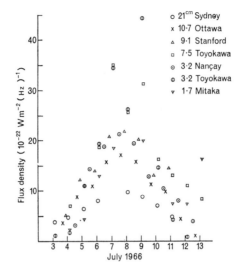

Fig. 3   Variations of flux density of the slowly varying component (from H. Tanaka, T. Kakinuma, and S. Enome, Paper 9) with the collaboration of many observatories.

More precisely, this feature of the high-frequency radio radiation was very likely associated with a change of the magnetic structure rather than with an increase of the sunspot area. It seems to be connected with the important changes in the optical aspect between 4 and 5 July, which leads to the classical configuration of the proton centres.

This fact is clearly seen in Fig. 5 where we have collected the data concerning the evolution of the flux at different frequencies and the evolution of the

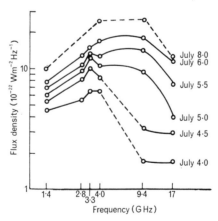

Fig. 4   Variation of spectrum of the slowly varying component (from H. Tanaka, T. Kakinuma, and S. Enome, Paper 9), with the collaboration of many observatories.

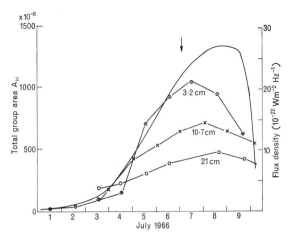

Fig. 5 Comparison between the daily variation of total sunspot area (from C. Popovici and A. Dimitriu, Paper 3), and flux density at centimetric and decimetric wavelengths.

sunspot area. For frequencies equal to or smaller than 4 GHz the radio development is similar to the optical. On the other hand, at 9.4 GHz we observe a discontinuity on 5 July.

1.2 Configuration and Activity of the Centre on 6 July

1.2.1 The Two Days preceding the Proton Flare. During the two days preceding the proton flare the active region exhibited some very striking phenomena summarized as follows: The remarkable *period of rapid growth* beginning on 5 July led to a configuration consisting of two parallel rows of spots. *The area of these spots was very large compared with* the area of the calcium plage (Fortini and Torelli, Paper 4). These spots extended in an *E–W direction while up to this date the extension was roughly N–S — with two main umbrae very close together.* On the white light records "the darkness [of the spots] and their close separation indicates strong magnetic fields and a steep magnetic field gradient" (McIntosh, Paper 5).

Between 5 and 6 July (see Fig. 1) the two main spots of opposite polarities reached a kind of "equilibrium" (in area and magnetic flux) (Mogilevsky *et al.*, Paper 35). *This step in the development does not coincide with the maximum of the area of the group but rather with the maximum of the spot which presented the δ configuration. More precisely, this may be called an A configuration, because equilibrium has been attained* (Avignon *et al.* 1963). *The A configuration is always a special case of the δ configuration.* The Hα brightness was greatest between the umbrae of these two spots and decreased eastward. Connected with the activity of subflares were several intensity fluctuations at microwave frequencies, in particular at frequencies around

9 GHz. Some of these fluctuations had the character of gradual rise and fall, others had more a burst character. The production of small high-frequency bursts continued also after the proton flare. The Type IV radio event on 7 July stood isolated from the rest of radio bursts as a giant.

1.2.2   Several Hours before the Proton Flare.   In white light a remarkable development was observed in the central portion *10 hours* before the flare: the *penumbra* between the two spots becomes unusually dark (McIntosh, Paper 5). Figure 6 reveals that *12 hours before* the proton flare the plage exhibited two

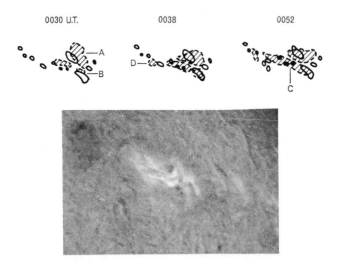

Fig. 6   Comparison between photograph of Hα taken on 6 July, 1153, 12 hours before the flare from Bucharest, and drawings of the proton flare itself from McCabe and P. A. Caldwell (Paper 24).

bright filaments which had a symmetrical disposition with respect to the axes of the group and just covered the penumbrae of the two ranges of spots (Popovici and Dimitriu, Paper 3). The abundance of absorbing material in the form of filaments, active dark flocculi and large regions of structureless, dark material is quite remarkable. In the south-eastern part of the region gases moved away from the observer, whereas on the opposite side there was a movement toward the observer. These motions show significant enhancement (and changes of location) in the two hours preceding the flare (Dodson and Hedeman, Paper 34). It is also reported that a continuous production of small flares occurred in the region where the proton flare was bound to appear (Fisher and Mann, Paper 22). They increased in area from one subflare to the following one. Associated with this flare activity was a strong variation of the X-ray flux. More precisely, X-ray emission increased from 5 July, remaining at a high level on 6 July; the mean intensity at this time reached the level commonly reported for flare events. At the same time a *hardening* of the

X-ray emission took place (see Fig. 7): the 0.3 Å emission was first observed above the background level on 6 July (Michard and Ribes 1968, Friedman and Kreplin, Papers 11, 20).

The several aspects mentioned may be looked upon as indications of a kind of "preparation" of the active region, which started about 3 July but which was accelerated suddenly during the twelve hours preceding the proton flare.

In conclusion the main aspects of the general evolution of the active centre appear to be:

Its development is completely anomalous, being made up of the successive births and intermingled evolutions of three bipolar groups, finally merging into an A-type configuration with a magnetic inversion line of E–W orientation.

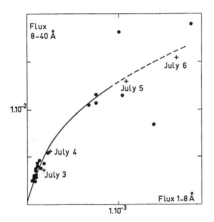

Fig. 7   Comparative evolution of 8–40 Å X-ray flux and 1–8 Å X-ray flux from Michard and Ribes (1968) with data of NRL solar X-ray monitoring satellite 1965–93A.

Parallel with this development a notable change occurs in the spectrum at radio frequencies. While the radio spectrum becomes flat toward the high frequencies, the X-ray emission becomes harder.

In Hα the plage attains an exceptionally high brightness, and several indications (minor flare activity, enhanced motions of absorbing material) point to the progressive building up of a major instability in the few hours preceding the proton flare.

2   Development of the Proton Flare

2.1   General

The proton flare first appeared essentially as a brightening of the plage. It commenced at 0026 at a position 35°N 45°W as two small *bright areas adjacent to the largest umbrae of the spot group.* The intensity increased rapidly

from 0026 onwards, at the same time as the area extended to the east along
the row of smaller spots. A first brightness maximum was reached between
0030 and 0036; a second maximum occurred between 0045 and 0052. At this
time most of the umbrae of the large spots were covered by flare material, as
well as a number of small spots. No significant movements along the line of
sight were noted for the flare material. At 0237 the flare had lost most of its
brightness (McCabe and Caldwell, Paper 24).

Simultaneously with the start of the optical flare, at 0026, there was a first
rise of intensity at microwave frequencies (Fig. 8), followed by a second,
larger one at 0033. At frequencies around 200 MHz a steep rise of intensity
occurred at 0035. The greatest intensity was reached at 0038, attaining a
value of over 6000×10^{-22} Hz^{-1} at frequencies above 6000 MHz. During the

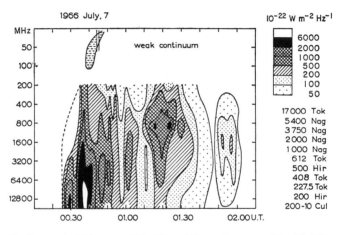

Fig. 8   Radio spectral diagram of the Type IV event, prepared by Kai (Paper 28).

subsequent decline some four secondary peaks occurred at microwave frequencies. At decimetric frequencies a very substantial fraction of the energy
was radiated between 0115 and 0140. The spectrum of this decimetric component peaked at around 800 MHz (see Fig. 8). A reversal of polarization
was observed at about 3000 MHz (Enome, Paper 27, Kai, Paper 28). At frequencies below 200 MHz the main feature was a Type II burst from 0038 to
0047 and a second intense portion of Type II burst from 0112 to 0113. Both
fundamental and harmonic components could be discerned (Stewart, Paper
25). Any continuum that may have followed the Type IV events was ill-
developed; this is perhaps due to an effect of directivity: the flare occurred
not far from the west limb. The metric Type IV continuum is reported as
being weak by many people. Nevertheless Warwick (Paper 26) observed a
well-defined Type IV emission at decametric wavelengths: the source of
emission "moves at a speed of 380 km s^{-1} outwards from the flare to a

distance 1.3 $R_\odot$ from the sun's centre at 0130 UT. After 0130 UT, the emission drifts slowly back towards the flare and fades at 0200 UT."

Associated with the proton flare was a strong flux of X-ray emission which, like the optical and radio radiation, started at 0026, judging from sudden ionospheric disturbances and a geomagnetic crochet. No significant ionospheric effect was associated with the decimetric radio emission peak at 0120. The sudden frequency deviation (SFD) on radio waves reflected from the F region lasted exceptionally long (Donnelly, Paper 32). The enhanced radiation in the 0–8 Å band lasted about 5 hours (Van Allen, Paper 30, Friedman and Kreplin, Paper 31, Pintér, Paper 33, Křivský and Nestorov, Paper 19).

2.2   Phenomena associated in Time with the Proton Flare

During the lifetime of the flare two small sympathetic flares occurred to the west of the sunspot group. The dark filament east of the region gradually disappeared, probably associated with a blast wave (S. Smith, private communication). It was again visible on 7 July at 1240 (McCabe and Caldwell, Paper 24).

In three directions perpendicular to the inversion line systematic variations of mean longitudinal gradient were noted: 0.1 G km^{-1} on 4 July, 1 G km^{-1} at 6.2 July; 0.2–0.1 G km^{-1} at 7.2 July (Severny, Paper 1). In white light the large umbra near the centre of the group is decreasing as a rapid growth continues both in the leading and following parts of the group (McIntosh and Sawyer, Paper 23). In good agreement with this, we note the relative increase of S-polarity flux as compared with N-polarity flux (Křivský, Paper 18).

These two remarks are probably not specific for proton flares: they support the description of the evolution of spots associated with flares which has been given by a thorough study of a small active region in the Co-operative Study on Solar Active Regions (CSSAR) project (Martres *et al.* 1968). Two other facts are remarkable: (*a*) Up to 5 July the elongation of the strong umbrae and the neighbouring penumbral filaments is along the N–S direction, but on 6 July it is strongly E–W (McIntosh, Paper 5) (the exact time has not been reported). (*b*) *A rotation of the horizontal component of the magnetic field* which is observed to be NE–SW on 6.2 July and more nearly E–W on 7.2 July (Severny, Paper 1).

2.3   Remarks on the Evolution of the active Centre after the Proton Flare

The part of the sunspot group where the proton flare occurred decreased and fragmented, but the total sunspot area still increased during the two days following the proton flare. This is due to the development of the east and west parts of the group (McIntosh and Sawyer, Paper 23).

Table I   Evolution of

Date 1966	Optical Features		
	White Light	K_3	$H\alpha$
June 28		decreasing old region	
29		bright grains	
30	1st pair of spots	development of bright flocculi	
July 1	2nd pair of spots		
2			
2.5			
3	3rd pair of spots		transformation of bright plage
4	increasing		
4.5			
5			
5.5		calcium plage area ~ spots area	
6			maximum of area
6.5	darkening of penumbra		two bright filaments very nearly along inversion line
7	Proton Flare	Proton Flare	Proton Flare
7.5	fragmentation of many umbrae and penumbrae		
8	maximum of whole area of spots		

the Active Region

Magnetic Configuration	X-rays	Radio Bursts	Radio
βp			
- - - - - - - - - - - - - - -			S component appears
complex ↓	- - - - - - - - - - - - -	beginning of flare activity	↓
	indication of increasing		flat spectrum 4 and 9.4 GHz
δ configuration ↓	↓	↓	
A configuration (state of equilibrium) ↓	hardening ↓	strongly increasing of number radio bursts ↓	↓
Proton Flare	Proton Flare	Proton Flare	Proton Flare
decrease of A configuration			

The radio evolution is not easy to study because the correction of the flux due to the heliographic position of the active centre is not well known and may be a function of frequency. It appears that on 8 July the radio spectrum still presents the same shape (Fig. 4).

The coronal data are difficult to interpret because the active centre was born on the solar disk and we have no information on the evolution of the centre while it passed from the east limb to the west limb. One interesting feature is that the maxima of the isophotes of coronal lines 6347 and 5303 were shifted toward the north pole (Leroy, Paper 6, Gnevyshev, Paper 7). From white light coronal observations it was found, on applying a method of deriving electron densities, that on 10 July the coronal density was higher than for an average coronal streamer. This anomalous electron density exists at low levels chiefly below 1.5 solar radii. It is interpreted as a "slowly expanding bubble" of dense coronal gas formed at the time of the proton flare (Newkirk, Hansen, and Hansen, Paper 8).

Two other important flares occurred while the region was still on the visible disk. The main conclusion that can be drawn from a comparison of these events with the proton flare is that the flare of 9 July was more typical for the "classical" proton flare picture than was the proton flare of 7 July itself. There was, however, a considerable difference in intensity, and it covered the fragmented umbrae of the region only partly.

Possibly the largest event in this region was produced when the centre had already passed the western limb; it was associated with the large eruptive prominence observed on 11 July. The big event started at 0905 and developed in two separate regions: one was parallel to the limb while the main part was inclined at an angle of 40° to the limb. The big blast in this latter region at about 0931 is worth comment. From spectra secured at Anacapri and from cinematographic pictures, velocities of as much as 500 km s^{-1} have been derived. The radial velocities were mainly in the direction of the observer, which indicates that the origin of the blast was well beyond the limb. The observations give an indication of twisted motions. More than half an hour after the time when no further activity was noted on narrow-band filtergrams, an active prominence of large dimensions was still visible on wide-band (5 Å) filtergrams. The fact that a part of the event was observable in integrated light, and its large dimensions (30 square degrees) would justify its classification as 4N flares.

3 Conclusion

The main details relating to the evolution of the active region are summarized in Table 1.

A certain number of features characteristic of proton flare regions can be ascertained in the present case. After a rapid growth the sunspot group reached a δ configuration on 5 July. A kind of equilibrium between the two adjoining and very strong magnetic polarities was reached on the day preceding the proton flare (A configuration). As from 5 July the microwave radio spectrum presented the form which is indicative of the occurrence of Type IV outbursts. The flare covered large parts of the umbrae; associated with it was Type IV radio emission and strong X-ray emission.

Acknowledgments

We are grateful to Dr. Michard for his interest in this work.

References

AVIGNON, Y., M. J. MARTRES, and M. PICK, 1963, Identification d'une classe d'éruptions chromosphériques responsables des absorptions ionosphériques polaires, *C.R. Acad. Sci., Paris*, **256**, 2112–2114.

—— 1966, Etude de la "composante lentement variable" en relation avec la structure des centres d'activité solaire associée, *Annls Astrophys.*, **29**, 33–42.

KUNZEL, H., 1960, Die Flare Harfigkeit in Fleckengruppen unterschiedlicher Klasse und magnetischer Struktur, *Astr. Nachr.*, **285**, 271–273.

MARTRES, M. J., R. MICHARD, I. SORU-ISCOVICI, and T. TSAP, 1968, A study of the localization of flares in selected, active regions, *Proc. IAU Symposium No. 35, Structure and Development of Solar Active Regions*, Ed. K. O. Kiepenheuer (Reidel Publ. Co., Dordrecht, Holland) pp. 318–325.

MICHARD, R., and E. RIBES, 1968, La composante lentement variable des rayons X solaires en relation avec la structure des centres d'activité, *Proc. IAU Symposium No. 35, Structure and Development of Solar Active Regions*, Ed. K. O. Kiepenheuer (Reidel Publ. Co., Dordrecht, Holland) pp. 420–430.

SWARUP, G., *et al.*, 1963, High resolution studies of ten solar active regions at wavelengths of 3.21 cm, *Astrophys. J.*, **137**, 1251–1257.

TANAKA, H., and T. KAKINUMA, 1964, The relation between the spectrum of slowly varying component of solar radio emission and solar proton event, *Rep. Ionosph. Space Res. Japan*, **18**, 32–41.

III

THE COSMIC AND GEOPHYSICAL EVENT

36

The Ground-Level Solar Proton Event of 7 July 1966 recorded by Neutron Monitors

H. Carmichael

Deep River Laboratory, Atomic Energy of Canada Ltd., Chalk River, Ontario, Canada

Abstract

Graphs are presented for ground-level neutron monitor observations at 34 stations. A ground-level solar proton event was detectable at some stations. Observations at Alert indicated that the solar particles arrived most strongly and promptly from the north in a direction perpendicular to the ecliptic, and observations at Leeds indicated the presence of particles of magnetic rigidity in excess of 2.2 GV.

Hourly counting totals for 18 days (1–18 July 1966) were collected from 12 stations operating IGY neutron monitors and from 22 stations using the new NM-64 monitors. A list of contributors is given in Table 1.

A very small ground-level solar proton event appeared to start within 5 minutes of 0055 UT on 7 July. Only at Alert where the NM-64 neutron monitor looks north along the spin axis of the earth was the effect clearly recognizable as a solar particle event. At Alert the maximum 5-minute counting rate excess due to solar particles was about 3 per cent during the 5-minute interval ending at 0150 UT. The event ended at 0600 UT. In the northern hemisphere the event was detectable at Inuvik, Deep River, Thule, Goose Bay, Sulphur Mt., Calgary, Victoria, and Leeds, but at Resolute, Oulu, and Durham it was not distinguishable from background. It could be seen in the south with maximum in the hour ending 0300 UT at McMurdo, South Pole, and Sanae. Detection at Leeds would indicate the presence of some particles of magnetic rigidity in excess of 2.2 GV. It appears that the solar particles

must have arrived most promptly and most strongly from the north in a
direction perpendicular to the ecliptic. Graphs for all stations are given in
Figs. 1 to 6.

Table I   List of Contributors

Station	Country	Person(s) responsible
IGY Neutron Monitors		
Ottawa	Canada	Dr. J. Katzman National Research Council Division of Pure Physics Ottawa 2, Ontario Canada
Chicago	USA	Dr. J. A. Simpson Laboratory for Astrophysics and Space Research University of Chicago Chicago, Illinois 60637 USA
London	United Kingdom	Dr. H. Elliot and T. Thambyahpillai Department of Physics Imperial College London SW 7 England
Climax	USA	Dr. J. A. Simpson Laboratory for Astrophysics and Space Research University of Chicago Chicago, Illinois 60637 USA
Lomnický štít	Czechoslovakia	Dr. J. Dubinsky and Dr. P. Chaloupka Ceskoslovenska Akademic Ved Fysikalni Ustav Praha 2, Vinicna Ul. 7 Czechoslovakia
Jungfraujoch	Switzerland	Dr. H. Debrunner Physikalisches Institut Universität Bern Bern Switzerland
White Mt.	USA	Dr. R. A. Nobles Lockheed Missiles and Space Company Palo Alto Research Laboratory 3251 Hanover Street Palo Alto, California 94304 USA

Table I   List of Contributors—*continued*

Station	Country	Person(s) responsible

IGY Neutron Monitors—*continued*

Station	Country	Person(s) responsible
Mexico City	USA	Dr. J. A. Simpson Laboratory for Astrophysics and Space Research University of Chicago Chicago, Illinois 60637 USA
Huancayo	USA	Dr. J. A. Simpson Laboratory for Astrophysics and Space Research University of Chicago Chicago, Illinois 60637 USA
Mina Aguilar	Argentina	Lic. Orestes R. Santochi Instituto de Fisica Universidad Nacional de Tucuman Ayacucho 482 S. M. de Tucuman Argentina
Wellington	Australia	Dr. A. G. Fenton Department of Physics University of Tasmania P.O. Box 252 C Hobart Australia
South Pole	USA	Dr. M. A. Pomerantz Bartol Research Foundation Whittier Place Swarthmore, Pennsylvania, 19081 USA

NM-64 Neutron Monitors

Station	Country	Person(s) responsible
Alert	Canada	Dr. H. Carmichael and J. F. Steljes Atomic Energy of Canada Ltd. Chalk River, Ontario Canada
Thule	USA	Dr. M. A. Pomerantz Bartol Research Foundation Whittier Place Swarthmore, Pennsylvania 19081 USA

Table I   List of Contributors—*continued*

Station	Country	Person(s) responsible

NM-64 Neutron Monitors—*continued*

Station	Country	Person(s) responsible
Resolute Bay	Canada	Dr. J. Katzman National Research Council Division of Pure Physics Ottawa 2, Ontario Canada
Inuvik	Canada	Dr. H. Carmichael and J. F. Steljes Atomic Energy of Canada Ltd. Chalk River, Ontario Canada
Churchill	USA	Dr. K. G. McCracken and Dr. Ricardo A. R. Palmeira Southwest Center for Advanced Studies P.O. Box 30365 Dallas, Texas 75230 USA
Goose Bay	Canada	Dr. H. Carmichael and J. F. Steljes Atomic Energy of Canada Ltd. Chalk River, Ontario Canada
Oulu	Finland	Prof. R. Tuomikoski and S. Niemi Department of Physics University of Oulu Kontinkangas Oulu, Finland.
Deep River	Canada	Dr. H. Carmichael and J. F. Steljes Atomic Energy of Canada Ltd. Chalk River, Ontario Canada
Calgary	Canada	Dr. B. G. Wilson and R. H. Johnson Department of Physics The University of Alberta Calgary, Alberta Canada
Sulphur Mt.	Canada	Dr. B. G. Wilson and R. H. Johnson Department of Physics The University of Alberta Calgary, Alberta Canada
Durham	USA	Dr. J. A. Lockwood Department of Physics University of New Hampshire Durham, New Hampshire 03824 USA

Table I   List of Contributors—*continued*

Station	Country	Person(s) responsible

NM-64 Neutron Monitors—*continued*

Station	Country	Person(s) responsible
Victoria	Canada	Dr. R. M. Pearce Physics Department University of Victoria Victoria, B.C. Canada
Swarthmore	USA	Dr. M. A. Pomerantz Bartol Research Foundation Whittier Place Swarthmore, Pennsylvania 19081 USA
Leeds	United Kingdom	The Physics Department The University of Leeds Leeds 2 England
Kiel	Federal Republic of Germany	Professor Erich Bagge Institut für Reine und Angewandte Kernphysik der Christian-Albrechts-Universität Kiel 23 Kiel Olshausenstrasse 40–60 Gebäude 32 Federal Republic of Germany
Denver	USA	Professor Robert L. Chasson Department of Physics University of Denver Denver, Colorado 80210 USA
Dallas	USA	Dr. K. G. McCracken and Dr. Ricardo A. R. Palmeira Southwest Center for Advanced Studies P.O. Box 30365 Dallas, Texas 75230 USA
Pic-du-Midi	France	Professor A. Fréon Laboratoire de Physique Cosmique Fort de Verrières Route des Gatines Verrières-le-Buisson (S.-et-O.) France

Table 1   List of Contributors—*continued*

Station	Country	Person(s) responsible

NM-64 Neutron Monitors—*continued*

Station	Country	Person(s) responsible
Hermanus	Republic of South Africa	Chief Hermanus Magnetic Observatory P.O. Box 32 Hermanus Republic of South Africa
Kerguelen	France	Professor A. Fréon Laboratoire de Physique Cosmique Fort de Verrières Route des Gatines Verrières-le-Buisson (S.-et-O.) France
Sanae	Republic of South Africa	Dr. P. H. Stoker Dept. of Physics University of Patchefstroom Patchefstroom, Transvaal Republic of South Africa
McMurdo	USA	Dr. M. A. Pomerantz Bartol Research Foundation Whittier Place Swarthmore, Pennsylvania 19081 USA

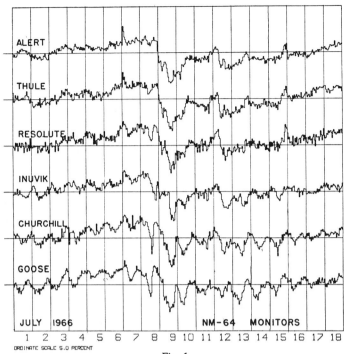

Fig. 1

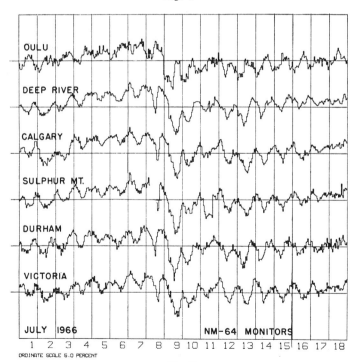

Fig. 2

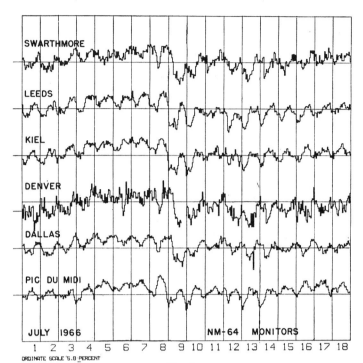

Fig. 3

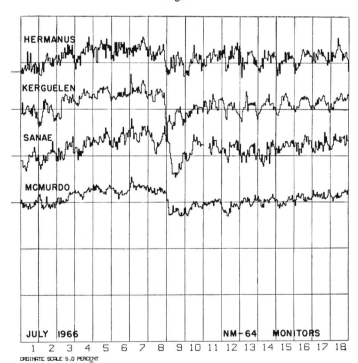

Fig. 4

252

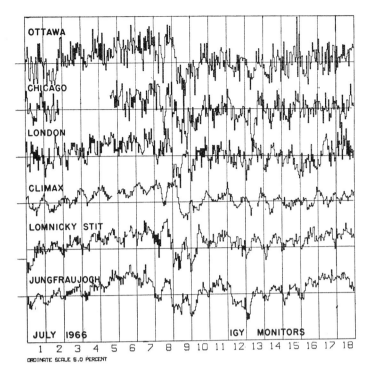

Fig. 5

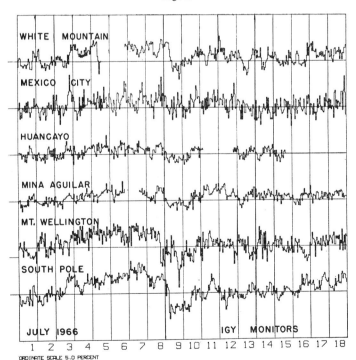

Fig. 6

253

37

The Increase in Low-Energy Cosmic Ray Intensity on 7 July 1966

H. S. Ahluwalia*, L. V. Sud, and M. Schreier

Laboratorio de Física Cósmica, Universidad Mayor de San Andrés, La Paz, Bolivia

Abstract

Some stations of the high-latitude network of high counting rate neutron monitors with vertical cut-off rigidity up to 2.3 GV registered a sharp simultaneous and rather conspicuous small increase between 0100 and 0300 UT on 7 July 1966. No increase was observed with meson telescopes at the same sites. The increase is the smallest ever recorded by ground-level detectors and is associated with the class 2B solar flare which occurred on the same day at 0020 UT in the McMath plage region 8362 with heliographic coordinates 34°N 47°W. The flare thus turns out to be in the most northerly location so far known to produce increase of cosmic-ray intensity in ground-level detectors. It is conjectured that the solar protons which produced the ground-level increase reached the earth after considerable scattering—they might have been deviated over 30° from the radial direction. Deductions as to the configuration of the prevalent interplanetary magnetic field and the propagation charac-teristics of solar protons are discussed.

Introduction

Ground-level cosmic ray increases associated with solar flares belong to that rare category of events when the rough position and the approxi-mate time of generation of energetic particles on the visible solar disk are known somewhat more unambiguously. One thereby has access to the complete history, in time, of these particles as they arrive on earth, and their

* Now at Department of Physics and Astronomy, University of New Mexico, Albuquerque, New Mexico, USA.

secondaries are registered by a skilfully deployed global network of neutron monitors. A careful study of the characteristics of the complete profile of such events thus enables one to gain a valuable insight into the gross features of the interplanetary magnetic field (IMF) in the vicinity of the sun and in the interplanetary medium as well as in the neighbourhood of the earth and beyond the earth's orbit. The information so derived is expected to be very valuable in understanding the general problem of modulation of galactic cosmic rays by the IMF. The significance of a study of this type is the more enhanced if the magnitude of the effect is large and it is preceded and followed by undisturbed solar, interplanetary, and geomagnetic conditions. If also the increase encompasses a wider range in the rigidity spectrum, the spectrometric action of the geomagnetic field may be used to reconstruct the variational spectrum (Dorman 1957) of the energetic particles involved and thereby some insight may be gained into the nature of the physical processes which lead to the generation of energetic particles. Such idealized situations are, however, very hard to come by, and it is no wonder that the present event occurred under far from ideal conditions. In fact the increase was the smallest ever recorded by the ground-level world-wide network of high-latitude neutron monitors and can be seen clearly only in the records of super neutron monitors (Hutton and Carmichael 1964) in the polar regions of the earth (see also Carmichael 1968). But for the existence of these very high counting rate instruments located at the appropriate sites, the increase most probably would not have been noticed at all in the records of ground-level detectors. Moreover the increase was confined to low rigidities ($\leqslant 2.3$ GV) where the trajectories in the magnetic field of the earth are quite complex (McCracken, Rao, and Shea 1962) and penumbral effects quite pronounced. As if to make the situation even more complex (Ahluwalia and McCracken 1966a, b) the geomagnetic field was moderately deformed, the magnetopause being at 10 R_e as shown in Fig. 2 of Krimigis *et al.* (1967). Nevertheless there are some interesting features associated with this event which make its study worth while. It must be pointed out that this is the first ground-level increase which has been extensively studied with balloons, satellites, and space probes (Krimigis *et al.* 1967, Heristchi *et al.* 1968).

2 The Data and Their Analysis

We have examined hourly pressure-corrected data from 22 stations of the world-wide network where 23 detectors were operating during the period of interest. Table 1 provides detailed information about the sites and the detectors considered. Figure 1 gives the plot of neutron monitor data obtained at sites listed in Table 1 from 0000 UT on 6 July to 1500 UT on 7 July 1966. A careful examination of Table 1 together with Fig. 1 shows that

a. The increase is definitely absent from records of stations having a vertical cut-off of 3.0 GV or more, e.g., increase is absent at Mt.

Table I   Particulars of Sites and Detectors used in Analysis

Serial No.	Station Name	Altitude (m)	Geog. Coord. Lat. (°)	Geog. Coord. Long. (°)	Vertical Cut-off Rigidity+ (GV)	Detector Type*	Poisson Error per hour (±%) N	Poisson Error per hour (±%) M	Whether Increase seen? N	Whether Increase seen? M
1.	Pic-du-Midi	2860	42.9	0.3	5.36	N	0.06		No	
2.	Lindau	140	51.6	10.1	3.00	N, M‡	0.17	0.48	No	No
3.	Kiel	54	54.3	10.1	2.29	N, M‡	0.13	0.14	Yes	No
4.	Oulu	SL	65.0	25.5	0.81	N, M	0.16	0.31	Yes	No
5.	Mawson	SL	−67.6	62.9	<0.22	N, M	0.52		Yes	No
6.	Kerguelen Is.	SL	−49.4	70.2	1.19	N	0.11		Yes	
7.	Wilkes	SL	−66.4	110.5	<0.05	N	0.50		‡	
8.	Hobart	725	−42.9	147.2	1.89	N, M	0.41	0.26	‡	No
9.	College†	SL	64.9	212.2	0.54	N	0.38		‡	
10.	Inuvik	21	68.4	226.3	<0.18	N	0.12		Yes	
11.	Victoria	71	48.5	236.6	1.86	N	0.15		‡	
12.	Banff	2283	51.2	244.4	1.14	N, M	0.11	0.14	Yes	No
13.	Calgary	1128	51.1	245.9	1.09	N	0.09		Yes	
14.	Climax	3400	39.4	253.8	3.03	N	0.17		No	
15.	Resolute	17	74.7	265.1	<0.05	N, M	0.24	0.14	‡	
16.	Churchill	39	58.8	265.9	0.21	N	0.12		Yes	
17.	Deep River	145	46.1	282.5	1.02	N	0.07		Yes	
18.	Mt. Washington	1917	44.3	288.7	1.24	N	0.26		Yes	
19.	Durham	SL	43.1	289.7	1.41	N	0.04		No	
20.	Alert	66	82.5	297.7	<0.05	N	0.12		Yes	
21.	Goose Bay	46	53.3	299.8	0.52	N	0.12		Yes	
22.	Mt. Chacaltaya	5200	−16.3	291.8	13.10	N	0.23		No	

* N = Neutron monitor, M = Meson telescope; † Only bihourly data available; ‡ Resolution of data too poor to discern any increase clearly; + Shea et al. (1965).

Chacaltaya, Pic-du-Midi, Climax, and Lindau. This indicates that there were no protons of solar origin of rigidity 3.0 GV or more in the vicinity of the earth.

b. None of the meson telescopes registered the increase although neutron monitors at some of the same sites (Banff, Mawson, Kiel) recorded the increase. This is not surprising in view of (*a*) above, because the atmospheric cut-off applicable to meson telescopes is about 4 GV compared with 1.1 GV applicable to neutron monitors (McCracken 1962).

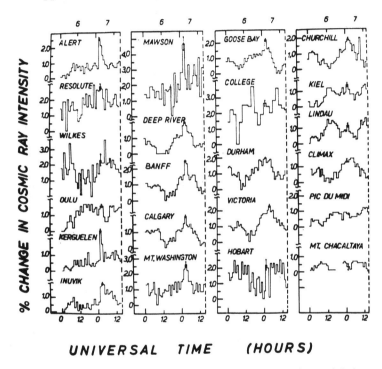

UNIVERSAL TIME (HOURS)

Fig. 1   Hourly pressure-corrected neutron monitor data plots from global network. Data are plotted from 0000 UT on 6 July to 1500 UT on 7 July 1966.

c. The increase is largest at Alert and Kerguelen Island and is smallest at Kiel. This point will be discussed below. A large increase is also indicated at Mawson but the inherent variability of these data is also large.

In Fig. 2 we have plotted 5-minute pressure-corrected neutron monitor data from Inuvik, Alert, Goose Bay, and Deep River, kindly supplied to us by Dr. J. F. Steljes. One notes rather large fluctuations in the rising as well as in the decaying phase of the increase at all the four stations. Our best estimates of the onset times at the four stations are indicated by arrows, and these are also listed in Table 2. There seems to be about half an hour of spread between the onset times, the mean onset time being 0.98 ± 0.02 hr

UT. Considering the paucity of data (we have only four stations from which 5-minute data are available) and the fact that rather large (~0.4 per cent) statistical errors are associated with these data, it is very difficult to draw any conclusions as to whether the solar proton flux was anisotropic in the initial phase, i.e. from onset to about 0125 UT. We would like to state, though, that such a possibility cannot be definitely ruled out. In fact weak support for this hypothesis is provided by the fact that Alert, Kerguelen Island, and Oulu recorded larger magnitudes of the increase, and the maximum at these stations occurred an hour earlier than at other stations having vertical cut-off

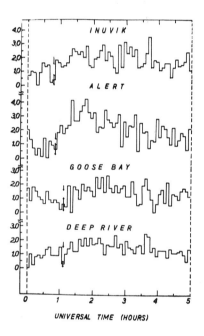

Fig. 2   Cosmic-ray increase seen at four locations in 5-minute data. Arrows indicate
time of onset of the increase. Scale at left indicates percentage change in cosmic-
ray intensity, 7 July 1966.

below atmospheric cut-off (see Table 2). This rather weak evidence could be taken to imply that the rising phase of the increase was anisotropic with maximum flux arriving from directions west of the earth–sun line (see also Fig. 3).

In Table 2 we list, among other things, the time when maximum flux was recorded at different locations as well as the magnitude of increase as deter-mined from hourly data (see Fig. 1). Some stations record the maximum at 0130 UT while others record it at 0230 UT. Above we have commented on the possible physical significance of this difference of 1 hour in the times of maximum at the two groups of stations as well as the fact that the largest

Table 2 Cosmic Ray Increase of 7 July 1966

Serial No.	Station Name	Mean Pressure Level for Correction (cmHg)	Pressure Coeff. used $(-\beta)$ $(\%(cmHg)^{-1})$	Time of Start* (hr UT)	Time of Maximum (hr UT)	Magnitude of Increase (%)†
1.	Alert	75.20	9.87	0.88 ± 0.04	1.5 ± 0.5	1.95 ± 0.17
2.	Oulu	75.00	10.07		1.5 ± 0.5	0.90 ± 0.23‡
3.	Kerguelen Is.	75.80	9.87		1.5 ± 0.5	1.90 ± 0.16
4.	Inuvik	75.80	9.87	0.79 ± 0.04	2.5 ± 0.5	1.20 ± 0.17
5.	Mawson	72.77	7.49		2.5 ± 0.5	1.80 ± 0.74
6.	Deep River	74.70	9.87	1.13 ± 0.04	2.5 ± 0.5	0.90 ± 0.10
7.	Banff	56.30	10.43		2.5 ± 0.5	1.20 ± 0.16
8.	Calgary		10.50		2.5 ± 0.5	0.80 ± 0.13
9.	Mt. Washington	60.50	9.84		2.5 ± 0.5	1.00 ± 0.37
10.	Goose Bay	75.80	9.87	1.13 ± 0.04	2.5 ± 0.5	0.70 ± 0.17
11.	Churchill	74.50	9.91		§	0.70 ± 0.17
12.	Kiel	75.50	10.50		1.5 ± 0.5	0.50 ± 0.18

* Time determined from 5-min data from the instant when monotonic increase began (see Fig. 2).
† Magnitude of increase is determined from hourly data and is reckoned from mean counting rate level during the interval 0000 UT to 0100 UT.
‡ Some uncertainty is involved in determining the magnitude of increase at Oulu since it was mixed up with the decaying phase of solar daily variation (see Fig. 1). The magnitude of increase could easily be 0.40% more than the value listed here.
§ Not possible to determine time within ± 0.5 hr due to statistical fluctuations.

increase was recorded at Alert and Kerguelen Island ($\sim$2 per cent). One may also note that Kiel recorded the smallest ($\sim$0.5 per cent) increase. Also from Fig. 1 one sees that increase is apparently indistinguishable from background at Resolute, Wilkes, Durham, Victoria, and Hobart, which sites have vertical cut-off less than that of Kiel (see Table 1). It is useful to bear in mind that Carmichael (1968) has reported that increase is also noticeable in data obtained at the southern polar station at McMurdo.

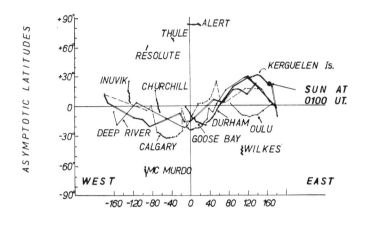

Fig. 3   A geographical map of asymptotic directions of vertical incidence of solar protons of rigidities 1.1–3.0 GV. The map is based on trajectories calculated by Shea *et al.* (1965). The direction of the sun at 0100 UT on 7 July 1966 is indicated by solid dot. The map indicates that solar protons may have arrived from directions to the west of the earth–sun line.

In Fig. 3 we have plotted the asymptotic direction of viewing (McCracken 1962) applicable to neutron monitors from 1.1 GV to 3.0 GV at different sites as given by Shea, Smart, and McCracken (1965) for vertical incidence in a Finch and Leaton (1957) type geomagnetic field. The following features stand out:

a. Kerguelen Island, Deep River, and Calgary have a rather wide cone of acceptance (McCracken 1962) in asymptotic longitudes with very good general tracking, and yet the maximum flux at Kerguelen Island is nearly twice as large as at the other two stations, being nearly equal to that received at the northern polar station at Alert; also, the maximum is reached nearly an hour earlier than at Deep River and Calgary. One of the explanations for this would be in terms of impact zones as indicated under the discussion of Fig. 2. Alternatively we note that the Kerguelen Island site is located near the Capetown magnetic anomaly and, as we have already pointed out, the geomagnetic field was moderately disturbed at the time of the increase. One should, therefore, investigate whether it is possible that some transient change takes place in the asymptotic cone associated with this site under disturbed conditions, thus explaining the larger flux observed in the present case.

b. Inuvik, Churchill, and Goose Bay have a very narrow asymptotic cone of acceptance in longitude compared with Deep River and Calgary, and yet within the error of observation the magnitude of increase observed by the first group of stations, in hourly data, is comparable with that observed by the second group. This indicates that by 0230 ± 0030 UT, the observed time of maximum, the solar proton flux had already become isotropic in the vicinity of the earth's orbit.

c. The asymptotic cone applicable to Durham links very well with that of Deep River part of the way and yet no increase above background is noticeable at Durham, whereas Deep River registered an increase of about 1 per cent. This point will be discussed below.

d. The polar stations Alert, Thule, Resolute, and McMurdo scan rather narrow regions of space at large asymptotic latitudes. Of this group, Resolute did not record any increase above the background, but Carmichael (1968) has reported that increase was registered at Thule and McMurdo. However, looking at the curve corresponding to Resolute in Fig. 1 it is clear that near the expected time there are rather large fluctuations characteristic of a low counting rate instrument. It is thus possible that the small increase is rendered indistinguishable from the background due to large inherent variability of data. These same comments apply to Wilkes.

In Table 3 we have listed the asymptotic directions of viewing for Deep River, Durham, Victoria, Hobart, and Kiel in the rigidity range 1.1–2.5 GV (Shea *et al.* 1965). It is at once clear that rather complex penumbra exist for Durham, Victoria, Hobart, and Kiel. The situation is bound to be more complex if deformation of the geomagnetic field is taken into account (Ahluwalia and McCracken 1966a, b). Moreover, we note from Fig. 1 that near the expected time of increase there exists a broad maximum of solar daily variation at Durham, Victoria, and Hobart; at Hobart the variability of the data is also large, the Poisson error being about 0.4 per cent. It is thus not surprising that the small increase is indistinguishable from background at these stations and is barely observable at Kiel where it occurred near the minimum of solar daily variation.

An important set of criteria thus emerge from this discussion. These are *that small solar-flare-associated increases in ground-level cosmic-ray intensity are best studied by examining data from high counting rate neutron monitors of comparable characteristics in polar regions where penumbral effects are absent and solar daily variation has a very small amplitude* (Sandstrom *et al.* 1962, Pomerantz *et al.* 1962, Kitamura 1966). Controversial results obtained in the past numerous attempts to detect small ground-level flare-associated increases

Table 3   Asymptotic Coordinates above Atmospheric Cut-Off for Selected Sites

Rigidity (GV)	Deep River Lat. (°)	Long. (°)	Durham Lat. (°)	Long. (°)	Victoria Lat. (°)	Long. (°)	Hobart Lat. (°)	Long. (°)	Kiel Lat. (°)	Long. (°)
1.10	3.6	−111.8	R*		F		F		R	
1.15	4.1	164.8	R		R		F		R	
1.20	28.7	112.5	F†		F		F		R	
1.25	not available		F		F		F		F	
1.30	15.8	72.5	F		F		R		R	
1.40	2.3	54.3	R		F		F		R	
1.50	−6.2	45.7	R		F		F		F	
1.60	−13.4	34.6	−1.1	178.0	R		R		F	
1.70	−16.8	28.1	28.4	121.2	F		F		R	
1.80	−19.7	23.7	19.7	88.5	3.6	−152.4	R		F	
1.90	−21.6	17.0	7.1	69.8	F		9.7	94.6	F	
2.00	−22.2	10.4	0.5	59.8	−3.4	16.9	R		F	
2.10	−22.9	6.4	−3.6	54.5	22.7	73.9	21.6	58.9	F	
2.20	−23.7	4.0	−8.0	50.1	21.5	38.5	−24.5	−13.4	F	
2.30	−23.9	1.5	−12.2	44.3	9.7	18.7	−25.0	−37.0	−3.7	−113.7
2.40	−23.3	−1.9	−15.2	37.6	−3.5	5.4	−20.2	−52.0	R	
2.50	−22.2	−5.6	−16.9	31.5	−13.1	−5.2	−12.6	−64.2	10.7	−120.1

* R = Forbidden trajectory.
† F = Failed to complete integration even after allowing large number of steps in modified Runge–Kutta integration process (Gill 1951). Such orbits are usually very complex.

of cosmic-ray intensity (Anderson *et al.* 1962, Wilson and Nehra 1962, and references therein) are in no small measure due to failure, in varying degrees, to observe the criteria outlined above.

3 Discussion

The solar and terrestrial relationships of the increase of 7 July 1966 have been extensively commented upon by several authors (Krimigis *et al.* 1967, Severny 1968, Kai 1968, Hakura 1968, Masley and Goedeke 1968). It suffices to say that the associated flare was of class 2B about which CRPL Report No. FB-267 (November 1966 issue) gives the following information as recorded by Culgoora Observatory in Australia: The flare occurred in McMath Plage No. 8362, heliographic coordinates 34°N 47°W at 0020 UT on 7 July 1966. The flare reached maximum intensity at 0052 UT and ended at 0239 UT; it thus had a duration of 139 minutes. Observing conditions were good (rating 3) and a complete sequence of photographs were taken. Also *Preliminary Reports of Solar Activity* from the High Altitude Observatory, Boulder, Colorado, USA (TR #775 and TR #776) indicate that the flare was followed by an intense Type IV outburst which started before 0053 UT and ended at 0146 UT. PCA was first observed at 0120 UT (Hakura 1968). We have already noted that the mean onset time for ground-level cosmic-ray increase was 00.98 hr UT, i.e. well before PCA set in.

The main feature to which we wish to draw attention concerns the location of the flare on the visible solar disk. The solar flare occurred in the most northerly location so far known to produce a cosmic-ray increase in ground-level neutron monitors. Since plasma must move radially outwards from the sun (Ahluwalia and Dessler 1962), the quiet-day field lines drawn out at the heliolatitude of 34°N must spiral out into the interplanetary medium along a conical surface. If this helical spiral is free of inhomogeneities and if cosmic rays are generated at a single point, defined by the heliolatitude of the visible solar flare, then in the present case all of them would have been "ducted" along the quiet-day field lines and hence would not have reached the earth at all. From simple considerations of the schematics of earth–sun relative positions, it is easy to show that, for cosmic rays generated under the above conditions to reach the earth, it is necessary to scatter them through about 30° from the radius through the point where they are generated on the sun, as illustrated in Fig. 4. It is quite probable, of course, that energetic particles are generated in a region of finite angular width in which case the total scattering, as applicable to the present case, would be less than 30°. We believe that this total scattering came about in several steps whereby energetic particles "jumped" across the IMF lines to approach the solar equatorial plane. Obviously to account for the anisotropic character of the initial phase of increase, a significant number of solar protons must be scattered perpendicular to the field lines very close to the sun, say within 10 to 20 solar radii (note that solar wind becomes supersonic after about 10 solar radii, Parker 1963). Since the IMF is derived from a magnetic field of about 1 gauss in the solar photosphere (Ahluwalia and Dessler 1962, Axford *et al.* 1963) the field at 20 solar radii, mainly radial, would thus have a value of some 250 γ ($1\gamma = 10^{-5}$ G). The cyclotron radius of 2 GV protons in this field is about 3×10^4 km which also gives the scale size of inhomogeneities in quiet-day field lines required to scatter effectively 2 GV protons (Parker 1964). Michel (1967) has proposed a model for the structure of quiet-day solar wind in which "granulations" on the solar surface play a dominant role in producing inhomogeneities. These solar structures have characteristic lengths in the range 10^3 km to 3×10^3 km with lifetimes of the order of 3×10^2 seconds. At 20 solar radii these lengths project from 2×10^4 km to 6×10^4 km. Considering a typical solar wind speed of 500 km s^{-1} (Neugebauer and Snyder 1962, Wolfe *et al.* 1966) one may in extreme cases expect

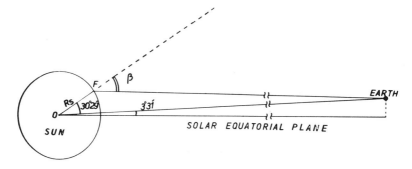

Fig. 4   An illustration of simple schematics of propagation of solar cosmic rays generated at point F on sun. Angle β indicates deviation from radial course suffered by these protons to reach earth.

of the order of 1000 inhomogeneities of the scale size indicated over the sun–earth distance. On the basis of Michel's model then one would expect continuous scattering of energetic particles right from the time they get projected into the quiet-day IMF. We suggest that a significant portion of these protons "jump" across the IMF lines equatorwards and polewards of the sun and part of them reach the earth's orbit. We wish to point out that these solar protons lose a significant amount of energy through adiabatic cooling (Singer 1958) on their way to the earth and hence their variational spectrum at the earth's orbit is not the same as at the source. Applied to the present case, for example, this would mean that solar protons of rigidity greater than 3 GV were indeed produced by the sun. An important consequence of this picture is that for energetic particles generated at higher heliolatitudes to be detected at least by ground-level neutron monitors located in polar regions two basic conditions must be satisfied: (*a*) the source spectrum must have an appreciable high-energy tail so that enough energetic particles arrive at the earth with sufficiently high energy to overcome the 1.1 GV effective atmospheric threshold for ground-level neutron monitors; (*b*) the frequency spectrum of inhomogeneities in quiet-day IMF should be of right type to enable sufficient energetic particles to "jump" across the field lines and ultimately find the right field lines which guide them to earth.

The magnitude of the ground-level increase would depend on how well the above two conditions are satisfied.

Acknowledgments

This research is supported in part by U.S. Air Force Office of Scientific Research under Grant No. AF-AFOSR-319-66.

We wish to thank Antonio Carrasco for computational assistance. One of us (L.V.S.) is supported in part by Universidad Mayor de San Andrés (UMSA) for which he wishes to express his gratitude to UMSA authorities. We are also very grateful to the investigators who very kindly supplied data used in the present analysis.

References

AHLUWALIA, H. S., and A. J. DESSLER, 1962, Diurnal variation of cosmic radiation intensity produced by a solar wind, *Planet. Space Sci.*, **9**, 195–210.

AHLUWALIA, H. S., and K. G. MCCRACKEN, 1966a, The influence of magnetopause on cosmic ray particle trajectories, *Proc. 9th Int. Conf. on Cosmic Rays, London 1965* (Institute of Physics and Physical Society, London), **1**, 568–570.

—— 1966b, Characteristic effects of the deformed magnetic field of the earth on medium energy cosmic rays, *Space Research VI*, Ed. R. L. Smith-Rose (Spartan Books Inc., Washington D.C.), pp. 872–890.

ANDERSON, J. C., R. L. CHASSON, and K. MAEDA, 1962, Characteristics of solar flare cosmic rays during I.G.Y., *J. Phys. Soc. Japan*, **17**, Suppl. A-II, 264–268.

AXFORD, W. I., A. J. DESSLER, and B. GOTTLIEB, 1963, Termination of solar wind and solar magnetic field, *Astrophys. J.*, **137**, 1268–1278.

CARMICHAEL, H., 1968, The ground level solar proton event of 7 July 1966 recorded by neutron monitors, *Ann. IQSY*, this volume, Paper 36.

DORMAN, L. I., 1957, *Cosmic Ray Variations* (State Publishing House for Technical and Theoretical Literature, Moscow).

FINCH, H. P., and B. R. LEATON, 1957, The earth's main magnetic field epoch 1955.0, *Mon. Not. R. Astr. Soc., Geophys. Suppl.* **1**, 314–317.

GILL, S., 1951, A process for the step-by-step integration of differential equations in an automatic digital computing machine, *Proc. Camb. Phil. Soc.*, **47**, 96–108.

HAKURA, 1968, The polar cap absorption on 7–10 July 1966, *Ann. IQSY*, this volume, Paper 45.

HERISTCHI, DJ., J. KANGAS, G. KREMSER, J. P. LEGRAND, P. MASSE, M. PALOUS, G. PFOTZER, W. RIEDLER, and K. WILHELM, 1968, Balloon measurements of solar protons in Northern Scandinavia on 7 July 1966, *Ann. IQSY*, this volume, Paper 38.

HUTTON, C. J., and H. CARMICHAEL, 1964, Experimental investigation of the NM-64 neutron monitor, *Can. J. Phys.*, **42**, 2443–2472.

KAI, K., 1968, The complete Type IV burst associated with the 7 July 1966 proton event, *Ann. IQSY*, this volume, Paper 28.

KITAMURA, M., 1966, The solar diurnal variation of the cosmic ray intensity, *Proc. 9th Int. Conf. on Cosmic Rays, London 1965* (Institute of Physics and Physical Society, London), **1**, 201–203.

KRIMIGIS, S. M., J. A. VAN ALLEN, and T. P. ARMSTRONG, 1967, Simultaneous observations of solar protons inside and outside the magnetosphere, *Phys. Rev. Lett.*, **18**, 1204–1207.

MASLEY, A. J., and A. D. GOEDEKE, 1968, The 7 July 1966 solar cosmic ray event, *Ann. IQSY*, this volume, Paper 46.

McCRACKEN, K. G., 1962, The cosmic ray flare effect: 1. Some new methods of analysis, *J. Geophys. Res.*, **67**, 423–434.

McCRACKEN, K. G., U. R. RAO, and M. A. SHEA, 1962, The trajectories of cosmic rays in a high degree simulation of the geomagnetic field, *M.I.T. Tech. Rep.* 77 (M.I.T., Cambridge, Mass.).

MICHEL, F. C., 1967, Model of solar wind structure, *J. Geophys. Res.*, **72**, 1917–1932.

NEUGEBAUER, M., and C. W. SNYDER, 1962, Solar plasma experiment: Preliminary Mariner II observations, *Science*, **138**, 1095–1097.

PARKER, E. N., 1963, *Interplanetary Dynamical Processes* (Interscience Publishers, New York).

—— 1964, The scattering of charged particles by magnetic irregularities, *J. Geophys. Res.*, **69**, 1755–1758.

POMERANTZ, M. A., S. P. DUGGAL, and K. NAGASHIMA, 1962, Solar diurnal variation of cosmic ray intensity, *J. Phys. Soc. Japan*, **17**, Suppl. A-II, 464–468.

SANDSTROM, A. E., E. DYRING, and S. LINDGREN, 1962, Direction of the cosmic ray diurnal anisotropy, *J. Phys. Soc. Japan*, **17**, Suppl. A-II, 471–476.

SEVERNY, A., 1968, The magnetic fields and proton flare of 7 July 1966, *Ann. IQSY*, this volume, Paper 1.

SHEA, M. A., D. F. SMART, and K. G. McCRACKEN, 1965, A study of vertically incident cosmic trajectories using sixth degree simulations of the geomagnetic field, *AFCRL Environmental Research Papers*, No. 141 (L.G. Hanscom Field, Bedford, Mass.).

SINGER, S. F., 1958, Cosmic ray time variations produced by deceleration in interplanetary space, *Nuovo Cim.*, Suppl. **8** (Series 10), 334–341.

WILSON, B. G., and C. P. NEHRA, 1962, Cosmic ray increases associated with solar flares, *J. Phys. Soc., Japan*, **17**, Suppl. A-II, 269–272.

WOLFE, J. H., R. W. SILVA, and M. A. MYERS, 1966, Observations of the solar wind during the flight of Imp I, *J. Geophys. Res.*, **71**, 1319–1340.

38

Balloon Measurements of Solar Protons in Northern Scandinavia on 7 July 1966

Dj. Heristchi*, J. Kangas†, G. Kremser‡, J. P. Legrand*, P. Masse*, M. Palous*, G. Pfotzer‡, W. Riedler§, and K. Wilhelm‡

* Laboratoire de Physique Cosmique, Meudon, France
† Department of Physics, University of Oulu, Oulu, Finland
‡ Max-Planck-Institut für Aeronomie, Institut für Stratosphärenphysik, 3411 Lindau/Harz, Federal Republic of Germany
§ Kiruna Geophysical Observatory, Kiruna C, Sweden

Abstract

Following the flare of importance 2B of 7 July 1966, 0020 UT, proton measurements were obtained from two balloon flights in northern Scandinavia. At balloon altitudes the integral proton flux ($E_p > 100\,\text{MeV}$) increased from 0110 UT onwards. The maximum proton flux of 2.6 protons $\text{cm}^{-2}\,\text{s}^{-1}\,\text{sr}^{-1}$ was reached at 0205 UT. The following decrease could be observed until about 2230 UT, when the detector stopped working. The exponent γ of the power law representing the differential energy spectrum was deduced for $E_p > 100$ MeV from the ratio of the counting rates of a single omnidirectional counter and a counter telescope. Up to about 0600 UT γ increased from about 2 to 3.5 and then varied between 3.5 and 3.8. Another estimate of γ by measuring the range spectrum of the protons was in good agreement with these values. The differential proton flux was calculated for several energies, using the above deduced values for γ and the counting rates of the telescope. The maximum of the differential flux occurred at about 0500 UT, 0400 UT, 0230 UT for 100 MeV, 150 MeV, 200 MeV protons, respectively.

The time variations of the proton flux could be explained with the formalism of diffusion theory as has been done for the special case of solar protons by Krimigis. A diffusion coefficient varying with the distance from the sun according to $D = D_0 r^{1.1}$ was needed. The mean free path L was estimated to be about 0.05 AU. The total number N of protons emitted during the flare can also be estimated by this method and is found to be $N \simeq 10^{31}\,\text{sr}^{-1}$.

1   Introduction

The measurements of solar protons with balloon instruments on 7 July 1966 were made subsequent to a "SPARMO Proton Alert" (SPARMO = Solar Particles and Radiation Monitoring Organisation) announced on 5 July. This kind of alert is based on observations of solar activity centres aiming at the prediction of flares associated with the emission of protons (Legrand and Simon 1966). From this day onwards, the SPARMO groups kept almost continuously at least one balloon at ceiling altitudes. The launchings were made from Sodankylä (Finland) and the signals from the westward drifting balloons were received by the other groups at Kiruna (Sweden) and Andenes (Norway), which were co-operating in a programme to measure auroral X-rays.

The measurements were made with a standardized threefold Geiger counter telescope, aperture about 50°. The counting rates of two single counters were also recorded to obtain additional information on the omni-directional intensity thereby obtaining an index for the zenithal angle and energy distributions, respectively (Keppler 1964a).

Actually, the time variations of the directional and omnidirectional proton fluxes above the atmospheric cut-off energy $E_0 \simeq 100$ MeV were recorded during a long term constant level flight at about 7 mb. The range distribution could be derived from the records obtained during the ascent of another detector launched during the proton event.

From these measurements assuming the differential energy spectrum to be

$$F(E, t)dE = A(t)E^{-\gamma(t)}dE$$

information could be obtained on the time variations of the exponent of the energy spectrum $\gamma(t)$ at the top of the atmosphere, the integral flux above about 100 MeV, and the differential flux (by means of $A(t)$) of the protons. Further, based on a diffusion-type model of propagation, the mean free path of the protons in interplanetary space and the total number of protons ($E > 100$ MeV) emitted during the flare could be estimated.

2   Observations

The counting rates obtained during the constant level flight (S3/66) are compiled in the upper part of Fig. 1. They began to increase at 0110 UT (50 minutes after the onset of the corresponding flare of importance 2B and 44 minutes after the onset of the Type IV radio burst associated with this flare). They reached a first maximum at 0206 UT. Further maxima were recorded at 0340 UT and perhaps also at 0440 UT. Thereafter the intensity decreased steadily until at least 2230 UT, when the detector stopped working.

Shortly before the solar proton event the counting rates of the single counters are slightly enhanced, but not those of the telescope. This part of the flight is shown in the upper left corner of Fig. 1 on an extended time scale.

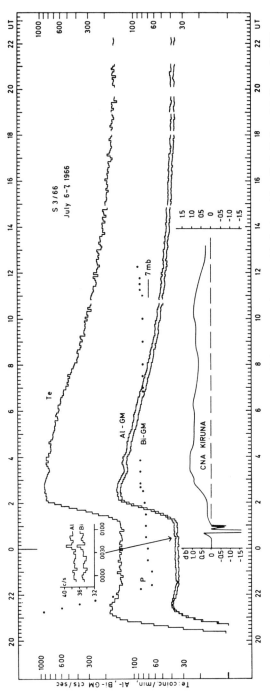

Fig. 1 Counting rate patterns during the constant level flight (S3/66). Te = Telescope, Al–GM = Al-walled Geiger–Müller tube (Victoreen 1B85), Bi–GM = Bi-coated Geiger–Müller tube (Victoreen 6306). The pressure during this flight is indicated by full dots. To obtain the pressure values the numbers at the scale for the counting rates have to be divided by 10. In the lower part of this figure the riometer recording of the cosmic-noise absorption at Kiruna is added.

The enhancement occurred between 0030 UT and 0100 UT with a maximum of about 7 per cent of the normal cosmic-ray level at 0037 UT (it should be kept in mind that the GM counters have a low efficiency for X-rays). It is very probably due to solar X-rays emitted during the flare. As the sun was 4° above the horizon at this time the X-rays had to traverse 84 g cm^{-2} of air. This points to a rather high X-ray energy.

The lower part of this figure shows the riometer recording of the cosmic-noise absorption at Kiruna. In this curve a burst of the 27 MHz flux starting at 0036 UT can be seen, which was due to the emission during the Type IV radio burst. The absorption only increased when the counting rates of the detectors had already reached their maximum. The maximum of absorption of 1.1 dB appeared at 0330 UT, approximately at the time of the second

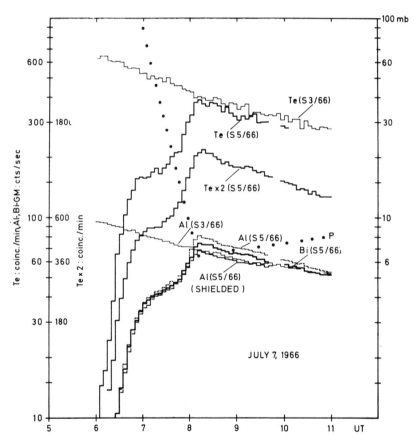

Fig. 2   Counting rate patterns during flight S5/66. For the explanation of Te,
Al, Bi see caption of Fig. 1. Te × 2 = counting rates of a twofold
coincidence telescope. The pressure is indicated by full dots. The
counting rates of the single Al–GM and the telescope of flight S3/66
are added for comparison.

maximum of the counting rates. Between 0330 UT and 1100 UT the absorption did not change appreciably, though the counting rates decreased continuously during the greater part of this interval. After 1100 UT the absorption diminished rather quickly. In comparing the counting rate pattern with the riometer curve one must keep in mind that these two curves are due to protons in different energy regions. The higher energy protons ($E > 100$ MeV) which are observed with the balloon-borne detector do not contribute significantly to the cosmic-noise absorption and vice versa. Further, these protons arrive earlier at the earth than the lower energy ones, thus explaining at least qualitatively the time lag between the maxima of these curves.

During the proton event a second balloon (S5/66) was launched at 0549 UT in order to measure the range distribution of the protons. For this flight Geiger–Müller counters were used again. The lowermost of the three counters forming the telescope was shielded with 1.3 g cm^{-2} of aluminium. In addition to the information usually telemetered the counting rates of this shielded counter and the twofold coincidences of the two uppermost counters were also transmitted to the ground. All these measurements are presented in Fig. 2; the counting rates of the telescope and the Al–GM counter of the constant level flight (S3/66) are added for comparison. This balloon reached a pressure level of 6.5 mb corresponding to an atmospheric cut-off of 88 MeV for protons (the calculated geomagnetic cut-off is about 120 MeV). The different counting rate patterns during both flights can be explained by the different altitudes of the balloons and the additional screening of the lowermost counter during flight S5/66. A more detailed description of the observations can be found in a preliminary report on these measurements (Heristchi *et al.* 1966).

3 The Energy Spectrum of the Protons

The method for the determination of the energy spectrum from our balloon observations is based on the fact that a proton flux which is isotropic at the top of the atmosphere is anisotropic inside the atmosphere. This is due to the increasing mass of air which particles from inclined directions have to traverse before reaching the detector. As the shape of the angular distribution inside the atmosphere depends on the slope of the proton energy spectrum at the top of the atmosphere, it is possible to determine this slope by measuring the angular distribution (Keppler 1964b). As is shown in Appendix 1 an angular distribution function

$$f(\theta) = \cos^{(\gamma-1)/1.8}(\theta) \equiv \cos^{\mu}(\theta) \tag{1}$$

is obtained if the differential energy spectrum at the top of the atmosphere can be written as

$$F(E) \, dE \sim E^{-\gamma} \, dE, \tag{2}$$

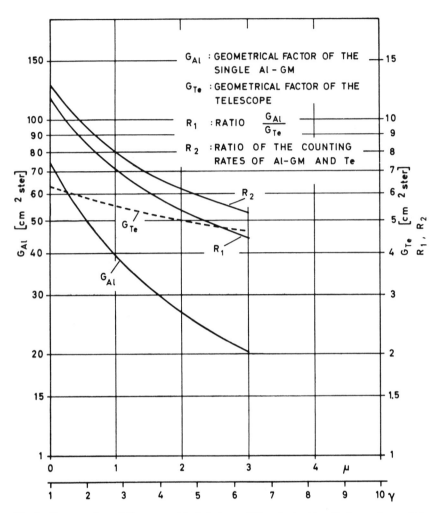

Fig. 3   Presentation of the geometrical factors of the single Al-walled counter and the
telescope, the ratio of these factors, and the ratio of the counting rates of the
single counter and the telescope. μ is the exponent of the angular distribution
$I(\theta) = I_0 \cos^{\mu}(\theta)$ inside the atmosphere; γ is the exponent of the differential
energy spectrum $F(E)dE = AE^{-\gamma}dE$ at the top of the atmosphere.

and the protons lose their energy by ionization only. In Appendix 2 it is
further shown how to deduce the exponent μ from the ratio of the counting
rates of the single omnidirectional counter and the telescope. To do this, the
dependence on μ of the geometrical factors of the detectors must be known.
In Fig. 3 the geometrical factors, their ratio, and the ratio of the counting
rates are plotted against μ. From μ the exponent γ can be calculated according
to

$$\gamma = 1.8\mu + 1 \qquad\qquad (3)$$

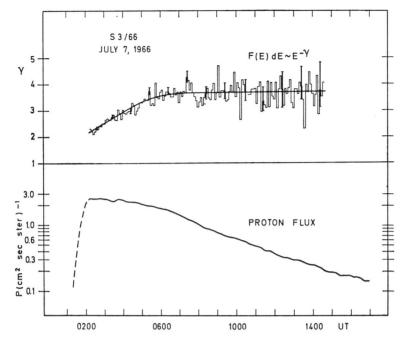

Fig. 4   The exponent γ of the differential energy spectrum and the integral proton flux ($E > 100$ MeV) during the solar proton event of 7 July 1966.

The values of $\gamma(t)$ obtained from the measurements during the constant level flight S3/66 are represented in the upper part of Fig. 4. Between 0200 UT and 0500 UT $\gamma(t)$ increased from 2 to 3.5, afterwards it varies between 3.5 and 4. Before 0200 UT this method is not applicable as during this early phase of the event the higher energy particles are in excess and no representation of the spectrum by a power-law function is possible. After 1700 UT the counting rates are too low to warrant sufficient accuracy.

These values can be compared with the results of another completely independent method based on the range measurements during the ascent of flight S5/66. In Fig. 5 the excess counting rates of a single counter and the telescope are plotted against pressure. Here we have taken into account the decrease of the proton flux during the ascent of the balloon as seen from the constant-level flight. From the slope of the straight lines drawn in this figure the exponent γ of the differential energy spectrum averaged over the time of the ascent can be calculated. One finds $\gamma_{Te} = 3.5$; $\gamma_{Al} = 3.6$. These values are in good agreement with the results represented in Fig. 4, where we find at 0700 UT, $\gamma = 3.7$.

In Fig. 5 the counting rates at high air pressures deviate from the straight line. It seems possible to explain this deviation by a cut-off of the proton flux at a certain energy E_{max}. Such a cut-off considerably reduces the geometrical

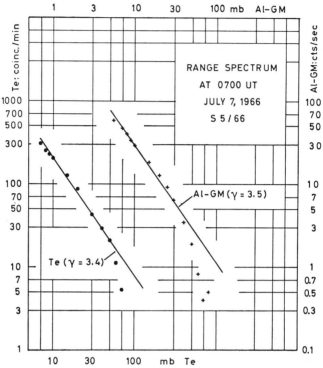

Fig. 5   Integral range spectrum of the protons obtained during the
ascent of flight S5/66. The values of the exponent γ of the
differential energy spectrum are derived from the slopes of
the straight lines.

factor, which is then a function of the air pressure. Choosing a cut-off at
$E_{max} = 500$ MeV, the values of the proton flux calculated with an appropriate pressure dependent geometrical factor all fit a straight line.

4   The Proton Flux

4.1   The Integral Proton Flux above the Atmospheric Cut-Off

With the angular distribution of the proton flux at balloon altitudes found
from the preceding section, it is possible to calculate the integral proton flux
above the atmospheric cut-off. We have

$$F(t) = \frac{\Delta N(t)}{\epsilon G(\mu(t))} \tag{4}$$

ΔN = additional counting rates due to the proton flux.

   ϵ = efficiency ($\epsilon_{Al} = 0.96$; $\epsilon_{Te} = 0.88$).

$G(\mu)$ = geometrical factor, depending on μ, the exponent of the angular
distribution.

The geometrical factor can be obtained from the calculated (G, μ) curves, which are shown in Fig. 3. The exponent $\mu(t)$ itself has been determined in the preceding section. The result of this calculation is shown in the lower part of Fig. 4. The integral proton flux above the atmospheric cut-off ($\simeq 100$ MeV) increased until about 0210 UT up to 2.6 protons $\text{cm}^{-2} \text{ s}^{-1} \text{ sr}^{-1}$. The decrease is fairly steady. At 1700 UT a flux of about 0.15 protons $\text{cm}^{-2} \text{ s}^{-1} \text{ sr}^{-1}$ was measured.

4.2 The Differential Proton Flux

As the slope of the differential energy spectrum is known (see Sec. 3), the differential proton flux can be calculated from the counting rates of the telescope. For this purpose it is necessary to know the parameter $A(t)$ of the differential energy spectrum

$$N(E, t)\, dE = A(t)E^{-\gamma(t)}\, dE \qquad (5)$$

Integrating (5) for energies above the atmospheric cut-off E_0, one gets the number of protons which reach the detectors and yield the following counting rate:

$$\Delta N_{\text{Te}} = \frac{A}{\gamma - 1} E_0^{-\gamma+1} G_{\text{Te}} \epsilon_{\text{Te}} \qquad (6)$$

With the aid of (6) the parameter $A(t)$ in (5) can be eliminated. For the differential proton flux one obtains

$$N(E)\, dE = \frac{(\gamma - 1)\, \Delta N_{\text{Te}}}{G_{\text{Te}} \epsilon_{\text{Te}}} \frac{1}{E_0} \left(\frac{E}{E_0}\right)^{-\gamma} dE \qquad (7)$$

The results of this calculation are shown in Fig. 6 for $E = 100, 150, 200, 300, 500$ MeV. Also drawn is the integral proton flux for energies above 500 MeV, which can be compared with the counting rate patterns of some high-latitude neutron monitors (e.g. Alert). These curves show a shift of the maximum towards earlier times with increasing energy. The maxima for 100, 150, and 200 MeV occur at 0500 UT, 0400 UT, and 0230 UT, respectively. It can further be seen that the decrease is faster for higher energy protons than for lower.

5 Diffusion of Protons in Interplanetary Space

The propagation mechanism of solar protons in interplanetary space is not yet fully understood. This is mainly due to the lack of knowledge about the influence of solar and interplanetary magnetic fields. Several authors (e.g. Bryant *et al.* 1962, Parker 1963, Hofmann and Winckler 1963, Krimigis 1965) have assumed that the protons are scattered at irregularities of the magnetic field, resulting in a diffusion-like propagation.

Proceeding from calculations by Krimigis (1965) we shall also compare

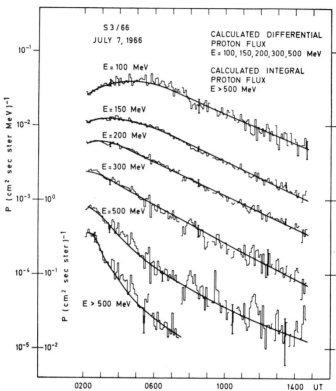

Fig. 6   The calculated differential proton fluxes for $E = 100, 150,$
200, 300, 500 MeV and the integral proton flux for
$E > 500$ MeV.

our measurements with results obtained by the application of the diffusion
theory to the propagation of solar protons. Krimigis (1965) has taken a
diffusion coefficient D varying with the distance r from the sun according to

$$D = D_0 r^\delta \tag{8}$$

We give here his results under the assumption of diffusion in three-dimensional space away from a point source. The solution of the diffusion equation
then shows that the values $\ln (It^{3(2-\delta)})$ plotted against t^{-1} should lie on a
straight line with slope

$$m = \frac{r^{2-\delta}}{(2-\delta)^2 D_0} \tag{9}$$

and intercept b with the ordinate, according to

$$b = \ln \left[\frac{Nv}{4\pi (2-\delta)^{(4+\delta)(2-\delta)} \Gamma(3/(2-\delta))} \left(\frac{1}{D_0}\right)^{3/(2-\delta)} \right] \tag{10}$$

N = number of particles per steradian emitted at $t = 0$

v = magnitude of the particle velocity

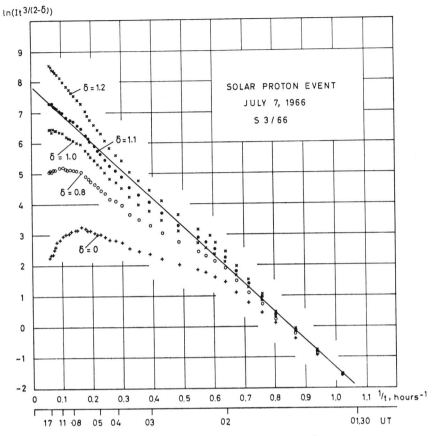

Fig. 7 Curves of ln $(It^{3/(2-\delta)})$ plotted against t^{-1}. δ gives the dependence of the diffusion coefficient D on the distance from the sun, according to $D = D_0 r^\delta$; t is the time after the onset of the Type IV radio burst.

For the event of 7 July 1966 we have plotted in Fig. 7 the values ln $(It^{3/(2-\delta)})$ against t^{-1} for $\delta = 0, 0.8, 1.0, 1.1, 1.2$ ($\delta = 0$ corresponds to the assumption of a diffusion coefficient independent of r, as was used in earlier papers); t is the time after the onset of the Type IV radio burst. It is obvious that the best approximation of the data points to a straight line is obtained for $\delta = 1.1$. With $\delta = 1.1$ we get the diffusion coefficient

$$D = D_0 r^{1.1} \tag{11}$$

The slope m of this straight line gives

$$\frac{D_0}{r_0^{2-\delta}} = 0.134 \text{ hour}^{-1} \tag{12}$$

(r_0 = distance from the sun to the earth). Then the average value of D

between the sun and the earth is

$$\bar{D} = \frac{1}{r_0} \int_0^{r_0} D\,dr = 0.064 r_0{}^2 \qquad (13)$$

and from the general equation

$$\bar{D} = \frac{v}{3}\bar{L} = \frac{c}{3}\beta\bar{L} \qquad (14)$$

where $\bar{L}$ = average mean free path, $\beta = v/c$, we obtain $\beta\bar{L} = 0.026$ AU. Thus the average mean free paths for 100 MeV and 300 MeV protons are $\bar{L} \simeq 0.06$ AU and $\bar{L} \simeq 0.04$ AU, respectively.

Taking a mean value for $\beta = 0.5$, we get as estimate of the total number N of protons emitted during the flare $N \simeq 10^{31}$ sr^{-1}. As can be seen from Fig. 7 our measurements compare quite well with the results of the diffusion theory. However, the values of the diffusion parameters which we have deduced can only be regarded as estimates. One reason is that they have been calculated with the aid of formulae which were derived for monoenergetic protons, but are used here for the integral proton flux above about 100 MeV. It should further be remarked that the value $\delta = 1.1$ for the variation of the diffusion coefficient is obtained under the assumption of a diffusion in three-dimensional space away from a point source. Such an assumption is necessary as experimentally one can only determine the following expression

$$Z = \frac{\alpha + 1}{2 - \delta}, \qquad (15)$$

where α is a parameter specifying the dimensionality of space (Parker 1963). In our case α is equal to 2. But if, for example, the diffusion is away from a plane or through a trumpet-shaped region, then $\alpha \neq 2$, and δ is greater or smaller than the value we have given. As the exact geometry of the diffusion region is not known, one should not stress this value of δ too much.

Appendix I   The Angular Distribution of the Solar Proton Flux at Balloon Altitudes

Assuming an isotropic proton flux at the top of the atmosphere with a differential energy spectrum given by

$$F(E)\,dE = AE^{-\gamma}\,dE \qquad (A1)$$

and energy losses in the atmosphere due to ionization only, the angular distribution of the proton flux and its dependence on the slope of the energy spectrum can easily be calculated. From (1) the number of protons having traversed an absorbing layer of air of p g cm^{-2} can be obtained by integration

$$N(p) = \int_{E_0(p)}^{\infty} AE^{-\gamma} \, dE = \frac{A}{\gamma - 1} E_0(p)^{-\gamma+1} \qquad (A2)$$

$E_0(p)$ is the minimum energy of protons required to traverse p g cm^{-2} of air. With the aid of the range–energy relation (e.g. Rich and Madey 1954) which can be approximated in the 50–500 MeV region by

$$p = BE^{1.8} \qquad (A3)$$

(Wilson 1947, Pfotzer *et al.* 1962) one gets

$$N(p) = \frac{A}{\gamma - 1} B^{(\gamma-1)/1.8} p^{(-\gamma+1)/1.8} \qquad (A4)$$

As the angular distribution function is defined by

$$f(\theta) = \frac{I_\theta}{I_0} \qquad (A5)$$

where I_θ is the intensity in the direction of a zenithal angle θ and I_0 is the intensity in the vertical direction, we get with the aid of (A4)

$$f(\theta) = \left(\frac{p_\theta}{p_0}\right)^{(-\gamma+1)/1.8} \qquad (A6)$$

where p_θ g cm^{-2} of air have to be traversed by protons coming from a direction with zenithal angle θ, and p_0 g cm^{-2} of air by vertically propagated protons. Neglecting the curvature of the atmosphere one gets

$$p_\theta = \frac{p_0}{\cos \theta} \qquad (A7)$$

The angular distribution function is then given by

$$f(\theta) = \cos^{(\gamma-1)/1.8}(\theta) \qquad (A8)$$

As can be seen the exponent of this function depends only on the slope of the differential energy spectrum and not on the atmospheric depth.

Appendix 2   Remarks on the Calculation of the Ratio R of the Counting Rates of the Single Counter and the Telescope

If the angular distribution function of the protons is of the form

$$f(\theta) = \cos^\mu(\theta) \qquad (A9)$$

it is possible to determine the exponent μ from the ratio of the counting rates of a single counter and a telescope. To do this one has to calculate R as a function of μ, plot the curve, and then take the values of μ for each measured ratio of the counting rates from it. The calculation of $R(\mu)$ starts from the following equation:

$$R(\mu) = \frac{\Delta N_{Al}}{\Delta N_{Ts}} = \frac{\epsilon_{Al} G_{Al}(\mu)}{\epsilon_{Te} G_{Te}(\mu)} \tag{A10}$$

where ΔN = additional counting rates due to the proton flux, ϵ = efficiency, and G = geometrical factor.

In this equation ϵ is independent of μ. It was determined experimentally for the Al–GM counter (Victoreen 1B85) by Keppler (1964b), who obtained $\epsilon_{Al} = 0.96$ and then calculated $\epsilon_{Te} = (0.96)^3 = 0.88$. The geometrical factors must be calculated. This has been done by different authors, but whereas the results for the single counter are in agreement, those for the telescope differ greatly according to what assumptions have been made in the derivation of the formulae and what approximation has been used in the numerical calculations. We have used values obtained by Newell and Pressly (1949) for $\mu = 0$ and 2. For $\mu = 1$ and 3 the values for $\mu = 0$ and 2 from Newell and Pressly were interpolated taking the form of the curve for $G(\mu)$ obtained from the formulae of Pomerantz (1949). Further, the values obtained above were multiplied by 0.97, a factor which takes into account the different effective dimensions of the Al counter (Victoreen 1B85) and Bi counter (Victoreen 6306). The latter has small dimensions due to the Bi screen inside the Al mantle (Heristchi and Masse 1966). The geometrical factors, calculated and corrected in the way described above are plotted in Fig. 4. For the ratio of the counting rates, the different efficiencies of the Al–GM counter and the telescope (according to (A10)) and the energy threshold of 14 MeV for the telescope were considered. The influence of the energy threshold of the single counter is negligible.

Acknowledgments

The research reported in this document has been sponsored in part through:

the Lindau group (Institut für Stratosphären-Physik am Max-Planck-Institut für Aeronomie), by the Bundesministerium für wissenschaftliche Forschung der Bundesrepublik Deutschland (WRK–10), by the Max-Planck-Gesellschaft granted mainly by the Deutsche Ländergemeinschaft and the Bundesrepublik Deutschland;

the Kiruna group (Kiruna Geophysical Observatory, Director Dr. B. Hultqvist), by the Swedish Natural Science Research Council,

the Meudon group (Laboratoire de Physique Cosmique, Director Prof. Dr. A. Fréon) by the Centre National d'Etudes Spatiales (CNES),

the Oulu group by the Finnish Academy of Science and the National Research Council for Sciences.

Note added in proof: Satellite measurements now available (T. L. Cline *et al.*, *J. Geophys. Res.*, 1968, **73**, 434–437) have confirmed our assumption on solar X-rays in Sec. 2.

References

BRYANT, D. A., T. L. CLINE, U. D. DESAI, and F. B. McDONALD, 1962, Explorer 12 observations of solar cosmic rays and energetic storm particles after the solar flare of September 28, 1961, *J. Geophys. Res.*, **67**, 4983–5000.

HERISTCHI, DJ., J. KANGAS, G. KREMSER, J. P. LEGRAND, P. MASSE, M. PALOUS, G. PFOTZER, W. RIEDLER, K. WILHELM, 1966, Preliminary report on measurements with balloon-borne detectors in northern Scandinavia during the solar proton event of July 7, 1966, *SPARMO Bull., No. 4, Dec. 1966*, pp. 3–15.

HERISTCHI, DJ., and P. MASSE, 1966, Influence de la géométrie du compteur GM-Bi sur son taux de comptage et celui du télescope standard SPARMO, *SPARMO Bull., No. 4, Dec. 1966*, pp. 16–19.

HOFMANN, D. J., and J. R. WINCKLER, 1963, Simultaneous balloon observations at Fort Churchill and Minneapolis during the solar cosmic ray events of July 1961, *J. Geophys. Res.*, **68**, 2067–2098.

KEPPLER, E., 1964a, Description and instruction manual for the Sonde SPARMO 64, *SPARMO Bull., No. 3, Oct. 1964*, pp. 21–29.

—— 1964b, Messung von Röntgenstrahlung und solaren Protonen mit Ballongeräten in der Nordlichtzone. *Mitt. Max-Planck-Inst. Aeronomie*, No. 15, 1964 (Springer-Verlag, Berlin–Heidelberg–New York).

KRIMIGIS, S. M., 1965, Interplanetary diffusion model for the time behavior of intensity in a solar cosmic ray event, *J. Geophys. Res.*, **70**, 2943–2960.

LEGRAND, J. P., and P. SIMON, 1966, La "SPARMO ALERTE" du 5 au 10 juillet 1966 *SPARMO Bull., No. 4, Dec. 1966*, pp. 1–2.

NEWELL, H. E., and E. C. PRESSLY, 1949, Counting with Geiger counters, *Rev. Scient. Instrum.*, **20**, 568–572.

PARKER, E. N., 1963, *Interplanetary Dynamical Processes* (Interscience Publishers, New York).

PFOTZER, G., A. EHMERT, and E. KEPPLER, 1962, Time pattern of ionizing radiation in balloon altitude in high latitudes. *Mitt. Max-Planck-Inst. Aeronomie*, No. 9, 1962.

POMERANTZ, M. A., 1949, The properties of cosmic radiation in the lower atmosphere, *Phys. Rev.*, **75**, 1721–1728.

RICH, M., and R. MADEY, 1954, Range energy tables, *Report of the University of California UCRL 2301* (University of California).

WILSON, R. R., 1947, Range, straggling and multiple scattering of fast protons, *Phys. Rev.*, **71**, 385–386.

39

The Proton Flares on 7 July, 2 September 1966, and 28 January 1967

P. N. Ageshin, V. V. Boyarevich, Yu. I. Stozhkov, A. N. Charakhchyan, and T. N. Charakhchyan

Lebedev Physical Institute, Institute of Nuclear Physics of the Moscow State University, Moscow, USSR

Abstract

The cases of the increases in the cosmic-ray intensity on 7 July, 2 September 1966, and 28 January 1967 were detected in the stratosphere in the Murmansk region (Olenya station) and at Mirny (the Antarctic). The energy spectrum and time dependences of the solar proton intensity were measured. The exponent γ of the integral energy spectrum of the solar protons in the 200–300 MeV energy range proved to be equal to $\gamma \simeq 2.4$ for the flare of 7 July, $\gamma \simeq 3.7$ for the flare of 2 September, $\gamma \simeq 3.0$ for the flare of 28 January. The maximum proton flux detected in the flare of 28 January at 1250 UT was about 1.8×10^6 particles $\text{cm}^{-2}\,\text{s}^{-1}\,\text{sr}^{-1}$.

On 7 July and 2 September 1966 and on 28 January 1967 the cosmic-ray bursts were detected from a balloon in the stratosphere over Murmansk and Mirny (the Antarctic). The measurements were carried out using the standard cosmic-ray radiosondes PK-1 and PK-2 (Ageshin and Charakhchyan 1966). The sensing element in PK-1 was a Geiger counter (CTC-6) whose wall thickness was 0.07 g cm^{-2} of steel. The sensing element in PK-2 was a telescope of two CTC-6 counters between which a filter of 2 g cm^{-2} Al thickness was inserted. Table 1 presents the date, point of observation, type of radiosonde, and times of launchings of the balloons from which the solar protons were detected. Also listed in the table is the time at which an instrument was at

Table I   Balloon Observations of Solar Protons

No.	Date	Time of Launching (UT)	Maximum Pressure (g cm^{-2})	Altitude Time (UT)	N_p (at 8 g cm^{-2}) (cm^{-2} s^{-1} sr^{-1})	Point of Observation	Type of Radio-sonde
	1966						
1	7.VII	0705	11	0842	0.7	Mirny	PK–1
2	2.IX	0700	6	0830	3.3	Murmansk	PK–1
3	2.IX	0715	20	0840	1.6	Mirny	PK–1
4	2.IX	1051	9	1200	3.8	Murmansk	PK–2
5	2.IX	1450	17	1610	5.4	Murmansk	PK–2
6	2.IX	1649	11	1850	7.6	Murmansk	PK–1
7	2.IX	2354	13	0130	1.1	Murmansk	PK–1
	1967						
8	28.I	1157	67	1250	180	Murmansk	PK–1
9	28.I	1355	54	1503	120	Murmansk	PK–1
10	29.I	0647	8	0836	7.3	Mirny	PK–1
11	29.I	0707	13	0830	6.5	Murmansk	PK–1
12	29.I	0911	8	1052	5.6	Mirny	PK–1
13	29.I	1042	16	1211	5.6	Murmansk	PK–1
14	30.I	0647	6	0847	1.7	Mirny	PK–1
15	30.I	0658	8	0846	1.7	Murmansk	PK–1
16	31.I	0647	6	0844	0.3	Mirny	PK–1
17	1.II	0657	4	0917	0.1	Murmansk	PK–2

maximum altitude and the pressure (in g cm^{-2}) corresponding to this altitude. The proton intensity at a pressure of 8 g cm^{-2} is also presented. In the cases when the maximum pressure was lower than 8 g cm^{-2} the intensity was obtained by extrapolating the altitude dependence to the pressure of 8 g cm^{-2}.

The pressure dependence of the number of protons is shown in Fig. 1. The numerals in the key correspond to the serial numbers in the table. The proton intensity in the flare of 7 July detected over Mirny at 0840 UT was equal to 0.7 cm^{-2} s^{-1} sr^{-1} and proved to be close to the proton intensity detected at the same time over Kiruna at a pressure of about 8 g cm^{-2} which was equal to 0.8 cm^{-2} s^{-1} sr^{-1} (Heristchi *et al.* 1966). The curve of the proton absorption in the atmosphere measured at Mirny (the data marked with an asterisk in the figure) corresponds to the integral proton energy spectrum in the power representation with the exponent $\gamma \simeq 2.4$ which is also in agreement with the data on the proton energy spectrum at Kiruna (Heristchi *et al.* 1966). Taking into account that the cosmic rays arriving from various directions were detected at Mirny and Kiruna the coincidence of the fluxes indicates the isotropy of the radiation in the vicinity of the earth.

The energy spectrum in the flare of 2 September was somewhat softer (the exponent of the integral spectrum $\gamma \simeq 3.7$). It follows from the character of the altitude dependence of the protons in the stratosphere over Murmansk that no considerable changes in the spectrum were observed during the flare.

The flare of 28 January was most powerful. The greatest proton flux was detected in the Murmansk region at 1250 UT; at a pressure of 8 g cm^{-2} this flux was approximately 1.8×10^6 m^{-2} s^{-1} sr^{-1}. As can be seen from Fig. 1

the proton intensities in the stratosphere for simultaneous measurements at Murmansk and Mirny on 29 and 30 January are in coincidence, i.e. an isotropic proton flux was observed in the vicinity of the earth for this flare as well.

The proton energy spectra obtained from the absorption curves in Fig. 1 are presented in Fig. 2. The exponent of the integral energy spectrum in the 300–600 MeV energy range for the measurements of 28 January was $\gamma \simeq 3.5$. In the measurements of 29 and 30 January and 1 February $\gamma \simeq 3.0$ in the 80–400 MeV energy range.

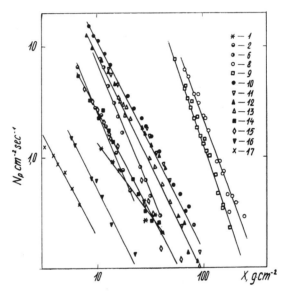

Fig. 1   The solar proton number N_p plotted against atmospheric pressure X(g cm^{-2}) for the measurements presented in Table 1. The numerals in the key correspond to the serial numbers in the table.

Figure 3 presents the time dependences of the proton intensity in the flares of 7 July, 2 September, and 28 January. Plotted as ordinates are the proton numbers in relative units, as the abscissa the time in hours counted, for the flares of 7 July and 2 September from the moment of the onset of the chromospheric flare on the sun, and for the flare of 28 January from 0800 UT, since in the latter case the chromospheric flare on the sun was not detected and the beginning of the increase was observed in the neutron monitor soon after 0800 UT.

For the flares of 7 July and 2 September the data presented were obtained in the stratosphere over Kiruna (Heristchi *et al.* 1966) at a pressure of about 8–10 g cm^{-2} and over Murmansk at a pressure of 8 g cm^{-2}, i.e. for protons of energies higher than 100 MeV. For the flare of 28 January the data presented were obtained in the stratosphere over Murmansk and Mirny for protons of energies higher than 300 MeV; the proton intensities were those at a pressure of 50 g cm^{-2}, where the data from all the flight were actually available. For this flare the data of the neutron monitor at Churchill are also presented; the maximum increase here was 17 per cent. These data were

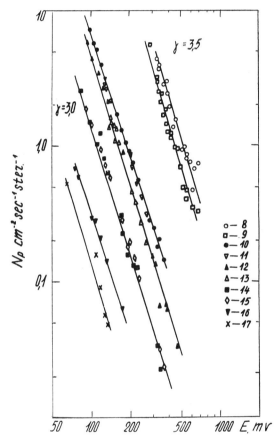

Fig. 2   The integral energy spectra of solar protons at the flare on 28 January 1967. The numerals in the key correspond to the serial numbers in Table 1.

kindly presented to us by Dr. R. A. R. Palmeira. The time dependence for the flare of 2 September was unusual: the intensity decrease was shorter than the increase and it is impossible to describe this increase by the usual diffusion curve. The time dependences in the flares of 7 July and 28 January can be rather well described by the diffusion curves on the assumption that the generation on the sun occurs for a comparatively short period and the protons propagate through interplanetary space with magnetic inhomogeneities the density of which is decreased with distance from the sun, i.e. the diffusion coefficient $D = D_0(\xi/R)^B$. In this case the time dependence of the particle intensity $N(t)$ is of the form (Parker 1963)

$$N(t) = \frac{A}{(D_0 t)^{3/(2-B)}} \exp\left(-\frac{R^2}{(2-B)^2 D_0 t}\right) \qquad (1)$$

where R is the distance to the earth's orbit. The diffusion coefficient D_0 near the earth's orbit is connected with t_{max} (the time where the particle intensity is maximum) by the relation

$$t_{max} = \frac{R^2}{3(2-B)D_0}$$

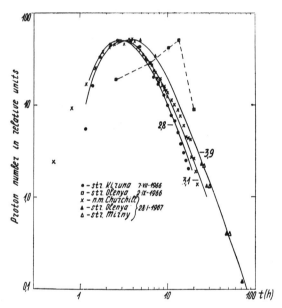

Fig. 3   The time dependence for the flares of 7 July
and 2 September 1966, and 28 January 1967.

The solid curves in Fig. 3 have been calculated from the formula (1) at $B = 1$ and $t_{max} = 2.8$, 3.1, and 3.9 hours. The corresponding values for the diffusion coefficients near the earth prove to be 7.4, 6.7, and 5.3×10^{21} cm^2 s^{-1}. If the difference in the velocities for the protons detected with the neutron monitor at Churchill and in the stratosphere is taken into account (in the first case the effective proton momentum is approximately 2 GeV c^{-1} and in the second case it is approximately 1 GeV c^{-1}) then for the flare of 28 January the path before the scattering proves to be independent of particle momentum.

For the flare of 7 July the mean path before the scattering proved to be 1.4×10^{12} cm, i.e. the same as for the flare of 28 September 1961. In the two cases the solar activity was identical (the monthly total sunspot group number $\eta = 120$). The same is observed for the flares of 28 January 1967, and 1 April and 4 May 1960 which occurred at identical solar activity ($\eta = 230$). In the three cases the free paths proved to be close to each other: 7.4, 7.1, and 9.8×10^{11} cm for the flares of 28 January 1967, 1 April and 4 May 1960, respectively.

References

AGESHIN, P. N., and A. N. CHARAKHCHYAN, 1966, A radiosonde for measuring cosmic rays in the stratosphere, *Geomagn. i Aeronomiya*, **6**, 617–618.

HERISTCHI, DJ., J. KANGAS, G. KRESMER, J. P. LEGRAND, P. MASSE, M. PALOUS, G. PFOTZER, W. RIEDLER, and K. WILHELM, 1966, Preliminary report on measurements with balloon-borne detectors in northern Scandinavia during the solar proton event of July 7, 1966, *SPARMO Bull.*, *No. 4, Dec. 1966*, pp. 3–15. See also *Ann. IQSY*, this volume, Paper 38.

PARKER, E. N., 1963, *Interplanetary Dynamical Processes* (Interscience Publishers, New York and London).

40

Sea-Level Observations of the 7 July 1966 Solar Proton Event

A. Fréon, J. Berry, and J. Folques

Laboratoire de Physique Cosmique, Fort de Verrières, 91-Verrières-le-Buisson, France

Abstract

From the beginning of the present solar cycle, the 7 July 1966 proton event is the first to give obvious effects in ground-level cosmic-ray detectors. Rather low but noticeable increases against background have been observed by several high-rate neutron monitors (NM 64), the two largest ones being recorded at Alert, Alaska, and Port-aux-Français, Archipelago Kerguelen. Here we analyse these results, especially the latter, in comparison with high-altitude measurements with balloon-borne detectors in Northern Scandinavia.

The main results are the following: it seems not to be necessary to assume an anisotropic distribution on earth of the solar particles to explain the relatively high increase observed at Kerguelen; the maximum momentum of the solar protons is of the order of 1.5 to 2 GeV/c; the proton event has been observed at ground level up to 0520 UT, i.e. during the whole increasing period of the exponent of the power law spectrum of the particle energy; the variations observed at sea level during the decrease of the event are probably related to the observed structure at balloon altitudes showing a second maximum.

According to the method developed by Fenton *et al.* (1959), Fedchenko (1965) and Ables *et al.* (1967), a cosmic-ray intensity time–direction map was compiled for the period 6–10 July 1966, in order to determine the propagation conditions in interplanetary space during the event.

The main results were as follows: the pre-flare interplanetary state was quiet and presented a normal diurnal effect; the anisotropic phase of the associated Forbush decrease occurred about 28 hours after the onset of the flare; the main phase of the storm began 43 hours after the event, i.e. the mean transit velocity of flare solar wind was 970 km s^{-1}.

As is known from observations of previous events, the 45° westward location of the flare on the sun lends support to the hypothesis of an anisotropic distribution on earth of the solar protons (impact zones). Such an assumption

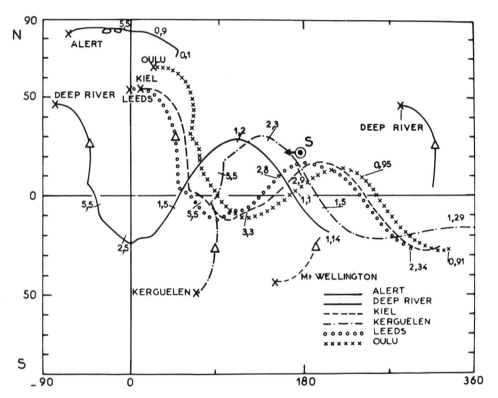

Fig. 1   Asymptotic directions of viewing, given in geographic coordinates for various stations. Crosses correspond to the geographic location of each station, triangles indicate the mean asymptotic direction for the cosmic spectrum, energy in GeV is plotted along each curve. The arrow corresponds to the apparent shift from south of the sun during the flare.

was put forward in order to explain the observed Kerguelen increase. On the other hand, the high latitude of the flare, 34°N, leads us to think that solar particles emitted far from the ecliptic plane are mainly controlled by diffusion processes on their path to the earth.

In Fig. 1, based on the calculations of McCracken *et al.* (1965), the asymptotic directions of viewing are plotted in geographic coordinates as a function of the rigidity for six cosmic-ray stations in which the proton event was recorded with noticeable amplitude. We also indicate on this diagram the position of the sun and its drift during the flare. Taking into account these asymptotic directions, the relative observed amplitudes of the increases are consistent with a space distribution shifted westward around the sun, similar to that previously determined by McCracken (1962) for the proton flare events during the last solar cycle.

At first sight, it does not seem essential to invoke impact zones to explain the relatively high increase observed at Kerguelen. The Alert increase appears to be at variance with the others. Taking into account the northern location of the flare, we think that it can be explained by the relative directions of the sun and earth spin axes at the time of the event, facilitating the diffusion of solar particles toward the north polar cap.

From this diagram, it is possible to make a rough approximation of the maximal solar particle energy. An upper limit of about 2 GeV is able to explain the observed effect at sea level.

It is also possible to estimate the maximum energy of the solar protons from a comparison between the relative increases observed in the Kerguelen super neutron monitor at sea level and in the balloon-borne detector flying at Sodankylä, Finland, near the 7-mb level.

The increase of intensity relative to the cosmic-ray background can be written as follows:

$$\frac{\Delta I}{I} \% = \frac{\int_{p(\Phi, x)}^{p_m} R(p, x) J_t^{fl}(p) F(\theta_p, \theta_\odot)\, dp}{\int_{p(\Phi, x)}^{\infty} R(p, x) J_t^{q}(p)\, dp} \tag{1}$$

In this formula, the denominator is the cosmic-ray intensity. $p(\Phi, x)$ is the minimum momentum required for a primary particle to give an observable effect in a detector located at geomagnetic latitude Φ and at atmospheric depth x; p_m is the maximal solar particle momentum, $J_t^{fl}(p)$ and $J_t^{q}(p)$ are the momentum spectra of flare particles and cosmic rays at time t.

$R(p, x)$ is the probability that a primary particle of momentum p will give an observable effect in the detector at atmospheric depth x, including the detector efficiency; $F(\theta_p, \theta_\odot)$ is a distribution function for the flare particles where $\theta_\odot$ and θ_p are the direction of the sun and the asymptotic direction for a particle of momentum p.

In the following lines we consider only the beginning of the flare event, during which the background cosmic-ray level can be considered as constant and equal to the mean pre-flare value. The ratio of balloon to sea-level increase can be expressed by

$$\delta = \frac{I_K \int_{p(\Phi, x)_S}^{p_m} R(p, x_S) J_t^{fl}(p) F_S(\theta_p, \theta_\odot)\, dp}{I_S \int_{p(\Phi, x)_K}^{p_m} R(p, x_K) J_t^{fl}(p) F_K(\theta_p, \theta_\odot)\, dp} \tag{2}$$

where S and K relate to Sodankylä and Kerguelen respectively, I_K and I_S being the mean pre-flare intensity.

It is known that the energy spectrum of flare particles can be expressed in the same form as the cosmic-ray energy spectrum, i.e.

$$S_t^{\,fl}(E)\, dE \sim A(t)E^{-\gamma_t}\, dE \tag{3}$$

Pfotzer *et al.* (1962) have shown that it is possible to deduce the exponent γ from the ratio of the counting rates of a single counter and of the telescope of the balloon-borne detector. This ratio gives the angular distribution of the particles in the atmosphere which depends on γ. According to this method, the variation of γ during the proton event has been computed (Heristchi *et al.* 1968). The results are plotted in Fig. 2, curve A. From these results γ may be estimated to be of the order of 2 at the beginning of the event, i.e. quite similar to the cosmic-ray spectrum.

As a first approximation, we made the following hypothesis: The asymptotic directions for Sodankylä, not plotted in Fig. 1, for the required energies are not far from the corresponding asymptotic directions for Kerguelen. If we assume that diffusion processes predominate, we can expect that the distribution function F is of the same order of magnitude in both cases. We assume also that $R(p, x)$ is not too different for $p(\Phi, x)_K$ and $p(\Phi, x)_S$. This latter assumption will be discussed further.

The values of the atmospheric depth at Sodankylä and of the magnetic cut-off at Kerguelen are such that, in both cases, the minimum observable kinetic energy is near to that determined by the geomagnetic threshold. For the Sodankylä balloon-borne detector, ceiling near 7 mb, the minimum kinetic energy $E_S = 95$ MeV ~ 0.1 GeV for a proton particle. At Kerguelen the cut-off rigidity $p_K \sim 1.15$ GeV/c, corresponding to a kinetic energy $E_K = 550$ MeV for a proton.

Thus, with the above approximations, according to formula (3), formula (2) takes the following form:

$$\delta = \frac{\int_{E_S}^{E_m} A(t)E^{-\gamma}\, dE}{\int_{E_K}^{E_m} A(t)E^{-\gamma}\, dE} = \frac{\int_{E_S}^{E_m} E^{-\gamma}\, dE}{\int_{E_K}^{E_m} E^{-\gamma}\, dE} \tag{4}$$

putting $E_K/E_S = k$ we obtain

$$E_m = E_S \frac{(\delta - 1)^{\gamma - 1}}{\delta k^{1-\gamma} - 1} \quad \text{and, with } \gamma \simeq 2, \quad E_m = E_S \frac{\delta - 1}{(\delta/k)^{-1}} \tag{5}$$

Comparison between Kerguelen data for the time intervals 0105–0115 and 0115–0130 UT gives a relative increase of 2.5 $\pm$ 0.3 per cent (see Fig. 2, curve E).

From the balloon data, the corresponding increases have been found to be equal to 44 $\pm$ 4.5 per cent, and the threefold telescope and single counters lead to the same value, within the limits of statistical error.

Thus we find $\delta = 17.6 \pm 2.6$ and, taking $k = 5.5$ as defined above, we finally obtain $E_m = 725 \pm 45$ MeV and $p_m = 1.4 \pm 0.1$ GeV/c.

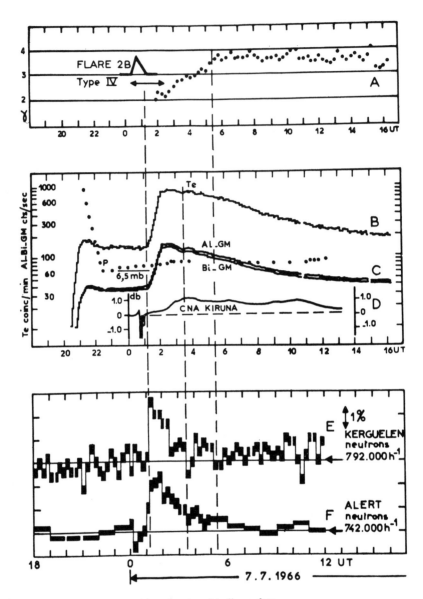

Fig. 2   Comparison between sea-level and balloon data.
Balloon observations: B, C, D, threefold coincidences, Al and Bi single counter counting rates at 5-minute intervals; statistical errors not plotted (from Heristchi *et al.* 1968). A, variation of γ with time, deduced from curves B and C. Error not plotted ~10 per cent at the beginning of the event.
Ground observations: E, Kerguelen neutron monitor; 15-minute values; statistical errors, black shading. F, Alert neutron monitor; 15-minute and hourly values; statistical errors, black shading.

In this calculation, we have assumed that $F_K \sim F_S$. It is easy to estimate the maximum energy and momentum of solar particles if $F_K \neq F_S$: we obtain $p_m = 1.15 \pm 0.05$ GeV/c if we assume that $F_K = 2F_S$ and $p_m = 2.15 \pm 0.4$ GeV/c if $F_K = 0.5\, F_S$.

As we have seen above, the data recorded by sea-level neutron monitors do not involve the presence of particles of energy higher than 2 GeV, otherwise the proton flare event would be recorded by more detectors. The present results seems consequently consistent with the predominance of a diffusion process.

The second hypothesis, assuming that $R(p, x)$ is slowly varying between the two minimum values of E_S and E_K, is less easy to discuss. The following remarks support this hypothesis: The comparison between relative increases avoids the correction for the difference of the coefficients of efficiency of the two detectors, taking into account that, at the period considered, γ is the same for the solar and the cosmic-ray spectrum. As we have seen above, the lower limit of energy corresponds in both measurements with the geomagnetic threshold. It seems likely therefore that the probability that a particle will hit the detector is not very different in the two cases, i.e. for a 0.1 GeV proton at 7 mb and for a 0.55 GeV proton at sea level. It can be admitted that the mean probability coefficient from p_K to p_m is less than from p_S to p_m, i.e. $R_K < R_S$. A calculation can be made as above for the F function and leads to similar results if $R_K \sim 0.5\, R_S$ and $p_m = 2.15 \pm 0.4$ GeV.

In conclusion, it is not possible from these results either to avoid completely the possibility of an anisotropic distribution of solar particles on the earth, or to confirm its presence.

The comparison of Kerguelen and Alert data (Fig. 2, curves E and F) with balloon results leads us to point out two remarks: At sea level the decreasing phase of the event was observed during the whole period in which γ was increasing from 2 to 4, i.e. as long as the contribution of fast particles remained noticeable (Fig. 2, curve A). The observed sea-level variations during the decreasing phase of the event seem to be correlated with those pointed out by Heristchi et al. (1968), indicating a secondary maximum in the time–intensity curves B, C, and D of Fig. 2.

References

ABLES, J. G., E. BAROUCH, and K. G. McCRACKEN, 1967, The cosmic radiation anisotropy as a separable function of time and radiation, *Planet. Space Sci.*, **15**, 547–555.

FEDCHENKO, K. K., 1965, Anisotropy of Forbush-type cosmic ray intensity decrease and electromagnetic conditions in interplanetary space, *Proc. Int. Conf. on Cosmic Rays, London 1965* (Institute of Physics and Physical Society, London), **1**, 254–256.

FENTON, A. G., K. G. McCRACKEN, D. C. ROSE, and B. G. WILSON, 1959, The onset times of Forbush-type cosmic ray intensity decreases, *Can. J. Phys.*, **37**, 970–982.

HERISTCHI, DJ., J. KANGAS, G. KREMSER, J. P. LEGRAND, P. MASSE, M. PALOUS, G. PFOTZER, W. RIEDLER, and K. WILHELM, 1968, *Ann. IQSY*, this volume, Paper 38.

McCracken, K. G., 1962, Cosmic ray flare effect: 3. Detection regarding the inter-planetary magnetic field, *J. Geophys. Res.*, **67**, 447–458.

McCracken, K. G., U. R. Rao, B. C. Fowler, M. A. Shea, and D. F. Smart, 1965, Cosmic ray tables: Asymptotic directions, variational coefficients and cut-off rigidities, *IQSY Instruction Manual No. 10*, pp. 1–23 (IQSY Secretariat, London). Reprinted as Chapter 14 of *Ann. IQSY*, Vol. 1.

Pfotzer, G., A. Ehmert, and E. Keppler, 1962, Time pattern of ionizing radiation in balloon altitudes in high latitudes, *Mitt. Max-Planck-Inst. Aeronomie*, No. 9.

41

Relativistic Solar Electrons detected during the 7 July 1966 Proton Flare Event

T. L. Cline and F. B. McDonald
NASA–Goddard Space Flight Center, Greenbelt, Maryland, USA

Abstract

The 7 July 1966 flare event provided the first opportunity to detect relativistic solar electrons in interplanetary space. The solar electrons, observed with the satellite IMP-3, have energies between 3 and 12 MeV, nearly two orders of magnitudes higher than any previously studied in space. Since they are relativistic electrons, they therefore provide a new parameter in the study of solar particle events. The electrons were separable from low-energy solar protons for several hours following the flare of 0027 UT and were, in fact, the only detectable low-energy particles between 0100 and 0200 UT. The electron energy spectrum and complete time history were measured from a position outside geomagnetic influence and show a compatibility with the general diffusion picture, having a delayed onset and profile similar to the high-velocity proton histories of other events. Other features of the event are outlined in this note.

Solar-flare electrons of energies above 100 MeV were first reported via balloons (Meyer and Vogt 1962). Recently, solar-flare electrons of energies above 40 keV were detected in interplanetary space by Van Allen and Krimigis (1965), adding a new feature to solar particle studies. Further, Anderson and Lin showed (1966) that events of such particles are highly anisotropic and (Lin and Anderson 1967) that the events can be categorized according to their temporal properties, with the well-collimated beams tending to originate from flares near the solar longitude where the earth-intercepting Archimedes-spiral field line originates.

Our observations were made with a detector on the IMP-3 satellite at times in 1966 when it was well outside geomagnetic influence. The detector used three scintillators in the familiar energy loss, total energy, and guard counter arrangement. The detector measures the rate of energy loss against the energy of a measured sample of those particles which satisfy the coincidence requirements. Thus, the absolute intensity of a particular particle species is determined as a function of time with statistical accuracy reflecting its sampled

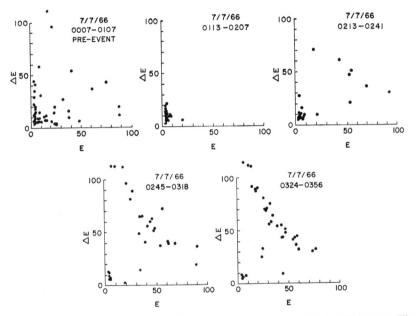

Fig. 1   Energy-loss versus energy grids before and during the 7 July 1966 event. The minimum-ionizing electron group and the proton group are clearly evident after the event begins.

proportion in that of the totality of particles detected. Figure 1 shows the energy loss plotted against energy tabulations of one period prior to, and several periods during, the 7 July 1966 event. The pattern in the pulse-height grid during the event is clean, having very few spurious events due to noise, random coincidences, scattered events, or penetrating particles which escape the anticoincidence cup. Thus, the identification of the two patterns of these particles with relativistic electrons and with slow protons can be unmistakably established.

The monitored counting rate of stopping particles is used to normalize the measured species in the energy-loss versus energy-pulse grid to produce the time histories shown in Fig. 2. It is seen that the relativistic electrons are not detected until after 0100 UT, whereas the onset of the solar microwave burst is 0027 UT, coincident with that of the flare X-ray burst at about 100 keV (Cline, Holt, and Hones 1968). The electrons are the only low-energy particles identified during the hour before the 80 MeV protons began to arrive at 0200 UT. Some higher-energy protons were present throughout, however; the Alert neutron monitor showed an increase of about 2 per cent at a maximum between 0100 and 0200, which decayed over a few hours.

We believe for several reasons that the electrons detected came from the sun and were not produced in or near the detector by high-energy solar

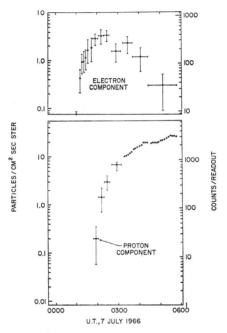

Fig. 2 Time histories of the 3–12 MeV electrons and 15–75 MeV protons during the 7 July 1966 event.

protons. First, their time history differs from that of the Alert proton event; and, second, the rate of stopping particles in the detector as a function of time for the first hour of the increase is half the total intensity of penetrating or telescoped particles. This means that each high-energy solar proton must produce at least one observed 3–12 MeV electron in order that the electrons be secondaries, a rate which seems much too high, especially when the proportion of such electrons in the quiet-time cosmic radiation is orders of magnitude lower.

The temporal history of the electrons seen in the 7 July event indicates that although the rise and decay times are short, the event is actually a delayed one, considering the 48°-west location of this flare, so that the direct field-line propagation time would be a little longer than 8.3 minutes. This delayed behavior contrasts that of the very low-energy electron histories of Lin and Anderson (1967), but is similar to those of relativistic protons (Bryant *et al.* 1965). We conclude either that considerable storage of particles must have taken place near the sun, if they were produced at the time of the X-ray burst, or that they were produced up to an hour later. Further, since the time history was approximately consistent with a fit to the standard diffusion equation using the time of the X-ray burst as origin, but not consistent with a fit using a time 40 minutes later as origin, it seems likely that the electron production took place near the time of the X-ray burst, in a manner analogous to that usually assumed for solar proton production, and that the interplanetary electrons which were observed were a sample of the electron population at the flare site.

References

ANDERSON, K. A., and R. P. LIN, 1966, Observations on the propagation of solar flare electrons in interplanetary space, *Phys. Rev. Lett.*, **16**, 1121–1124.

BRYANT, D. A., T. L. CLINE, U. D. DESAI, and F. B. McDONALD, 1965, Studies of solar protons with Explorers XII and XIV, *Astrophys. J.*, **141**, 478–499.

CLINE, T. L., S. S. HOLT, and E. W. HONES, JR, 1968, Very high-energy solar X-rays observed during the proton event of 7 July 1966, *Ann. IQSY*, this volume, Paper 29.

LIN, R. P., and K. A. ANDERSON, 1967, Electrons > 40 keV and protons > 500 keV of solar origin, *Solar Phys.*, **1**, 446–464.

MEYER, P., and R. VOGT, 1962, High-energy electrons of solar origin, *Phys. Rev. Lett.*, **8**, 387–389.

VAN ALLEN, J. A., and S. M. KRIMIGIS, 1965, Impulsive emission of ~40 keV electrons from the sun, *J. Geophys. Res.*, **70**, 5737–5751.

42

Spatial Gradients of Energetic Protons and Electrons observed after the 7 July 1966 Solar Flare

S. W. Kahler and R. P. Lin

Physics Department and Space Sciences Laboratory, University of California, Berkeley, California, USA

Abstract

Simultaneous observations of the 7–9 July 1966 solar particle event by energetic particle detectors on three satellites, IMP-3, OGO-3 and Explorer 33 are utilized to show that large spatial gradients are present in the fluxes of 0.5–20 MeV protons and $\gtrsim 45$ keV electrons. The event is divided into three parts: the ordinary diffusive component, the halo, and the core. The core co-rotates with the interplanetary field, and therefore it and the surrounding halo are interpreted as spatial features which are connected by the interplanetary magnetic field lines to the vicinity of the flare region. Upper limits to the interplanetary transverse diffusion coefficient at 1 AU are derived from the width of the halo for 3–20 MeV protons. These are at least two orders of magnitude less than the parallel diffusion coefficient for particles of the same energy.

It is argued that the observed flux variations cannot be explained by an impulsive point source injection for any physically reasonable diffusion model. Instead, since the interplanetary transverse diffusion coefficient is small for these low-energy particles, the observed spatial features are interpreted as the projection to 1 AU by the interplanetary field lines of an extensive injection profile at the sun. The geometry of the injection mechanism is discussed and it is suggested that some temporary storage of the flare particles occurs in the solar atmosphere.

I Introduction

In this paper we shall utilize simultaneous observations of the 7–10 July 1966 solar particle event by the three satellites, IMP-3, Explorer 33 and

OGO-3 to show that large spatial gradients exist in fluxes of 0.5–20 MeV protons and $\gtrsim 45$ keV electrons, and that these spatial gradients are due to the channelling of these particles by the interplanetary magnetic field. Furthermore, we shall reconstruct the instantaneous spatial intensity profile in the interplanetary medium for protons between 3 and 20 MeV and show that the spatial gradient is a decreasing function of the proton energy; that is, the intensity variation of the proton flux is larger for low-energy protons than for high-energy protons over the same spatial region.

Evidence will be presented that the observed increases in particle densities are due to the satellites passing through a region which is connected by the interplanetary magnetic field to the vicinity of the flare region at the sun. The spread of the >3 MeV protons is interpreted as being due to transverse diffusion of the particles either in interplanetary space or at the sun.

2   Experimental Details

The locations of the satellites during the event of 7–9 July 1966 are shown in Fig. 1. IMP-3 and Explorer 33 were outside the magnetosphere for the duration of the event. OGO-3 made one pass through the radiation belts during which no solar proton data could be obtained.

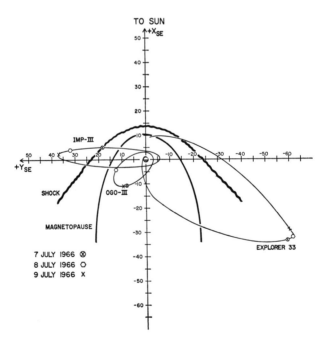

Fig. 1   Locations of the IMP-3, Explorer 33, and OGO-3 satellites during 7–9 July 1966 projected onto the ecliptic plane. OGO-3 is at high geomagnetic latitude (14–37°) and therefore outside the magnetosphere during most of this period.

The University of California experiments aboard IMP-3 and Explorer 33 are quite similar. Both satellite packages carry two Geiger–Müller tubes and and an ion chamber. One GM tube in each package observes the particle flux backscattered off a high atomic number foil, so that its directional response is only to > 45 keV electrons. The other GM tube in each package is open and counts both protons and electrons. For IMP-3 the open counter is sensitive to > 40 keV electrons and > 0.5 MeV protons. The Explorer 33 open counter is sensitive to > 22 keV electrons and > 0.3 MeV protons.

Protons of 3 MeV $< E < 33$ MeV are observed by the University of California scintillation counter on the OGO-3 satellite. The detector consists of a CsI crystal 1 in. thick and $1\frac{1}{4}$ in. in diameter surrounded by a plastic anticoincidence shield. Pulses from the photomultiplier are sorted into 32 energy channels by pulse-height analysis.

3   Description of the Particle Event

Figure 2 provides a summary of the mixed-particle event as observed by IMP-3, Explorer 33 and OGO-3. One-hour averages of the count rates are plotted for the GM tubes and ion chamber aboard Explorer 33, for the ion chamber aboard IMP-3 and for six different proton energies from the OGO-3 scintillation counter. The count rates of the GM tubes aboard IMP-3 are similar to Explorer 33. Since this is the case for the open counters, despite their energy threshold difference, we shall henceforth refer to the particles observed only as $\gtrsim 45$ keV electrons and $\gtrsim 0.5$ MeV protons.

The onset of the main particle event occurs at 0058 ± 2 UT. The initial rise is apparently due primarily to electrons. Cline and Hones (private communication 1967) report observations of 3–10 MeV electrons by the IMP-3 (E, dE/dx) counter beginning about 0100 UT and lasting for about five hours. Figure 2a(v) shows that the lower-energy $\gtrsim 45$ keV electrons are also present at this time. Low-energy (3–33 MeV) protons are observed by the OGO-3 detector after 0135 UT. The count rates of all the detectors rise to a maximum and decay away smoothly until about 1900 UT on 7 July. After this time the count rates of the $\gtrsim 20$ MeV channels continue to decay away as before, but the lower-energy proton channels rise to a second maximum. At about 0600 UT there is a sharp rise of the $\gtrsim 45$ keV electron and $\gtrsim 0.5$ MeV proton flux. The electron flux decreases after 1100 UT while the high proton flux continues until it decreases at 1600 UT. The proton fluxes observed by the energy channels below 20 MeV of the OGO-3 detector show broad peaks in the interval 0000–0800 UT. About 2–3 hours after the sudden commencement at 2102 UT all the particle fluxes drop and then rise slowly again.

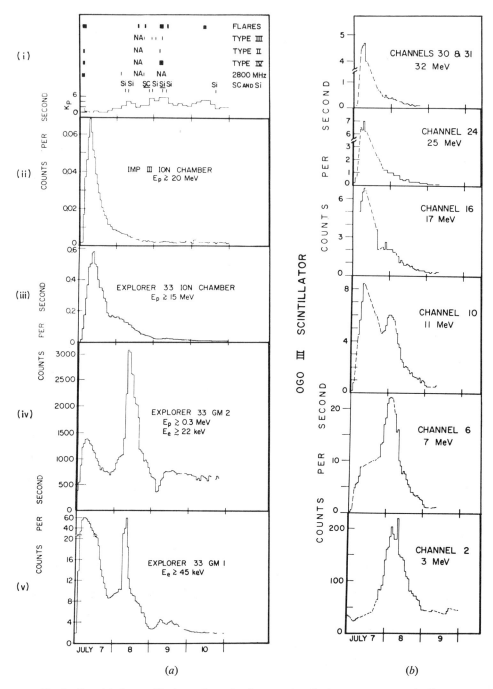

Fig. 2   Part (*a*) shows: (i), the major solar flares and radio bursts, geomagnetic disturbances and *Kp* for the period 7–9 July 1966; (ii), (iii) (iv), (v), the counting rates
of particle detectors on IMP-3 and Explorer 33. Part (*b*) shows the count rates
of six different energy channels of the OGO-3 detector for the same time interval.

302

4 Channelling of $\gtrsim 0.5$ MeV Protons and $\gtrsim 45$ keV Electrons by the Interplanetary Magnetic Field

Figure 3 shows the 10-minute average count rates of the Geiger–Müller tubes aboard IMP-3 and Explorer 33 for the period 7 July 1800 UT, to 9 July 0300 UT. The upper two plots are of the scatter counters, which have a directional sensitivity only to >45 keV electrons, and the lower two plots are of the open counters. The variations in the count rate of the IMP-3 scatter counter, which are observed from 0400 to 1100 UT, 8 July, are seen

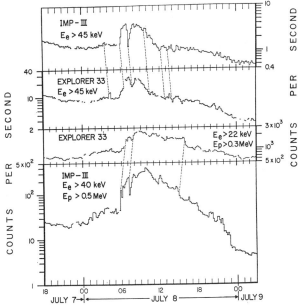

Fig. 3   The 10-minute average count rates of the GM tubes aboard IMP-3 and Explorer 33 are shown for the period 7 July, 1800 UT to 9 July 1966, 0300 UT. The two scatter counters are shown in the upper two graphs and the two open counters in the bottom two graphs.

to be followed 50 ± 10 minutes later by the variations of the Explorer 33 scatter counter. Similarly, the count rate of the open counter aboard Explorer 33 follows the count rate of the open counter aboard IMP-3 by 50 ± 10 minutes, for the period 0600 UT to 1600 UT, 8 July. The comparison of the open counters, however, is not so direct as for the scatter counters since the open counter aboard Explorer 33 has lower energy thresholds for both electrons and protons than the open counter aboard IMP-3. No increase is observed in the ion chambers during this time (see Fig. 2a (ii) and (iii)) indicating that this rise is an increase in the flux of the low-energy particle component and not an increase in the energetic penetrating radiation.

This delay in observation of these features between the two satellites is easily explained as a spatial structure carried past the two satellites by the solar wind. The time delay can be calculated simply by knowing the solar wind velocity, the angle of the interplanetary magnetic field, and the positions of the satellites in space. The angle of the interplanetary magnetic field to the sun–earth line was supplied by D. S. Colburn (private communication) and is about 30°. Since we also know the time delay of the IMP-3 scatter counter features, we can calculate that the solar wind velocity must be about 400 km s^{-1}, which agrees well with the theoretical and experimental values. Thus, we can identify the features with magnetic field flux tubes which are carried past the earth by the solar wind. It should be noted that this situation is exactly the co-rotation effect observed by O'Gallagher and Simpson (1966) and Fan *et al.* (1966). The co-rotation effect arises from the transport of the spiral interplanetary magnetic field lines radially outward by the solar wind. Particles which are trapped on the field lines will then appear to co-rotate past the satellites.

We will now show that this observed increase in directional particle flux is due to an increase in the particle density on these field lines. Then we will estimate the widths of these particle structures and the spatial gradients of the fluxes across the interplanetary field lines.

This rise in the count rates of the GM tubes cannot be entirely attributed to a change in the direction of an anisotropic pitch angle distribution of the particles since the detectors on the two satellites are pointed in quite different directions relative to the magnetic field. Furthermore, both GM tubes aboard Explorer 33 and the scatter counter aboard IMP-3 average counts over a wide cone as the satellite spins. The changes must therefore be due primarily to a spatial gradient in the particle density across the interplanetary magnetic field lines.

From the time interval of the counting rate rise in the two counters we may estimate the width d of the spatial regions:

$$d = TV_P \sin \theta \qquad (1)$$

where T is the time interval, V_P is the solar wind velocity, and θ is the angle between the interplanetary magnetic field direction and the sun–earth line.

The widths and maximum fluxes in the rise are given in Table 1 for both electrons and protons. The flux values from the two satellites are in good agreement considering that the counters on the two satellites point in different directions. The maximum observed spatial gradients in the particle intensities are also included in Table 1. These are calculated from the maximum change in flux observed by both satellites between the 40.96-second readouts. These large spatial gradients indicate that propagation across these field lines is very limited during the time of the observation.

Although there is a magnetic sector crossing between 0600 and 0800 UT, the magnetic field direction and magnitude stay steady from about 0800 UT on 8 July until the sudden commencement at about 2100 UT on 8 July

Table I   Parameters of 0.5 MeV Protons and 45 keV Electrons

Particle Species	Width (°)	Maximum Flux (cm² sr s)⁻¹	Maximum observed Flux Gradient (cm² sr s 10⁶ km)⁻¹
Electrons > 45 keV (IMP-3)	2.5	1.4×10^3	4.8×10^4
Electrons > 45 keV (Explorer 33)	2.5	0.9×10^3	1.8×10^4
Protons > 0.5 MeV (IMP-3)	5.0	8×10^3	3.7×10^4
Protons > 0.3 MeV (Explorer 33)	5.0	8×10^3	5.5×10^4

(D. S. Colburn and C. P. Sonett, private communication). Thus, it appears that the gradients are not due to local bunching of the field lines. The steady field may also be taken as evidence against interplanetary acceleration processes near the point of observation.

Since the direction of the field is approximately at the quiet-time spiral field angle, we interpret the rise in flux as being due to the satellite passing through magnetic field lines which are connected close to the flare region on the sun. For a constant solar wind speed V_P the solar longitude of the spiral field line from the earth to the sun is

$$\phi = \Omega t \qquad (2)$$

where $t = 1/V_P$ (AU) and $\Omega = $ solar rotation velocity $\simeq 13°/$day.

For $V_P = 350$ km s⁻¹, which is about the quiet-time plasma velocity, $\theta \simeq 66°$. The flare at the beginning of 7 July is located at 48°W so that the line from the flare will rotate over the earth in $18°/(13°/\text{day}) = 1.4$ days. This is about the observed delay of this rise in particle flux from the flare. The gradients observed are then interpreted as being due to the nonuniform filling of the field lines at the sun with particles and/or the mixing of interplanetary magnetic flux tubes with different particle densities.

Figure 2a (iv) and (v) shows that this sharp rise is actually superimposed on a much wider, relatively featureless, "pedestal" of $\gtrsim 0.5$ MeV protons and $\gtrsim 45$ keV electron fluxes. This pedestal occurs at the same time as the rise in the MeV protons observed by OGO-3. The interpretation of this pedestal, then, is that it represents a large region at the sun over which these particles were released or diffused. In the next section we shall examine this pedestal in more detail.

5 Spatial Structure of the 3–20 MeV Protons

It can be seen from Fig. 2b that the lowest energy channels on the OGO-3 scintillation counter show a very large increase in counting rate starting about

1000 on 7 July and lasting to the beginning of 9 July. This proton flux increase coincides with the pedestal observed on both IMP-3 and Explorer 33. That this is predominantly an increase in the low-energy proton flux can be seen from Figs. 2 and 4. The IMP-3 ion chamber and the highest channels of the OGO-3 detector exhibit a nearly exponential decay in time while channels 2, 4, 6, and 10 exhibit marked increases in flux.

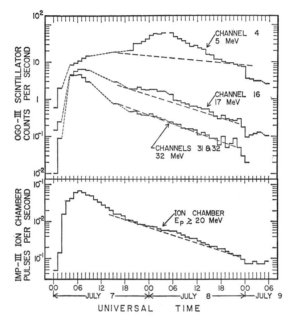

Fig. 4   Channels 4, 16, and 31 + 32 of the OGO-3 detector graphed together with the IMP-3 ion chamber to show the exponential time decay of the high energy (≥20 MeV) fluxes.

In this section we shall show that the rise in the lowest-energy channels of the OGO-3 scintillator is due to the earth moving through a spatial region in interplanetary space which is more densely populated with low-energy protons. Then we shall attempt to reconstruct an instantaneous spatial profile of the region, and finally we obtain values for the average spatial gradients of the particle flux across this region.

5.1   Spatial Origin of the 3–20 MeV Proton Structure

The origin of this low-energy proton flux cannot be due to another flare for several reasons. First, the only solar flares observed between 0100 and 2000 UT on 7 July were subflares, and one flare of importance 1 at about 0800 UT. Second, no ionospheric effects of solar flares were reported during this time and no continuum radio bursts were reported by western hemisphere radio observatories. Third, the injection time indicated by the energy dispersion in the OGO counting-rate peaks is after the onset of increase in flux, even if the background from the earlier flare is subtracted out. Therefore, we feel that it is very unlikely that the low-energy proton flux resulted from a second injection of particles at the sun.

It is well known that a few MeV protons may be trapped and stored, usually in a sudden commencement plasma cloud, and then observed at the earth with a fairly sharp onset a day or two after the flare (Bryant *et al.* 1962). These events always tend to continue to steepen the observed proton-energy spectrum due to their predominantly low energies (Webber 1964).

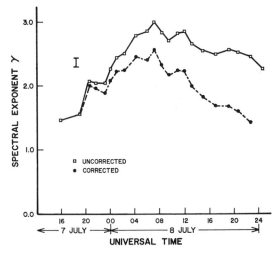

Fig. 5   The spectral index γ (from $dJ/dE = J_0 E^{-\gamma}$) is plotted against time. The upper curve is the index of the uncorrected time varying fluxes. The lower curve is the index corrected for the exponential decay in time of the fluxes. The lower plot approximates the variations of γ across the spatial structure at 7 July 1900 UT. I estimated error range for the values of γ, which were derived from fittings by eye to the data.

This event differs from secondary components of other solar flares in having no associated sudden commencement (ssc). The spectrum of the protons has been measured on the OGO-3 detector throughout the event. At all times after 1500 UT on 7 July the differential energy spectrum above 4 MeV is well fitted by a spectrum of the form $dN/dE = J_0 E^{-\gamma}$. The exponent γ is plotted in Fig. 5 as a function of time. It can be seen that, from the time of the flux increase at 1900 until about 0700 on 8 July, the exponent is increasing. After that time, however, it decreases significantly. This is in marked contrast to the behavior of the secondary components of other flares which are associated with ssc's. The spectrum is always expected to continue to steepen in time because the decay times decrease with increasing energy of the particles.

The above facts can be explained by assuming that during this event the earth went through a large spatial structure which was preferentially populated by low-energy protons from the 7 July solar flare at 0036 UT. We have argued in the previous section that Explorer 33 and IMP-3 observations show large spatial structures of 5–10 hours in duration for $\gtrsim 45$ keV electrons and $\gtrsim 0.5$ MeV protons. It is reasonable, then, that spatial features should also be seen for the $E > 3$ MeV protons observed on OGO-3.

The variations observed for the $\gtrsim 0.5$ MeV protons can also be seen to a lesser degree in the > 3 MeV protons. Over most of the rise of the > 3 MeV

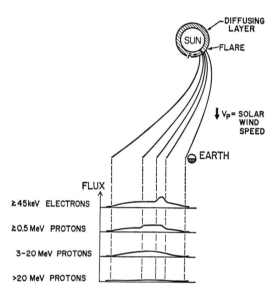

Fig. 6   A schematic of the core and halo of the energetic particle fluxes on 7 July. The core and halo are convected by the solar wind past the earth. The lower left graph indicates the spatial variation of the particle fluxes. The upper diagram shows the thin diffusing layer around the sun postulated by Reid (1964) and Axford (1965). ρ is the distance away from the flare measured in the diffusing layer.

protons the field is again at approximately the spiral field angle. Therefore, we also interpret this > 3 MeV proton spatial structure as being connected by the interplanetary magnetic field lines to the vicinity of the flare region on the sun. The situation is shown in Fig. 6.

5.2   Reconstruction of the Instantaneous Spatial Profile

The instantaneous particle population across the spatial feature can be constructed for some given time t_0 if we are able to identify the time dependence of the fluxes and if this dependence is separable from the spatial dependence of the fluxes. In principle, we may separate the time dependence into two types. The first is the variation of the shape of the spatial intensity profile with time such as would be expected for transverse diffusion. Obviously this type of time dependence would be difficult to remove from the fluxes. The second type of time dependence is the variation of the amplitude of the spatial intensity profile with time. This would be due to processes of diffusion and/or loss of particles in interplanetary space along the field lines. It is this type of time dependence which we shall attempt to remove from the data.

It is clear that this procedure will only give a crude approximation to the actual instantaneous intensity profile since we shall still have left the dependence of the shape on time. However, we expect that the variation of the shape will be small since the spatial structure sweeps past the earth many hours after the onset of the particle event.

Thus, in this section we attempt to determine the amplitude variation with time; then that variation will be removed from the fluxes to obtain a crude approximation to the instantaneous spatial intensity profile of the fluxes.

Figure 4 shows that the decay of 32 MeV protons and $E \gtrsim 20$ MeV protons is approximately exponential in time. Protons of these energies apparently show little or no response to the spatial feature, since this type of decay is observed for many other events (Webber 1964, Burlaga 1966). We therefore make the assumption that without the presence of the feature, protons of all energies would show an exponential decay in time. We feel that we are justified in assuming an exponential decay for the low-energy OGO-3 channels if there were no spatial feature because (*a*) as indicated above, high-energy protons ($E > 20$ MeV) show exponential decay during this time; (*b*) the times in the feature are at least 6 to 30 hours after the maximum for > 0.3 MeV protons (Fig. 2*a*(iv)), at times when exponential decay may be reasonably expected; (*c*) counting rates at 1600 and 1900 on 7 July and 2200 on 8 July lie close to a straight line on a semilogarithmic counting rate plot.

Since a large flux decrease was seen at 0005 UT on 9 July, presumably associated with the ssc seen at 2102 UT on 8 July, we have taken a time (8 July 2200 UT) before the drop in particle flux to extrapolate the exponential decay of the fluxes.

We have taken 7 July 1900 UT as the time for which we shall reconstruct the proton population in the spatial feature. By plotting the counting rates at 7 July 1900 UT and 8 July 2200 UT on a semilogarithmic graph the decay constants for each energy could be measured. The extrapolated decay constants appear reasonable because the higher-energy particles show a faster decay than the lower-energy particles.

For a given channel the flux is assumed to be

$$N(x, t) = N(x)\, e^{-\alpha t} \tag{3}$$

where $N(x)$ is the instantaneous flux across the feature at 1900 UT, α is the decay constant, and t is the time after 1900 UT.

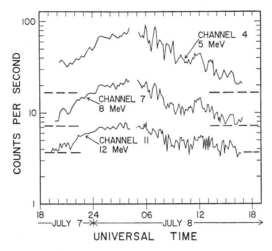

Fig. 7   The count rates of three low-energy channels of the OGO-3 scintillator, corrected for the exponential time decay. These curves approximate the spatial profiles of the particle fluxes across the halo at 7 July 1900 UT.

Figure 7 shows the results of calculating $N(x)$ by multiplying N by $e^{\alpha t}$ for three channels. Other low-energy channels are very similar. The percentage increases of the particle fluxes in the feature have been calculated for several channels and are presented in Table 2. Also presented in Table 2 are average flux gradients measured across the spiral magnetic field lines. For this calculation, we use the perpendicular distance across the spiral magnetic field (see Eq. (1)). The gradients are clearly decreasing functions of the energy as expected. The decay-corrected exponent of the energy spectrum is also shown in Fig. 5. This represents the exponent one would measure across the feature at one instant of time.

There are several possibilities for the origin of the spatial structure. One is that the particles were released in a small localized region at the flare site and then spread laterally in space by interplanetary diffusion. Another plausible

Table 2   Parameters of 3–20 MeV Spatial Structure

Proton Energy (MeV)	Flux Change (MeV cm² sr s)⁻¹	Percentage of Flux Change	Average Flux Gradient (cm²sr s MeV × 10⁶km)⁻¹
5	35	400	2.7
6	24	340	1.7
8	8	190	0.62
10	4.1	120	0.32
12	2.2	100	0.17

model is that most of the diffusion took place in the solar corona with the more energetic particles spreading over a wider coronal region. In this case the interplanetary field lines are populated near the sun and interplanetary diffusion plays a smaller role. Such models have been postulated by Reid (1964) and Axford (1965).

6 Summary and Discussion

The discussion above can be summarized as follows:

1. Large spatial gradients in the flux of electrons $\gtrsim 45$ keV and protons $\gtrsim 0.5$ MeV have been observed in structure convected outward by the solar wind.

2. These spatial gradients have been shown to be due to the preferential population of interplanetary magnetic flux tubes by particles at the sun and to the lack of propagation across the interplanetary magnetic field lines.

3. Evidence was presented for the connection of these interplanetary flux tubes to the flare region.

4. Protons of 3–20 MeV energy were shown to occupy a large spatial structure surrounding the lower-energy particle structure.

5. It was argued that this larger spatial structure is also connected back to the vicinity of the flare by the interplanetary field lines.

6. Evidence was presented that the particle fluxes in this large structure were decaying approximately exponentially in time at the time of observation, and the instantaneous spatial profile of the fluxes at 1900 UT on 7 July was constructed assuming this to be the case.

7. The spatial gradients of the proton flux in this structure were shown to be decreasing functions of energy between 3 and 20 MeV energy.

8. The spatial structure can be interpreted as either interplanetary diffusion of particles from the flare region or as coronal diffusion in which the particles populate the interplanetary spiral field lines at the base of the lines.

Note added in proof: Professor J. A. Simpson has kindly provided us with spectra and fluxes derived from the University of Chicago experiment on OGO-3 for the same period. This has allowed us to recalibrate the energy levels of the University of California OGO-3 detector. Although there are slight changes in the energy levels (each channel is approximately 1 MeV higher than stated here) and in spectra from those presented, the arguments remain unaltered.

References

Axford, W. I., 1965, Anisotropic diffusion of solar cosmic rays, *Planet. Space Sci.*, **13**, 1301–1309.

Bryant, D. A., T. L. Cline, U. D. Desai, and F. B. McDonald, 1962, Explorer XII observations of solar cosmic rays and energetic storm particles after the solar flare of September 28, 1961, *J. Geophys. Res.*, **67**, 4983–5000.

BURLAGA, L. F., 1966, Anisotropic diffusion of solar cosmic rays, *University of Minnesota Cosmic Ray Group publication CR-88*, December 1966 (University of Minnesota).

FAN, C. Y., J. E. LAMPORT, J. A. SIMPSON, and D. R. SMITH, 1966, Anisotropy and fluctuations of solar proton fluxes of energies 0.6–100 MeV measured on the Pioneer 6 space probe, *J. Geophys. Res.*, **71**, 3289–3296.

O'GALLAGHER, J. J., and J. A. SIMPSON, 1966, Anisotropic propagation of solar protons deduced from simultaneous observations by earth satellites and the Mariner-IV space probe, *Phys. Rev. Lett.*, **16**, 1212–1217.

REID, G. C., 1964, A diffusion model for the initial phase of a solar proton event, *J. Geophys. Res.*, **69**, 2659–2667.

WEBBER, W. R., 1964, A review of solar cosmic ray events, in *AAS-NASA Symposium on the Physics of Solar Flares*, NASA SP-50 (NASA, Washington D.C.).

43

Observations of the Solar Particle Event of 7 July 1966 with University of Iowa Detectors

T. P. Armstrong, S. M. Krimigis, and J. A. Van Allen
Department of Physics and Astronomy, University of Iowa, Iowa City, Iowa, USA

Abstract

Nearly complete time histories from 7 July to 17 July of the intensities of 0.31–10 MeV protons and of 2.1–17 MeV alpha particles emitted from the solar flare of 0023 UT on 7 July 1966 have been obtained with University of Iowa particle detectors on Explorer 33. The peak intensity of $3.5 \times 10^3 (\text{cm}^2 \text{ s sr MeV})^{-1}$ of 0.82–1.9 MeV protons occurred between 1000 and 1100 UT on 8 July, approximately 34 hours after the flare. At the same time the peak intensity of 2.1–17 MeV alpha particles was $190 \ (\text{cm}^2 \text{ s sr})^{-1}$. The abundance ratio of protons to alpha particles has been measured for the first time in the energy range from 0.5 to 4 MeV/nucleon and is found to range from 28 to 55 in this event. The time profiles of protons and alpha particles are complex and rapid variations of proton intensities are observed to occur in times as small as 82 seconds, the interval between data samples.

I Introduction

The satellite Explorer 33 was launched on 1 July 1966, into a highly elliptical earth orbit with initial apogee of 440,000 km (69.0 earth radii, R_e) and perigee of 50,000 km (7.84 R_e). The orbital period is approximately 12 days. Beginning on 7 July, the University of Iowa particle counters on Explorer 33 detected the arrival of solar protons, electrons, and alpha particles emitted in a solar flare at 0023 UT. The X-ray emission by the flare was also observed (Van Allen 1968). Some preliminary observations of the 7 July solar events with this experiment have been given elsewhere (Krimigis,

Van Allen, and Armstrong 1967, Krimigis, Armstrong, and Van Allen 1967, Van Allen, Krimigis, and Armstrong 1967, Van Allen 1967, Van Allen and Ness 1967).

Essentially complete time profiles of the intensities of low-energy protons in three energy ranges from 0.31 to 10 MeV and separately identified alpha particles in the range from 2.1 to 17 MeV have been obtained for the period from 7 to 17 July, the duration of the effects of the 7 July flare. From 7 July

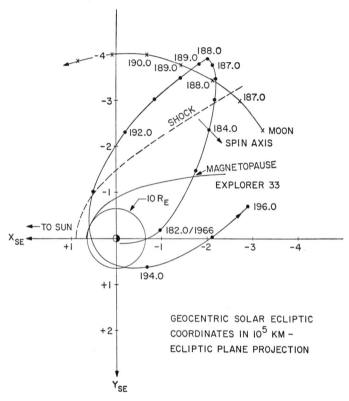

Fig. 1   Projection of the orbits of Explorer 33 and of the moon on the ecliptic plane. Decimal days are indicated on the orbits (e.g., decimal day 187.0 = 7 July, 0000 UT).

to 12 July Explorer 33 was in the interplanetary medium and from 13 July through 16 July in the outer portion of the earth's magnetosphere. Figure 1 shows the projection of the Explorer 33 orbit on the ecliptic plane from launch until 16 July. Protons of solar origin are observed continuously from 7 July to 16 July except for a period of about 14 hours on 13 July when trapped proton fluxes obscured the solar protons. Information is also obtained on solar electrons ($E_e \gtrsim 45$ keV) and penetrating ($E_p \gtrsim 55$ MeV) protons from the GM counters, although these particles are not separately identified by the counters.

The details of the experiment are discussed in Sec. 2. We discuss the gross time history of the various components of the event in Sec. 3. Section 4 gives an analysis of the composition and energy spectra and Sec. 5 a discussion of the local angular distribution of the protons.

2 Experimental Details

The proton and alpha-particle detector is a 26.5-μm thick silicon surface barrier detector of 10.4 mm^2 area situated inside a conical collimator of 60° full open angle with shielding sufficient to stop protons $E_p \lesssim 60$ MeV over the remaining solid angle. The silicon detector output pulses are amplified and clipped to 200 nanoseconds width to minimize accidental coincidences. Four discrimination levels are set to correspond to the passband labeled P1, P2, P3, and P4. P4 is set well above the maximum proton energy loss and responds only to particles more massive than deuterons, which we presume

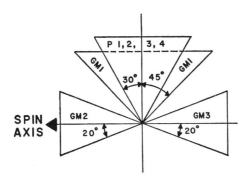

PI, 2, 3, 4, GM2, GM3 CONICAL
GMI±I5° IN AZIMUTH

Fig. 2 Arrangement of University of Iowa detectors on Explorer 33, showing the collimator angles in the spacecraft meridional plane.

in the present observation to be alpha particles. Because of the thinness of the detector and the fast clipping time of the electronics, the silicon detector system is insensitive to electrons.

The three GM counters are EON type 6213 detectors whose properties are summarized in Table 1. The orientation of the various detector collimators is shown in Fig. 2. The spin axis of the spacecraft points to 225° right ascension and −21° declination in celestial coordinates. The outputs of P1 and GM1 (perpendicular to the spin axis) are sorted into four equal angular sectors as the spacecraft spins ($\sim$26 rev min^{-1}) thereby providing information on the angular distribution of the radiation in the equatorial plane of the rotating

Table I   Principal Characteristics of Explorer 33 Detectors

Detector	Thresholds for Detectable Radiation	Collimator Full Angle	Collimator Axis Direction	Reciprocal Unidirectional Geometric Factor $(\text{cm}^2 \text{ sr})^{-1}$
P1	$0.31 \leqslant E_p \leqslant 10$ MeV† $0.59 \leqslant E_\alpha \leqslant 225$ MeV†	Conical, 60°	⊥ to spin axis, sectored	12.2
P2	$0.50 \leqslant E_p \leqslant 4.0$ MeV† $0.78 \leqslant E_\alpha \leqslant 98$ MeV†	Conical, 60°	⊥ to spin axis	12.2
P3	$0.82 \leqslant E_p \leqslant 1.9$ MeV† $1.13 \leqslant E_\alpha \leqslant 46$ MeV†	Conical, 60°	⊥ to spin axis	12.2
P4	$2.1 \leqslant E_\alpha \leqslant 17$ MeV†	Conical, 60°	⊥ to spin axis	12.2
GM1	$E_e \gtrsim 50$ keV* $E_p \gtrsim 830$ keV*	Fan, 45° equatorial 79° meridian	⊥ to spin axis, sectored	28
GM2	$E_e \gtrsim 45$ keV* $E_p \gtrsim 730$ keV*	Conical, 40°	Parallel to spin axis	50
GM3	$E_e \gtrsim 45$ keV* $E_p \gtrsim 730$ keV*	Conical, 40°	Antiparallel to spin axis	42

* GM tubes also sensitive to X-rays ($2 < \lambda < 12$ Å) and omnidirectionally to protons $E_p \gtrsim 55$ MeV.
† Upper thresholds are accurate to ±10 per cent, axial incidence assumed.

Table 2 Solar Ecliptic Coordinates of the Iowa
         Detectors on 7 July 1966

Detector		θ_{se}	ϕ_{se}
P1, GM1 Sector	I*	$-5°$	$216°$
	Sector II*	$+83°$	$82°$
	Sector III*	$5°$	$38°$
	Sector IV*	$-83°$	$263°$
GM2		$-4°$	$122°$
GM3		$+4°$	$302°$
P2, P3, P4 are spin-averaged			

*Angles are quoted for the midpoints of the 90° sectors.

spacecraft. The solar ecliptic polar coordinates (θ_{se}, ϕ_{se}) of the Iowa detectors on 7 July are given in Table 2. Sectors II and IV accept particles from the ecliptic north and south respectively. Sectors I and II are centered nearly in the ecliptic plane and accept particles from the antisolar and solar directions respectively.

3 Gross Temporal Structure of the Particle Intensities and Associated Geophysical Events

The onset of particle intensities at Explorer 33 occurred at 0058 ± 05 UT on 7 July as shown in Fig. 3, in which we have plotted the counting rate of GM1 with time resolution of 81.81 sec. The burst of X-rays which signalled the flare was measured in Sector III of GM1 and is discussed in detail by Van Allen (1968). The onset of particle intensities as detected by GM1, Sector I, and GM3 occurred at 0058 ± 05 UT or 35 minutes following the flare onset. Because the GM tubes are sensitive to both electrons ($E_e \gtrsim 45$ keV) and protons ($E_p \gtrsim 0.8$ MeV) directionally, as well as to protons with $E_p \gtrsim 55$ MeV omnidirectionally, the identification of the particles causing the GM counting rates is difficult. Protons of energy less than 10 MeV can be shown not to contribute significantly to the rates of the GM tubes until much later in the event by comparison with the rates of P1 (also designated PN1, see Fig. 3). The counting rates of the GM tubes during the onset phase may be due either to a nearly isotropic flux of electrons ($E_e \gtrsim 45$ keV) and/or protons ($E_p \gtrsim 10$ MeV) entering through the collimators and/or to a flux of protons ($E_p \gtrsim 55$ MeV) penetrating the sidewall shielding. Simultaneous data from a shielded GM tube on Injun 4 (Krimigis, Van Allen, and Armstrong 1967) indicate that the response of G1AV up to about 0230 UT is mainly due to penetrating protons, although the presence of a small flux at 45 keV electrons (up about 30 per cent of the counting rate) cannot be excluded. The onset of the polar-cap absorption (PCA) is indicated in Fig. 3. Also shown in Fig. 3 is the sudden cosmic-noise absorption (SCNA) accompanying the flare X-ray burst (ESSA, CRPL-FB-265, September 1966).

The full time history of the counting rates from 6 July through 17 July of GM1 (excluding Sector III, which has a contribution from solar X-rays) and of P3 (0.82–1.9 MeV protons) is shown in Fig. 4. GM1 and P3 have similar directional thresholds for protons. The counting rates plotted are spin-averaged counting rates. Some items (not a comprehensive summary) of solar–geophysical data (ESSA, CRPL-FB-265, 267, 270, Hakura 1967) are

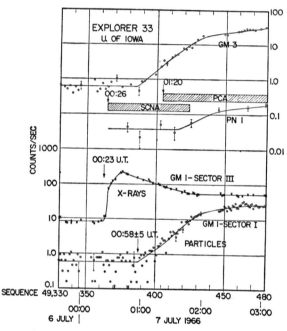

Fig. 3   Onset of X-rays and particle intensities at Explorer 33. PCA data are from Hakura (1967), and SCNA from ESSA Report CRPL-FB-265, September 1966.

shown in Fig. 4 for comparison with some features of the observed particle intensities. The PCA event noted above is fully discussed by Hakura (1967). Of the SCNA events of importance 2 or greater, only the initial event of 7 July is clearly related to the solar flare which produced energetic particles.

Although the McMath region 8362 remained active as long as it was visible (Fig. 4 gives a summary of the more intense outbursts) no impulsive emission of energetic corpuscular radiation by other than the initial burst on 7 July can be distinguished in the time profiles of the intensity. The modulation of particle intensities arriving at the earth is attributed to the effects of the interplanetary medium on the propagation of the flare particles from the sun to the earth. We will return later to a discussion of propagation.

The geomagnetic sudden commencement (ssc) of 8 July observed at the earth was also detected by Explorer 33 in both the magnetic records and the proton intensities which underwent a discontinuous decrease simultaneously with the ssc (Van Allen and Ness 1967). There was no detectable effect on proton intensities at Explorer 33 due to the ssc's of 11 July and 15 July.

The maximum spin averaged directional intensity of 0.82–1.9 MeV protons was 3.48×10^3 (cm^2 s sr MeV)$^{-1}$ between 1000 and 1100 UT on 8 July. The time-integrated flux of these protons was approximately

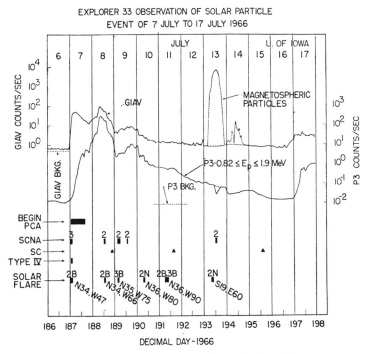

Fig. 4   Gross temporal profile of particle intensities at Explorer 33 and some associated solar and geophysical events.

1.38×10^8 (cm^2 sr MeV)$^{-1}$ for the entire event. The complex temporal structure of the particle intensities is evident from Fig. 4. The rate of decay of proton intensities after the maximum is about one-half decade per day, in a very gross sense.

The relative maximum on 7 July in the average counting rate of the three sectors of GM1 not exposed to the sun (G1AV) occurred between 0600 and 0700 UT and is not observed in the proton detector. As discussed above the response of G1AV may be due to either electrons $E_e \gtrsim 45$ keV and/or protons $E_p \gtrsim 830$ keV directionally and/or protons $E_p \gtrsim 55$ MeV omni-directionally. The corresponding maximum fluxes are 2.5×10^3 (cm^2 s sr)$^{-1}$

if purely directional or 3.3×10^2 (cm^2 s)$^{-1}$ if purely omnidirectional response is assumed.

The peaks in the response of G1AV late on 12 July and on 13 and 14 July are due to the trapped magnetospheric electrons and electron fluxes in the magnetosheath. The depression of 1.9 MeV proton intensity observed on 13 July coincident with the large peak on G1AV is believed due to the exclusion of the solar protons from the ordered magnetic field of the near ($\lesssim 8\ R_e$) magnetosphere.

No solar event has been identified as the source of the increase of particle intensities on 16 and 17 July, although this is apparently another event of solar origin.

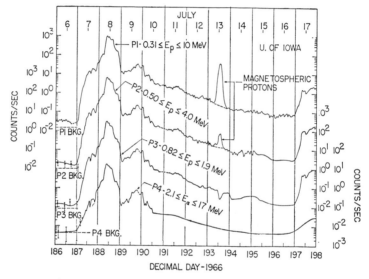

Fig. 5   Full-time history of low-energy 0.31–10 MeV protons in three energy intervals and of alpha particles 2.1–17 MeV following the flare of 7 July: Explorer 33 observation.

The time histories for 6 through 17 July of the counting rates of all the proton and alpha-particle channels from the silicon detector are shown in Fig. 5. It is apparent that the intensities of low-energy protons in the several intervals from 0.31 to 10 MeV in energy and of alpha particles from 2.1 to 17 MeV are modulated in a very similar way in the propagation from the sun to the earth. There are, however, significant time variations of the ratios P2/P1 and P3/P1, indicating changes in the spectrum of protons, and of the ratio P2/P4, indicating changes in the relative abundance of protons to alpha particles. The relative maxima of P1 and P2 on 13 July are due to magnetospherically trapped protons. The spectrum of trapped protons at large radial distances ($\sim 8\ R_e$) is very much softer than that of the solar protons. The quite different spectra of solar protons and of trapped protons at large radial distances place limitations on the possibility of direct injection of energetic solar protons as an important source of outer zone trapped protons.

4 Comments on the Proton Energy Spectrum and on the Relative Abundance of Alpha Particles

The interpretation of the counting rate ratios from the three proton channels of the silicon detector in terms of a spectral slope is complicated because of the fact that the respective energy ranges are nested within each other (Table 1). A given value of the ratio of two channels has two corresponding spectral slopes, depending on whether the differential intensity dj/dE is increasing or decreasing with energy. In principle, the fact that there are three energy channels allows a unique choice of a rising or falling two-parameter spectrum to be made. In practice, however, the uncertainties in the upper edges of the passbands make the interpretation of a differential spectrum which increases with energy very uncertain. When it is evident that the differential spectrum decreases with increasing energy then the interpretation is simple.

Figure 6 shows plots of the counting rate ratios P2/P1 and P3/P1 (three-hour averages) for 7 through 12 July and of the net counting rate of P1. We interpret the increase of the ratios from the inception of the event until 8 July 0300 UT as being due to a differential spectrum of protons which rises with energy over the interval 0.31–10 MeV and which becomes progressively less steeply rising as the event develops. This interpretation appears the most plausible and also consistent with the results of other workers who observe copious quantities of protons $E_p > 10$ MeV during this time period (Krimigis, Van Allen, and Armstrong 1967, Kahler and Lin 1968). A similar effect has been observed before in the early phase of the solar particle event of 5 February 1965 (Krimigis and Van Allen 1967a).

After 8 July 0300 UT we presume the differential spectrum to decrease with energy increase from 0.31 to 10 MeV and can therefore extract from the ratios the parameters characteristic of a power law or exponential spectral form. Table 3 gives a list of some values of γ and E_0 in a power law and an exponential fit to the differential proton-energy spectrum at selected times. The exponential form fits the observed ratios more successfully than the power law. The quoted range of the parameters E_0 and γ is due to the slightly different values obtained from the two ratios P2/P1 and P3/P1. The over-all time development of the proton spectrum from 0.31 to 10 MeV is inferred from the observed ratios to be initially very hard, becoming softer as the lower-energy protons arrive for the first two days and changing less markedly thereafter.

The abundance of solar protons relative to alpha particles can be inferred from the ratio of the counting rates of channel P2 to P4 under certain

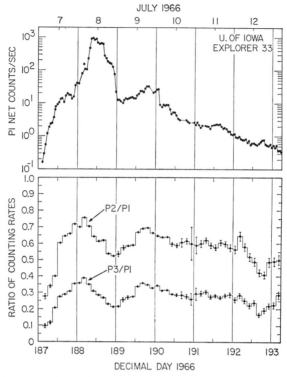

Fig. 6   Counting rate ratios P2/P1 and P3/P1 (3-hour averages) for 7 to 12 July compared with the intensity of 0.31–10 MeV protons.

circumstances: The passbands of P2 and P4 are very similar for protons and alpha particles when expressed in terms of energy per nucleon (P2 covering $0.50 \leqslant E_p \leqslant 4$ MeV/nucleon and P4 $0.52 \leqslant E_\alpha \leqslant 4.2$ MeV/nucleon), the difference being unimportant for this discussion. The ratio of P2 to P4 (3-hour averages) is plotted in Fig. 7, as is the net counting rate of P2.

Table 3   Spectral Parameters for Selected Times*

Time Period	E_0 (MeV)	γ	Comments
8 July 0900–1200	0.43–0.48	†	Max. int.
8 July 2100–2400	0.29–0.33	2.05–2.22	Rel. min. of ratios
9 July 1800–2100	0.53–0.57	†	Rel. max. of ratios
10 July 1200–	0.36–0.44	†	Extended plateau
11 July 2400			of ratios
12 July 1800–2100	0.21–0.31	2.29–2.82	Softest spectrum

*Derived from the expressions: $\dfrac{dj}{dE} = \dfrac{K}{E_0} \exp\left(-\dfrac{E}{E_0}\right)$, $\dfrac{dj}{dE} = K'E^{-\gamma}$.

†No fit possible with power law.

In order to establish the validity of P2/P4 as the ratio of proton to alpha-particle fluxes one must first establish that the response of P4 is due to alpha particles and not spurious counts and that the alpha-particle contribution to the rate of P2 is negligible. Considering first the response of P4, there are several possible sources of spurious response which must be investigated. The response of P4 to the observed fluxes and spectra of low-energy protons (0.3 to 10 MeV) incident through the collimator can be shown to be completely negligible in this case on the basis of laboratory calibrations. The

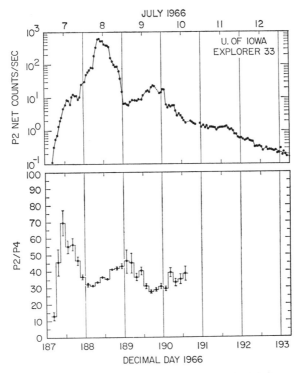

Fig. 7   Counting rate ratio of P2/P4 for 7–12 July compared with the rate of P2. After 7 July 1200 UT, P2/P4 can be interpreted directly as the p/α ratio for 0.5–4 MeV/nucleon.

omnidirectional response of P4 early in the event may not be negligible due to the presence of protons with energy $E_p \geqslant 60$ MeV sufficient to penetrate the collimator shielding (Heristchi *et al.* 1968). The response of a similar detector to such omnidirectional radiation is discussed in full detail by Krimigis and Van Allen (1967b). The intensity of penetrating protons apparently rises sharply to a maximum early on 7 July and by 0800 is decreasing significantly (Heristchi *et al.* 1968). The counting rate of P4, however, is still rising in this period of time with only brief interruptions, indicating that by about 1200 on 7 July the contribution to the rate of P4 due to penetrating protons is negligible.

Assuming that the response of P4 after 7 July 1200 UT is due to alpha particles and further assuming that the differential energy spectra of protons and alpha particles are identical when expressed in MeV/nucleon, it is found that the contribution of alpha particles to the counting rate of P2 is negligible.

We come to the tentative conclusion that from 0300 to 0600 on 7 July the ratio P2/P4 is probably not a valid ratio of the intensities of protons and alpha particles. From 0600 to 0900 and from 0900 to 1200, the ratio P2/P4 is probably a lower limit. After 1200 UT on 7 July we believe that the plotted ratios represent the ratios of proton to alpha-particle intensities in the range from 0.5 to 4 MeV per nucleon. We believe this to be the first observation of the ratio of energetic solar proton to alpha-particle intensities in this energy range.

The largest reliably observed p/α ratio was about 55 and the smallest about 28 for this event. At the time of maximum alpha-particle intensity (8 July, 0900–1200, 54 (cm^2 s sr MeV/nucleon)$^{-1}$) the ratio was 36.5. The p/α ratio was initially large and decreased during the first day of the event, and varied by about 50 per cent thereafter, indicating that an appreciable fraction of the alpha particles observed required up to one day longer to reach the vicinity of earth than protons of the same velocity. Also, the 50-per cent modulation of the p/α ratio from 8 to 10 July is apparently due to propagation effects in the interplanetary medium.

For comparison, Freier and Webber (1963) give a summary of p/α ratios observed in the solar events of 1959 to 1961 for rigidities about 0.5 GV (130 MeV for protons) which range from 1 to 40. On the basis of energy per nucleon, Ney and Stein (1962) find a ratio $j_p/j_\alpha = 40$ (>95 MeV/nucleon) for the event following the flare of 12 November 1960. The present results for j_p/j_α (0.5–4 MeV/nucleon) are roughly consistent with prior measurements at higher energies during flare events in the last solar maximum period, although such a definitive comparison is precluded by the wide variability of the p/α ratio from event to event (Freier and Webber 1963).

5 Local Angular Distribution and Temporal Fine Structure

The significant feature of the local angular distribution of solar protons on 7, 8, 9 July is their persistent net outward flow from the sun as illustrated by Fig. 8. The spacecraft equatorial plane is nearly perpendicular to the ecliptic plane and the intersection of the two planes passes about 30° east of the sun. Sector III is centered approximately on the solar direction and Sector I on the antisolar direction. The excess of counts in Sector III shows the net flow of protons away from the sun. Such a net outward flow is a necessary consequence of the gradual escape of the particles from the inner solar system.

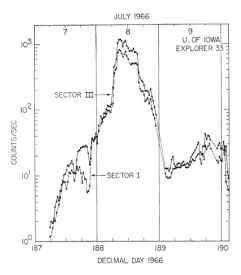

Fig. 8 Comparison of 0.31–10 MeV proton intensities arriving from the approximately solar (sector III) and antisolar (sector I) directions for 7, 8, 9 July. Note the persistent excess from the solar direction throughout the 3-day period.

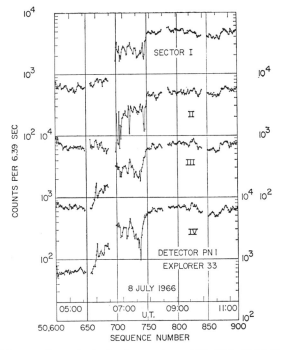

Fig. 9 Plot of the counting rates in the four sectors of P1 (0.31–10 MeV protons) with maximum time resolution (1 sequence = 81.81 seconds). Note the rapid fluctuations in intensity.

It has been observed earlier by Bartley *et al.* (1966) in the event of 29 December 1965.

Although we will not give an extensive treatment of the fine scale angular structure of the solar proton intensities we emphasize two features of the observations. First, we note significant fluctuations of the intensity of protons arriving at the spacecraft on time scales as short as the 82-second resolution of the data. Figure 9 shows an example of such rapid variations occurring around the time of maximum intensity on 8 July. An explanation of the orientation of the sectors is given in Sec. 2. Similar rapid variations in the intensity of solar protons have been observed in other events (Fan *et al.* 1966, Krimigis and Van Allen 1967a). These rapid intensity variations can be attributed to a filamentary spatial structure of proton intensities partially confined in the interplanetary magnetic field which is convected past the spacecraft by the solar wind (Bartley *et al.* 1966, Kahler and Lin 1968, Krimigis and Van Allen 1967a). The observed diversity in the directions of arrival as well as the prolonged (~ 1 week) storage of ~ 1 MeV protons in interplanetary space indicate that there are also significant diffusive effects for these energies, reminiscent of the diffusive propagation observed at higher energies (Krimigis 1965).

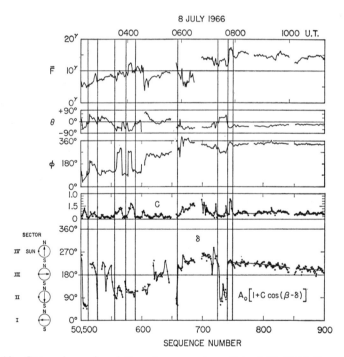

Fig. 10 Comparison of variations in parameters of the 0.31–10 MeV proton angular distribution with the variations in the local magnetic field (magnetic field data by courtesy of N. F. Ness, Goddard Space Flight Center).

Finally, although the full interpretation is not yet available, we show in Fig. 10 a comparison of the time variations of the local magnetic field vector (data by courtesy of N. F. Ness, Goddard Space Flight Center) with the parameters of the anisotropy of 0.31–10 MeV protons. The magnetic field is expressed as $\bar{F}$ the amplitude of magnetic field, θ its latitude in solar ecliptic coordinates, and ϕ its corresponding longitude. The parameters C and δ of the proton flux are from a fit of the function $A_0[1 + C \cos (\beta - \delta)]$ to the counting rates of the four sectors. The amplitude C ranges from 0 for an isotropic flux to 2 for a unidirectional flux and is characteristically about 0.2 for these data. The angle δ is the direction of maximum flux in the spacecraft equatorial plane (180° = maximum from the direction of the sun, 0° = antisolar, 90° = ecliptic north, 270° = ecliptic south). It is apparent that the anisotropy of solar protons is intimately related to the local magnetic field. We note, for example, in Fig. 10 the association of two peaks in the parameter C with reversals of the longitude of the field near 0400 and an abrupt change in the direction δ of the anisotropy coincident with a change in the magnetic field from pointing south to north. The detailed study of this association of anisotropies and the magnetic field is deferred to another paper.

Acknowledgments

We thank Dr. L. A. Frank and Mr. D. Klumpar for the use of the GM tube data. We also thank Dr. N. F. Ness and Mr. K. W. Behannon for the use of magnetic field data. Messrs. E. W. Strein, D. Camp, B. A. Randall, and others at the University of Iowa contributed to the construction, testing, and calibration of the experiment. We appreciate the cooperation of personnel of Goddard Space Flight Center, especially Dr. N. F. Ness and Messrs. P. Marcotte, J. Madden, and J. Brahm in executing the Explorer 33 experiment.

The research was supported in part by the National Aeronautics and Space Administration under contract No. NAS5-9076.

References

BARTLEY, W. C., R. P. BUKATA, K. G. McCRACKEN, and U. R. RAO, 1966, Anisotropic cosmic radiation fluxes of solar origin, *J. Geophys. Res.*, **71**, 3297–3304.

FAN, C. Y., J. E. LAMPORT, J. A. SIMPSON, and D. R. SMITH, 1966, Anisotropy of solar proton fluxes of energies 0.6 to 100 MeV measured on the Pioneer 6 space probe, *J. Geophys. Res.*, **71**, 3289–3296.

FREIER, P. S., and W. R. WEBBER, 1963, Exponential rigidity spectrums for solar-flare cosmic rays, *J. Geophys. Res.*, **68**, 1605–1629.

HAKURA, Y., 1967, The polar cap absorption on July 7–10, 1966, Goddard Space Flight Center Preprint No. X-641-67-116, March 1967 (NASA, Washington D.C.).

HERISTCHI, DJ., J. KANGAS, G. KREMSER, J. P. LEGRAND, P. MASSE, M. PALOUS, G. PFOTZER, W. RIEDLER, and K. WILHELM, 1968, Balloon measurements of solar protons in Northern Scandinavia on 7 July 1966, *Ann. IQSY*, this volume, Paper 38.

KAHLER, S. W., and R. P. LIN, 1968, Spatial gradients of energetic protons and electrons observed after the 7 July 1966 solar flare, *Ann. IQSY*, this volume, Paper 42.

KRIMIGIS, S. M., 1965, Interplanetary diffusion model for the time behavior of intensity in a solar cosmic ray event, *J. Geophys. Res.*, **70**, 2943–2960.

KRIMIGIS, S. M., T. P. ARMSTRONG, and J. A. VAN ALLEN, 1967, Solar particle events, July–December, 1966, *Trans. Amer. Geophys. Un.*, **48**, 161 (title only).

KRIMIGIS, S. M., and J. A. VAN ALLEN, 1967a, Observations of the February 5-12, 1965, solar particle event with Mariner 4 and Injun 4, *J. Geophys. Res.*, **72**, 4471–4486.

—— 1967b, Geomagnetically trapped alpha particles, *J. Geophys, Res.*, **72**, 5779–5797.

KRIMIGIS, S. M., J. A. VAN ALLEN, and T. P. ARMSTRONG, 1967, Simultaneous observations of solar protons inside and outside the magnetosphere, *Phys. Rev. Lett.*, **18**, 1204.

NEY, E. P., and W. A. STEIN, 1962, Solar protons, alpha particles and heavy nuclei in November, 1960, *J. Geophys. Res.*, **67**, 2087–2105.

VAN ALLEN, J. A., 1967, Solar X-ray ($\lambda < 14$ Å) emission by the sun since July 1, 1966, *Trans. Amer. Geophys. Un.*, **48**, 177(A).

—— 1968, The solar X-ray flare of 7 July 1966, *Ann. IQSY*, this volume, Paper 30.

VAN ALLEN, J. A., S. M. KRIMIGIS, and T. P. ARMSTRONG, 1967, Temporal and angular fine structure of solar proton and electron beams in interplanetary space, *Trans. Amer. Geophys. Un.*, **48**, 161 (title only).

VAN ALLEN, J. A., and N. F. NESS, 1967, Observed particle effects of an interplanetary shock wave on July 8, 1966, *J. Geophys. Res.*, **72**, 935–942.

44

Pioneer 6 Observations of the Solar Flare Particle Event of 7 July 1966

U. R. Rao*, K. G. McCracken†, and R. P. Bukata‡

* Physical Research Laboratory, Ahmedabad, India
† University of Adelaide, Australia
‡ Southwest Center for Advanced Studies, Dallas, Texas, USA

Abstract

The solar flare effects and Forbush decrease occurring during the period 5–15 July 1966, as observed by a detector on the Pioneer 6 spacecraft some 45° away from earth in solar longitude, are discussed. We conclude that the phenomena observed throughout the interval are completely typical of solar flare effects: thus a non-equilibrium anisotropy was observed from the "garden hose" direction at early times, a bi-directional anisotropy was observed subsequent to the onset of the Forbush decrease, and a equilibrium anisotropy due to convective removal of the cosmic rays from the solar system was observed at late times during the period. We infer that the velocity of propagation of the plasma disturbance responsible for the Forbush decrease was not significantly different (± 25 per cent) over a range of 45° of heliographic longitude.

I Introduction

In this paper we present detailed information on the time dependence, the degree of anisotropy and the spectral composition of cosmic radiation generated during a series of flares which occurred during the period 5–20 July 1966, with the major flare occurring on 7 July 1966. The observations presented here were made by a cosmic-ray detector on board the Pioneer 6 spacecraft which was launched into a heliocentric orbit on 16 December 1965. During the period 5–20 July 1966, the spacecraft was at a distance of approximately 0.8 AU from the sun and the spacecraft–sun–earth angle was about 45°.

Detailed descriptions of the cosmic-ray detector and the techniques used to study solar flares are given elsewhere (Bartley, McCracken, and Rao 1967a, McCracken, Rao, and Bukata 1967). Briefly the detector records cosmic rays from four directions for each of three energy windows of nominal energy 7.5–45, 45–90, and 150–350 MeV. Each directional counting rate is obtained by counting the pulses from the detector with a data accumulator as the axis of the detector sweeps out a fixed range of azimuths. The range of spacecraft azimuths corresponding to each directional counting rate is indicated in Fig. 1. Since any differences in the data corresponding to the four

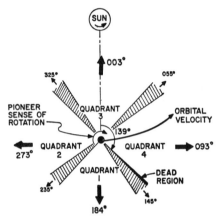

Fig. 1   The range of directions swept out by the axis of symmetry of the Pioneer cosmic-ray anisotropy detector for each quadrant is indicated, along with the mean direction of viewing of each quadrant (the heavy arrows). This diagram is as seen from the North ecliptic pole. The shaded sectors are the directions swept out in the Enhanced Dynamic Range mode of operation.

directions will be attributed to the existence of an anisotropy in the cosmic radiation, extreme care has been taken to ensure that such differences do not arise from unequal accumulation times in the different quadrants. An accuracy to better than 2.5 parts in 10^5 in the accumulation time has been achieved by using a self-calibrating, accurate time-dividing circuit (Bartley, McCracken, and Rao 1967b) on board the spacecraft.

In addition to the measurement of directional counting rates described above, the integral counting rate of all particles of energy greater than 7.5 MeV is also recorded. The counting rate of this integral channel is extremely high (about 130 counts/second), and consequently we are able to record cosmic-ray intensity changes with a very great statistical accuracy.

2   Data Reduction

A detailed account of the procedures employed in the data reduction is presented elsewhere (Bartley *et al.* 1966, McCracken, Rao, and Bukata 1967).

For the analysis presented in this paper, data averaged over 7.5 minutes have been employed. For each 7.5-minute interval, the four directional counting rates for each of the energy windows constitute a "snapshot" of the cosmic-ray anisotropy for that particular energy channel. By fitting a sinusoid to each of the 7.5-minute snapshots, the amplitude A and the direction θ_A of the anisotropy are obtained which provide a quantitative description of the cosmic-ray anisotropy.

Almost continuous data coverage is available for the periods 16 December 1965–30 April 1966, (Pioneer 6) and 17 August 1966–30 November 1966 (Pioneer 7). During the intervening period 1 May 1966–17 August 1966 the data coverage for Pioneer 6 is incomplete, due to tracking limitations. In Fig. 2 are plotted the available Pioneer 6 data for the period 5–12 July 1966 along with the Deep River neutron-monitor data.

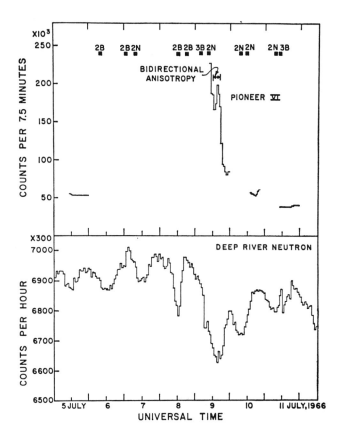

Fig. 2   The time profile of the cosmic-ray intensity of energy greater than 7.5 MeV during the period 5–12 July 1966 is plotted together with the hourly counting rate as observed by the Deep River neutron monitor. The typical features observed in the solar flare are indicated in the diagram.

The period 5–20 July was extremely disturbed insofar as interplanetary conditions were concerned. A large number of solar flares of importance greater than 2B were observed, many of which will have generated sufficient cosmic radiation to be detected by our instrument (80 per cent of all flares of importance 2B are observed to do so). The majority of our data during this period of time were obtained after 0800 UT on 9 July, at which time the cosmic-ray flux was rapidly decaying as a function of time. The fact that a flare which occurred at 7 July 0022 UT generated sufficient relativistic cosmic rays to be detected by ground-based neutron monitors, suggests that the majority of the cosmic rays observed on 9 July were released by this flare. However, this identification of the actual flare responsible for the particle acceleration is of no consequence in the following discussion.

A Forbush decrease was observed at the earth commencing at about 0000 UT on 9 July, minimum intensity being observed at about 1500 UT on the same day. During the period 1200–1600 UT on 9 July, the solar cosmic ray fluxes observed at Pioneer 6 were bi-directional, as is shown in Fig. 3;

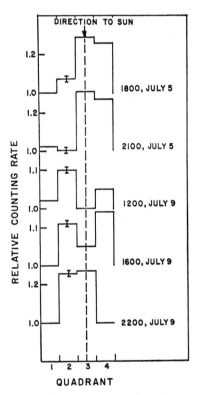

Fig. 3   Anisotropy snapshots of the cosmic-ray flux during the transition from uni-directional anisotropy to bi-directional anisotropy at the time of the minimum intensity phase of the Forbush decrease. The subsequent conversion to unidirectional anisotropy is also shown.

that is, the cosmic-ray flux was showing a maximum from two directions differing by approximately 180°. We have shown that such bi-directional fluxes are invariably associated with the minimum intensity phase of a Forbush decrease (Rao, McCracken, and Bukata 1967), and therefore conclude that a Forbush decrease occurred at Pioneer 6 prior to 0800 UT on 9 July, and that the minimum intensity phase occurred in the vicinity of 1200–1600 UT. This implies that the Forbush decrease at Pioneer 6 occurred simultaneously, or *earlier* than at the earth. This is consistent with the assumption that (*a*) the Forbush decrease was due to a shock wave originating in the flare which occurred 45° west of the central solar meridian (as seen

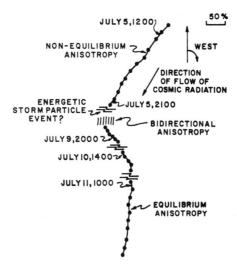

Fig. 4   The amplitude and azimuth of the cosmic-ray anisotropy (7.5–45 MeV) plotted as a vector addition diagram for the period 5–12 July 1966. Notice the long persistent anisotropy of mean amplitude about 18.0 per cent which commenced at 0900 UT on 11 July 1966.

from the earth) at 0022 UT on 7 July; (*b*) that the shock wave expanded radially outwards at approximately the same velocity (± 20 per cent) over at least 45° of solar longitude.

Figure 4 demonstrates the manner in which the cosmic-ray anisotropy varies throughout the period of interest. This diagram is essentially a vector addition diagram, each vector being of a length proportional to the amplitude of the anisotropy, and being in the "direction of flow" of the cosmic rays. The figure shows all of the phenomenological changes in the state of the anisotropy which are typically associated with solar flare and Forbush decrease events (McCracken, Rao, and Bukata 1967, Rao, McCracken, and Bukata 1967). Thus the anisotropy is of the non-equilibrium variety at early times, it becomes bi-directional soon after the onset of the Forbush decrease,

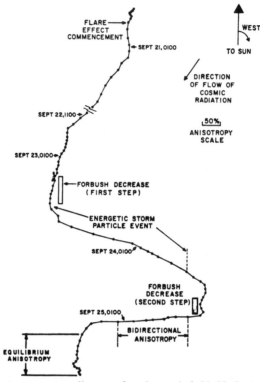

Fig. 5   The anisotropy vector diagram for the period 21–23 September 1966. The typical two-step profile of the Forbush decrease indicated in the diagram is discussed by Rao, McCracken, and Bukata (1967).

and is of the "equilibrium anisotropy" variety at late times. This time sequence is very typical and, in Fig. 5, we present a similar sequence of events (flare, Forbush decrease, etc.) observed in September 1966, for which greater continuity of data acquisition was achieved. This latter event serves as a useful guide in interpreting the phenomena observed during the July events.

3   Phenomena observed during the July Events

3.1   The Non-Equilibrium Anisotropy, 5 July 1966

Figure 4 shows that on 5 July the maximum cosmic-ray flux arrived at the spacecraft from a direction approximately 45° west of the spacecraft–sun line. This observation is consistent with the hypothesis that the cosmic rays were streaming along the lines of force of the interplanetary magnetic field (the typical "garden hose" angle being 45° west). This behaviour is typical of the initial stages of a flare effect (see Fig. 5, the commencement of the cosmic-ray enhancement being at 0300 UT on 21 September), in that the direction of maximum cosmic-ray flux is always aligned with the interplanetary magnetic field vector (parallel, or antiparallel). This situation is indicative of a non-homogeneous distribution of cosmic radiation throughout the solar system, the cosmic radiation flowing along the magnetic lines of force in order to eliminate these inhomogeneities. It has been shown (McCracken, Rao, and Ness 1968) that the cosmic-ray anisotropy direction is very strongly corre-lated with the magnetic field direction during the non-equilibrium anisotropy phase of a cosmic-ray flare effect.

3.2 The Equilibrium Anisotropy

Figure 4 shows that on 10 and 11 July, the cosmic-ray anisotropy was such that the maximum flux was always from the general direction of the sun. A similar behaviour is evident in Fig. 5 after 0500 UT on 25 September, and we find that anisotropies such as these, exhibiting time invariant amplitudes and phases, are commonly observed at late times during a solar flare effect. This species of anisotropy is normally associated with the decay phase of the flare effect, when the cosmic-ray flux is monotonically decreasing with time. It has been suggested (McCracken, Rao, and Bukata 1967) that the equilibrium anisotropy is an indicator of the cosmic radiation being in diffusive equilib-rium in the portion of the solar system accessible (magnetically) to the spacecraft.

The mechanism advanced to explain the equilibrium anisotropy (Rao, McCracken, and Bukata 1967) is that the cosmic radiation is essentially uniformly distributed throughout the solar system, and that it is being swept radially outwards by the solar wind. The cosmic-ray population is therefore moving with a bulk velocity of V_P (the plasma velocity), and consequently an observer in a stationary frame of reference will see an anisotropy of amplitude $(3 + \beta)V_P/V$ (Compton and Getting 1935), where V is the cosmic-ray particle velocity, and β is the exponent of the differential energy spectrum which varies as $E^{-\beta}$. Comparison of the 7.5–45 MeV and 45–90 MeV Pioneer 6 data for 11 July indicates a spectrum varying as $E^{-3.8}$, and this, together with the mean value of 18 per cent for the anisotropy on 11 July, indicates a solar wind velocity of approximately 1100 km s^{-1}.

4 Conclusions

We conclude that the cosmic-ray flare effects observed during 5–15 July were completely typical of other solar flare effects observed during 1965–1966 by the Pioneer 6 and 7 spacecrafts. In particular, the period in question exhibited non-equilibrium (field aligned) anisotropies at early times, followed by bi-directional anisotropies during the minimum of the Forbush decrease on 9 July, and equilibrium (convective removal) anisotropies thereafter. The cosmic-ray anisotropy data indicate that the interplanetary magnetic field was of the typical "Archimedes Spiral" configuration on 5 July, and that the solar wind velocity was approximately 1100 km s^{-1} on 11 July. The approximately simultaneous onset of a large Forbush decrease at the spacecraft and earth on 9 July indicates approximate equality of the plasma disturbance propagation velocity over a range of about 45° in solar longitude.

Acknowledgments

The cosmic-ray detector was developed at the Southwest Center for Advanced Studies, Dallas, Texas. The research was supported by the National Aeronautics and Space Administration under contracts NAS2-1756 and NSR-44-004-043, by a grant from the Indian Atomic Energy Commission, and by funds provided by the Australian Research Grants Committee. The authors are grateful to Mr. W. C. Bartley for help of many kinds during the development, construction and integration of the detector.

References

BARTLEY, W. C., R. P. BUKATA, K. G. MCCRACKEN, and U. R. RAO, 1966, Anisotropic cosmic radiation fluxes of solar origin, *J. Geophys. Res.*, **71**, 3297–3304.

BARTLEY, W. C., K. G. MCCRACKEN, and U. R. RAO, 1967a, The Pioneer VI detector to measure the degree of anistotropy of the cosmic radiation in the energy range 7.5–90 MeV/nucleon, *Rev. Scient. Instrum.*, **38**, 266–272.

—— 1967b, A digital system for accurate time sector division of a spin stabilized vehicle, *Inst. Elect. Electronics Engrs. Trans. Aerospace and Electronic Systems*, **AES 3**, 230–235.

COMPTON, A. H., and I. A. GETTING, 1935, An apparent effect of galactic rotation on the intensity of cosmic rays, *Phys. Rev.*, **47**, 817–821.

MCCRACKEN, K. G., U. R. RAO, and R. P. BUKATA, 1967, Cosmic ray propagation processes, I: A study of the cosmic ray flare effect, *J. Geophys. Res.*, **72**, 4293–4324.

MCCRACKEN, K. G., U. R. RAO, and N. F. NESS, 1968, The inter-relationship of cosmic ray anisotropies and the interplanetary magnetic field, *J. Geophys. Res.*, **73**, 4159–4166.

RAO, U. R., K. G. MCCRACKEN, and R. P. BUKATA, 1967, Cosmic ray propagation processes, II: The energetic storm particle event, *J. Geophys. Res.*, **72**, 4325–4341.

45

The Polar-Cap Absorption on 7–10 July 1966

*Y. Hakura**

NASA–Goddard Space Flight Center, Greenbelt, Maryland, USA

Abstract

The time history of a polar-cap absorption (PCA) on 7–10 July 1966 was analyzed using 16 riometers in the northern polar region and concurrent satellite observations of solar cosmic radiations. The first onset of PCA was noticed at 0120 UT at Shepherd Bay, Canada, which is located 10° from the North Pole, and the slight enhanced ionization of a few tenths of 1 dB covered the whole North Pole region before 0200 UT. On the other hand, auroral zone stations observed the PCA after 0200. The two-stepped onset of the PCA corresponds to the differential arrival of ionizing electrons and protons at the earth, detected by the satellites. The flux of 40 keV electron bursts observed by the satellites Explorer 33 and IMP-3 can explain the first onset of a slight PCA near the geomagnetic pole. The PCA in the polar region marked a maximum of 2.5 dB on 30 MHz at 1300 on 7 July, and then decayed gradually until it went down below 0.3 dB after 2345 on 8 July. The lowest latitude of the PCA during the geomagnetically calm period was some 63° in corrected geomagnetic latitude. After the onset of geomagnetic disturbances, the PCA superposed upon it the auroral zone absorption (AZA) that appeared even in the lower auroral zone.

1 Introduction

The general morphology of polar-cap absorption (PCA) events has been studied extensively by means of riometers, world-wide ionograms, and other

* On leave from Radio Research Laboratories, Tokyo, Japan.

radio propagation techniques, using a number of events that were observed during the last sunspot cycle (Bailey 1964, Obayashi 1964 and papers cited there). The most detailed spatial patterns of PCA events were obtained during the IGY, 1957–1958, when a comprehensive network of ionosphere soundings was in operation (Hakura and Nagai 1964, Hakura 1965). In recent years, artificial satellites have been instrumented appropriately and have detected in space the solar cosmic radiations responsible for the PCA. Comparisons between solar cosmic radiations and riometer absorptions have increased knowledge of spatial and time variations in PCA events (Van Allen, Lin, and Leinbach 1964, Leinbach, Venkatesan, and Parthasarathy 1965, Chivers and Burrows 1966, Reid and Sauer 1967).

The 7–10 July 1966 events constitute one of the typical solar–terrestrial disturbances in the current solar cycle, where more sophisticated observations of the solar cosmic radiations are available. It is believed worth while to analyze the world-wide time history of the PCA and compare the results with the concurrent satellite observations. Special attention will be paid to the onset phase of the PCA in connection with the differential arrival of solar electrons and protons observed by the satellites (Cline and McDonald 1968, Lin and Anderson 1967). Previous analyses of the present PCA event are also reviewed (Imhof *et al.* 1966, Masley and Goedeke 1968).

2 A Solar Flare responsible for the PCA on 7–10 July 1966

The PCA on 7 July 1966 may be correlated with a solar Hα flare of importance 3 observed at 35°N 48°W in the McMath plage region 8362 at 0025 UT. The flare was accompanied by major radio outbursts of Type IV which displayed complex features over a wide frequency range. Figure 1 shows a dynamic spectrum of the outbursts in a frequency interval 200–9400 MHz, inferred from seven single-frequency observations listed in Table 1. The increments of flux density from pre-burst levels (see Table 1) are graded into eight steps shown on the far right of Fig. 1.

Table I   Solar Radio Observatories, Frequencies and Corrected
             Pre-Burst Levels

Observatory	Frequency (MHz)	Corrected Pre-Burst Flux Level
Nagoya, Japan	9400	284
Nagoya, Japan	3750	120
Penticton, Canada	2700	93
Nagoya, Japan	2000	75
Nagoya, Japan	1000	57
Hiraiso, Japan	500	38
Hiraiso, Japan	200	12

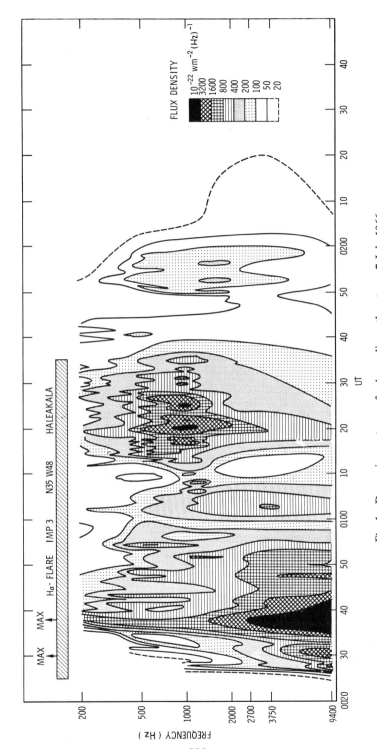

Fig. 1   Dynamic spectrum of solar radio outbursts on 7 July 1966.

339

The outbursts in the present frequency range are characterized by six main peaks that appeared with different peak frequencies in the course of the solar disturbance. The first and second outbursts were observed at 0028 and 0030 UT with their peak intensities at frequencies greater than 9400 MHz. The most outstanding outburst, covering a wide frequency range down to 200 MHz, occurred around 0038 with peak intensity at about 9400 MHz. The second and third outbursts are related to two maxima in the Hα flare shown at the top of Fig. 1, and classified as impulsive microwave bursts. An impulsive microwave burst is ascribed to gyrosynchrotron radiation from energetic electrons created in the flash phase of a flare and gyrating in the sunspot magnetic field. A major part of high-energy electrons stream into the middle chromosphere in which they lose their energy by hard (20–500 keV) X-rays (Winckler 1963). Arnoldy *et al.* (1967) observed a burst of X-rays (10–50 keV) at the time of the impulsive microbursts on 7 July. Cline, Holt,

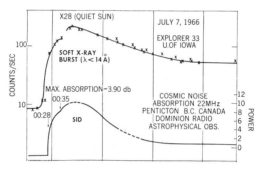

Fig. 2   A soft X-ray burst observed by Explorer 33 (Van Allen and Ness 1967) and a simultaneous SID effect on cosmic-noise intensity observed at Penticton, Canada.

and Hones (1968) using OGO-3 data showed that the impulsive bursts coincide accurately in their commencements and even in detailed features with the hard X-ray burst (≥ 75 keV and ≥ 450 keV).

Figure 2 shows a soft X-ray burst observed by Explorer 33 (Van Allen and Ness 1967) and a simultaneous sudden ionospheric disturbance (SID) effect on cosmic-noise intensity observed at Penticton, Canada. Two-stepped onset times of both the events at 0028 and 0035 correspond to those of the major impulsive microwave bursts.

After the microwave impulsive bursts followed the second phase of outbursts; the fourth, fifth and sixth peaks of radio emission are observed around 0102, 0124, and 0157 respectively in the lower micrometer- and decimeter-wave regions. The Type IV outbursts extend down to the meter-wave region, suggesting the production of 10 keV–1 MeV electrons in the higher corona. It has been statistically established that the Type IV outburst has a close correlation with the onset of a PCA event (Hakura and Goh 1959).

3　Onset Phase of the PCA Event

According to a private communication from G. C. Reid, most Antarctic stations were in darkness during the 7 July event and the absorption was barely noticeable and cannot be measured with any accuracy. Thus, further discussion will be confined to the PCA event observed at northern hemisphere stations.

Information of enhanced ionizations used in the present study were obtained from 16 riometers, 6 additional vertical soundings, and 2 VLF propagation records located in the northern hemisphere. The station names, abbreviations, operating frequencies, and station locations in geographic and corrected geomagnetic coordinates are shown in Table 2. The abbreviated station names and their locations (dots) are shown in geographic coordinates in Fig. 3, where isocorrected latitudes 40°, 50°, 60°, 70°, 80° are expressed by oval-shaped thick lines. All the riometers except at Penticton, Canada, used antennas with a half-power beamwidth of about 60° and operated on a

Table 2　Station Names, Abbreviations, Operating Frequencies, and Station Locations used for the present analysis

Station	Abr.	Freq. (MHz)	Geographic		Corrected Geomagnetic	
			Lat.	Long.	Lat.	Long.
Thule, Greenland	TH	30	76.6°N	291.3°E	86.0°	38.1°
Resolute Bay, Canada	RE†	30 and f_{min}	74.7	265.1	84.3	306.0
Shepherd Bay, Canada	SH	30	68.8	266.6	79.5	321.3
Churchill, Canada	CC	30	58.8	265.8	70.3	325.9
Great White Rv., Canada	GW	30	55.3	282.2	68.2	354.1
Dixon Is., USSR	DX	32	73.5	80.4	67.9	154.7
Fort Yukon, Alaska	FY	30	66.6	214.7	67.1	260.7
Reykjavik, Iceland	RY	20, 30, 40	64.1	338.3	66.5	71.2
Tromsö, Norway	TR	27.6	69.4	19.0	66.0	105.2
College, Alaska	CO	30	64.9	212.2	64.9	260.3
Moosonee, Canada	MS	30(p)	≥51.5	279.3	≥64.6	348.5
Kiruna, Sweden	KR	27.6	67.8	20.5	64.3	104.9
Kotzebue, Alaska	KZ	30	66.7	197.5	64.2	247.8
Healy, Alaska	HY	30	63.8	211.0	63.7	260.2
Ottawa, Canada	OT†	30(p) and f_{min}	≥45.4	284.3	≥58.9	355.7
Penticton, Canada	PE	22	49.5	240.4		
Lycksele, Sweden	LY*	f_{min}	64.6	18.8	61.2	101.4
Kenora, Canada	KE*	f_{min}	49.9	262.6	61.1	323.5
St. John's, Canada	ST*	f_{min}	47.6	307.3	58.3	29.8
Nurmijärvi, Finland	NU*	f_{min}	60.5	24.6	56.6	103.5
Slough, England	SL ⎱	NPM	51.5	359.4		
Maui, Hawaii	MU⎰	26.1 kHz	20.8	203.5		
Payerne, Switz.	PY⎱	NPG	46.8	6.9		
Jim Creek, USA	JC⎰	18.6 kHz	48.2	238.1		

*f_{min} record used completely; † f_{min} record used in part; (p) receiving antenna directed poleward.

frequency near 30 MHz. The absorption values ΔA(dB) were obtained by subtracting the quiet-day variation for each system. When no riometer data are available, absorptions on 30 MHz are estimated from f_{min} values, using an empirical relation

$$\Delta A(\text{dB}) = \tfrac{1}{2}\Delta f_{min} \text{ (MHz)}$$

where Δf_{min} is the deviation of f_{min} from its monthly median.

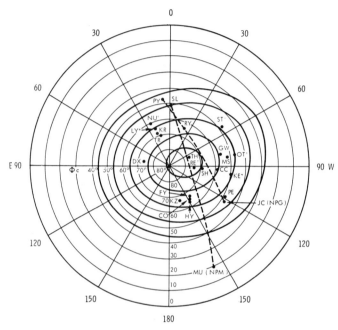

Fig. 3   Locations of ionosphere observatories in the northern hemisphere in geographic coordinates. Oval-shaped thick lines show the corrected geomagnetic latitude in 10° steps. The abbreviations refer to Table 2, where marks * and † indicate that the f_{min} record was used fully and partly, respectively.

Absorptions observed at 11 stations in the time interval 0000 through 0600 UT on 7 July are shown in the lower part of Fig. 4. They are arranged in order of their corrected geomagnetic latitudes which are indicated in parentheses. Following the immediate SID effect which was typically shown by Penticton data (hatched portion), polar stations north of Shepherd Bay marked the onset of a PCA before 0200 UT. The first onset of PCA was observed at 0120 UT at Shepherd Bay which was located 10° from the

---

Fig. 4   Initial phase of PCA on 7 July 1966. Upper figure: latitude dependence of definite PCA onset time, and the SID observed at Penticton (hatched). Lower figures: variations in absorption observed at 11 stations, where definite onset times are indicated by arrows.

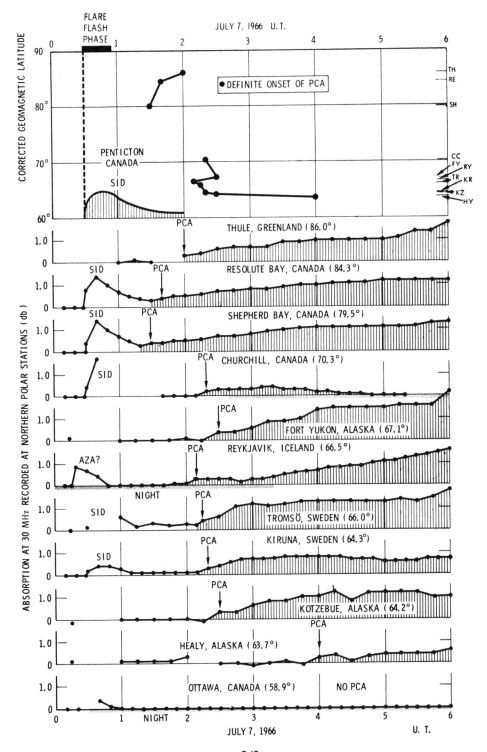

343

North Pole (Masley and Goedeke 1968). However, auroral zone stations including Churchill, Canada (79.5°), and Kotzebue, Alaska (64.2°), observed PCA after 0200 UT. The lowest latitude station of appreciable PCA was Healy, Alaska (63.7°), where a PCA started at about 0400 UT.

Since the absorption recorded by a riometer during a PCA event varies by a factor of about 4 between day and night, a standardized absorption should be used for detailed discussions. However, an onset time could easily be determined except for Moosonee (64.6°) where it was difficult to fix an onset time because of slightness of a PCA (D. H. Jelly, private communication). The latitude dependence of the definite onset of PCA is shown in the upper part of Fig. 4. In spite of the small number of observing points, the general sequence is quite similar to the pattern of the PCA initial phase obtained from the analysis of world-wide f_{min} records during the IGY 1957–1958: that the initial phase of PCA consists of at least three characteristic stages; the first stage is observed as a slightly enhanced ionization near the geomagnetic pole, the second stage as a remarkable development of PCA in the polar cap above 65°, and the third stage as an extension of the enhanced ionization to lower latitude zones (Hakura 1967). It has been suggested that the result is due to differential precipitation of ionizing solar electrons, protons, and α-particles.

Actually, the satellites IMP-3 and Explorer 33 detected a differential invasion of ionizing solar electrons and protons during the initial phase of the July event. According to Cline and McDonald (1968), the IMP-3 observed a 3-MeV electron burst that started at about 0100 UT and lasted about 2 hours. The energy spectrum in the interval 3–10 MeV was expressed by a power law $(kE)^{-5}$. Concurrently with the MeV electrons, a burst of ~ 40 keV electrons was observed by the satellites IMP-3 and Explorer 33 (Lin and Anderson 1967). According to a private communication from Lin, the Explorer 33 observed the onset of the electron burst at about 01 h UT. A flux value of more than 1500 electrons $cm^{-2}\,s^{-1}\,sr^{-1}$ was obtained before about 0200, and it became difficult to detect further time variations in electrons because of considerable proton contributions to the Geiger counter, starting at about 0200 UT. The empirical relationship between the precipitating flux $(cm^{-2}\,s^{-1}\,sr^{-1})$ of $E > 40$ keV electrons and the magnitude of broad beam absorption at 30 MHz could be expressed as

$$A(\mathrm{dB}) = 3.3 \times 10^{-3}[N(>40 \text{ keV})]^{1/2}$$

when the precipitation is isotropic (Parthasarathy *et al.* 1966). Taking the 40-keV electron flux of more than $1500\ cm^{-2}\,s^{-1}\,sr^{-1}$, an estimated absorption is

$$A(\mathrm{dB}) > 1.3 \times 10^{-1}$$

which is comparable with the absorption of a few tenths of 1 dB observed in the pole stations in the first phase of the PCA, at 0120–0200 UT on 7 July.

On the other hand, the satellite IMP-3 observed the onset of 15 ∼ 100 MeV protons only after 0200 UT (Cline and McDonald 1968). Since the energy range of solar protons effective on PCA is 1–100 MeV, the protons invading after 0200 UT explain the second phase of the PCA observed over the whole polar cap. Protons with higher energies were observed before 0200 UT; a ground-level solar proton event ($E_p \sim 2$ GeV) started at about 0100 UT (Carmichael 1968, Ahluwalia *et al.* 1968). At balloon altitudes the integral proton flux ($E_p > 100$ MeV) increased from 0110 UT onward and reached a maximum at 0205 UT (Heristchi *et al.* 1968). However, the maximum proton flux of 2.6 cm^{-2} s^{-1} sr^{-1} observed in this energy range cannot produce any appreciable absorption effect on a 30 MHz riometer, an estimated absorption being of the order of 10^{-4} dB. It is believed that the main part of PCA, i.e. the proton PCA, started at 0200 with the attainment of 15–100 MeV protons.

It has been known that a trans-polar-cap very low frequency (VLF) propagation is a sensitive detector of PCA events (Bates and Albee 1964). During the July event, VLF experiments along two transpolar circuits (broken lines in Fig. 3) were in operation by HRB-Singer Inc. (Imhof *et al.* 1966). Figure 5 shows the phase deviations (middle) and relative amplitude variations

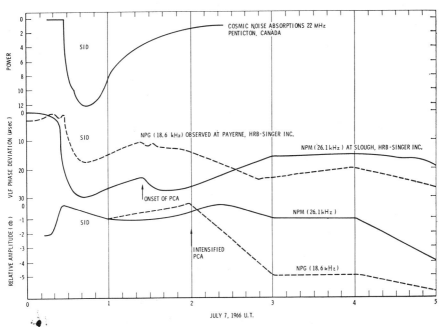

Fig. 5 Initial phase of 7 July 1966 events observed by Penticton riometer (top), VLF phase deviations (middle), and relative amplitudes (bottom) of NPM and NPG signals to Europe (Imhof *et al.* 1966). An SID and two-stepped onset of PCA are clearly seen.

(bottom) of NPG (18.6 kHz) and NPM (26.1 kHz) received in Europe, together with the Penticton riometer (top), in the time interval of 0000 through 0500 UT on 7 July. Concurrently with the Penticton SID, sudden phase anomalies (SPA) were produced over both of the high-latitude VLF paths. At approximately 0120 UT, a second but slower phase advance began on both signals, showing an onset of a slight PCA event. At about 0200 UT the signal strength (bottom) also began to decrease because of intensified PCA. The two-stepped onset pattern in the VLF PCA seems to correspond to that in the riometer PCA discussed above.

4   General View of Absorption Event observed on 7–10 July 1966

Figure 6 shows the time history of cosmic-noise absorptions at Thule (86.0° in corrected geomagnetic latitude), Fort Yukon (67.1°), and Healy, Alaska (63.7°), on 7 through 10 July 1966. Figure 7 shows latitude profiles of 30 MHz absorptions, together with the time variation of geomagnetic activity expressed by planetary Kp indices. The absorption is graded into three ranges as shown in the right top of Fig. 7.

Since Thule is located near the geomagnetic pole and since the event occurred in July when the ionosphere above Thule was continuously sunlit, the time history of the Thule record shows a time variation of solar cosmic-ray flux. Chivers and Burrows (1966) obtained an empirical relation

$$N(1.3 < E < 7 \text{ MeV}) = (2 \times 10^3)A^{2.0}$$

at the South Pole with a 30-MHz riometer during 21 September 1963 events. The PCA at Thule marked a maximum of 2.5 dB at 1300 UT on 7 July, showing that the maximum flux of 1.3–7 MeV protons was some $1.25 \times 10^4 \text{ cm}^{-2} \text{ s}^{-1} \text{ sr}^{-1}$. The PCA then decayed gradually until it went down below 0.3 dB after 2345 UT on 8 July.

The absorption at Fort Yukon (67.1°) showed a typical time variation which is usually seen at the lower edge of the polar cap (Leinbach, Venkatesan, and Parthasarathy 1965). The ratio of absorption Fort Yukon/Thule decreased in the local afternoon on 7 July, but increased after 0000 UT on 8 July along with the enhanced geomagnetic activity. In the pregeomagnetic disturbance period, Healy, Alaska (63.7°), was the lowest latitude station which marked the PCA effect.

At the time of sudden commencement, 2102 UT on 8 July, the auroral zone stations including Churchill (70.3°) and Healy (63.7°) observed a pronounced enhancement of absorption, called the sudden commencement absorption (SCA). Intermittent but outstanding absorptions were observed throughout the geomagnetically active period, especially in the local nighttime of the observatories. The auroral-zone absorption (AZA) is associated with polar geomagnetic disturbances and auroral displays.

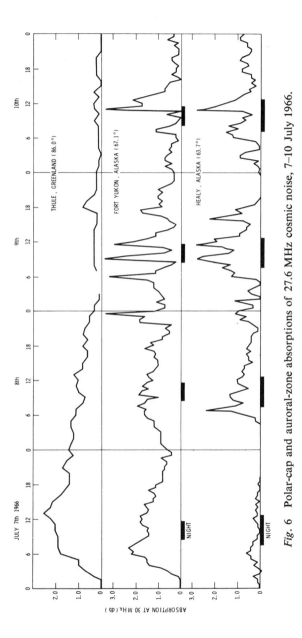

Fig. 6 Polar-cap and auroral-zone absorptions of 27.6 MHz cosmic noise, 7–10 July 1966.

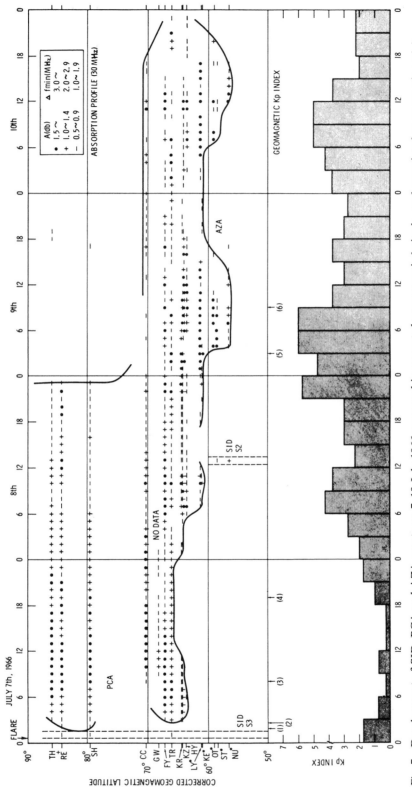

Fig. 7 Development of SID, PCA and AZA events on 7–10 July 1966 expressed in corrected geomagnetic latitude, and associated geomagnetic activity.

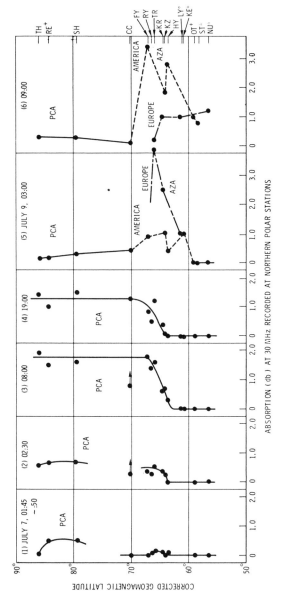

Fig. 8   Latitude profiles of cosmic noise absorptions at 6 stages during PCA and AZA events on 7–9 July 1966.

Figure 8 shows the latitude profiles of cosmic-noise absorptions at six selected stages in the course of the PCA and AZA events. The numbers (1) through (6) correspond to those shown in Fig. 7. These profiles are preliminary and need some correction, since the absorption in the polar-cap edge is subject to a diurnal change in the geomagnetic cut-off as well as to the sunlight effect (Chivers and Burrows 1966). However, these figures give a general idea of time sequence of absorption profiles throughout the event. At 0145 on 7 July (1), an absorption of a few tenths of 1 dB was observed in the pole region, while all riometers above 64.2° observed the PCA at 0230 (2). At 0800 on 7 July (3), the lowest latitude of PCA attained to 63.7°. The broken and chain lines in the profiles (5) at 0300 on 9 July and (6) at 0900 show the auroral zone absorptions in American and European regions respectively.

5 Summary

16 riometers, 6 vertical soundings, and 2 VLF propagation records in the northern polar region were used to analyze the development pattern of a PCA on 7–10 July 1966. The results obtained are summarized as follows:

1. The PCA is attributed to a solar flare of importance 3 observed at 0025 UT on 7 July that was accompanied by a major radio outburst of Type IV.

2. The first onset of PCA was observed at 0120 UT at Shepherd Bay, Canada, which is located 10° from the North Pole, and the slight enhanced ionization of a few tenths of 1 dB covered the whole North Pole region before 0200 UT. On the other hand, auroral zone stations observed the PCA after 0200. The two-stepped onset of the PCA corresponds to the differential arrival of solar electrons and protons at the earth, observed by the satellite IMP-3 (Cline and McDonald 1968). The flux of 40 keV electron bursts, > 1500 electrons $cm^{-2} s^{-1} sr^{-1}$, observed by the same satellite can explain the first onset of a slight PCA near the geomagnetic pole (Lin and Anderson 1967).

3. The PCA in the pole region marked a maximum of 2.5 dB at 1300 on 7 July and then decayed gradually until it went down below 0.3 dB after 2345 on 8 July. The auroral zone stations including Churchill (70.3°) and Healy (63.7°) observed a pronounced SCA.

The lowest latitude of enhanced ionization in the pregeomagnetic storm stage was some 63° in the corrected geomagnetic latitude. After the onset of geomagnetic disturbances, the PCA superposed upon it the AZA that appeared even in the lower auroral zone.

Acknowledgments

The author is most grateful to those in many establishments who collaborated in this subject by providing their useful data and giving valuable comments.

The present work was carried out while the author was a senior post-doctoral resident research associate of the NAS-NAE at the NASA–Goddard Space Flight Center, on leave of absence from the Radio Research Laboratories, Tokyo, Japan. He is grateful to Dr. W. N. Hess, GSFC, for his kind hospitality. His thanks are due to Drs. F. B. McDonald and T. Cline, GSFC, for their discussions and comments.

References

AHLUWALIA, H. S., L. V. SUD, and M. SCHREIER, 1968, The increase in low energy cosmic ray intensity on 7 July 1966, *Ann. IQSY*, this volume, Paper 37.

ARNOLDY, R. L., S. R. KANE, and J. R. WINCKLER, 1967, Energetic solar flare X-rays observed by satellite and their correlation with solar radio and energetic particle emission, *Tech. Rep.* CR-97, University of Minnesota.

BAILEY, D. K., 1964, Polar-cap absorption, *Planet. Space Sci.*, **12**, 495–541.

BATES, H. F., and P. R. ALBEE, 1964, High latitude VLF propagation, *Rep. Geophys. Inst. Univ. Alaska*, UAG-R154.

CARMICHAEL, H., 1968, The ground level solar proton event of 7 July 1966 recorded by neutron monitors, *Ann. IQSY*, this volume, Paper 36.

CHIVERS, H. J. A., and J. R. BURROWS, 1966, Simultaneous satellite and ground-based observations of solar protons, *Planet. Space Sci.*, **14**, 131–142.

CLINE, T. L., S. S. HOLT, and E. W. HONES, JR, 1968, Very high energy solar X-rays observed during the proton event of 7 July 1966, *Ann. IQSY*, this volume, Paper 29.

CLINE, T. L., and F. B. MCDONALD, 1968, Relativistic solar electrons detected during the 7 July 1966 proton flare event, *Ann. IQSY*, this volume, Paper 41.

HAKURA, Y., 1965, Initial phase of the PCA events and compositions of the solar cosmic radiations, *J. Radio Res. Labs Japan*, **12**, 231–273.

—— 1966, Time variations in the solar X-rays producing SID's, *Rep. Ionosph. Space Res. Japan*, **20**, 30–32.

—— 1967, Entry of solar cosmic rays into the polar cap atmosphere, *J. Geophys. Res.*, **72**, 1461–1472.

HAKURA, Y., and T. GOH, 1959, Pre-SC polar cap ionospheric blackout and type IV solar radio outburst, *J. Radio Res. Labs Japan*, **6**, 635–650.

HAKURA, Y., and M. NAGAI, 1964, Synthetic study of severe solar terrestrial disturbances of February 9–12, 1958, *J. Radio Res. Labs Japan*, **11**, 197–249.

HERISTCHI, DJ., J. KANGAS, G. KREMSER, J. P. LEGRAND, P. MASSE, M. PALOUS, G. PFOTZER, W. RIEDLER, and K. WILHELM, 1968, Balloon measurements of solar protons in Northern Scandinavia on 7 July 1966, *Ann. IQSY*, this volume, Paper 38.

IMHOF, G. W., J. M. MUSSER, E. J. OELBERMANN, and C. VOLZ, 1966, Coordinated high-latitude experiments for the simulation of nuclear-burst effects on VLF systems, *Ann. Tech. Rep.* 356-R-8 of HRB-Singer, Inc., State College, Pa., USA.

LEINBACH, H., D. VENKATESAN, and R. PARTHASARATHY, 1965, The influence of geomagnetic activity on polar cap absorption, *Planet. Space Sci.*, **13**, 1075–1095.

LIN, R. P., and K. A. ANDERSON, 1967, Electrons > 40 keV and protons > 500 keV of solar origin, *Solar Phys.*, **1**, 446–464.

MASLEY, A. J., and A. D. GOEDEKE, 1968, The 7 July 1966 solar cosmic ray event, *Ann. IQSY*, this volume, Paper 46.

OBAYASHI, T., 1964, Interaction of solar plasma streams with the outer geomagnetic field, *J. Geophys. Res.*, **69**, 861–867.

PARTHASARATHY, R., F. T. BERKEY, and D. VENKATESAN, 1966, Auroral zone electron flux and its relation to broadbeam radiowave absorption, *Planet. Space Sci.*, **14**, 65–83.

REID, G. C., and H. H. SAUER, 1967, The influence of the geomagnetic tail on low-energy cosmic-ray cutoffs, *J. Geophys. Res.*, **72**, 197–208.

VAN ALLEN, J. A., W. C. LIN, and H. LEINBACH, 1964, On the relation between absolute solar cosmic ray intensity and riometer absorption, *J. Geophys. Res.*, **69**, 4481–4491.
VAN ALLEN, J. A., and N. F. NESS, 1967, Observed particle effects of an interplanetary shock wave on July 8, 1966, *J. Geophys. Res.*, **72**, 935–942.
WINCKLER, J. R., 1963, Energetic X-ray bursts from solar flares, *Proc. Amer. Astr. Soc.–NASA Symposium on the Physics of Solar Flares*, GSFC, NASA-50, pp. 117–129 (NASA, Washington D.C.).

46

The 7 July 1966 Solar Cosmic-Ray Event

A. J. Masley and A. D. Goedeke

Space Sciences Department, Douglas Missile and Space Systems Division, Santa Monica, California, USA

Abstract

Absorption was in progress at 0120 UT on 7 July 1966, when the sudden cosmic-noise absorption (SCNA) was reduced and particle absorption began to dominate. This start time, indicating about a one-hour delay from the flare start time, is in good agreement with satellite observations. The absorption reached a maximum of near 2 dB at 1220 UT on 7 July, decayed steadily to 0.3 dB during the next 36 hours and stayed near this level for several days. The event was observed in continuous daylight at Shepherd Bay while McMurdo was in continuous darkness.

This paper is based on observations with 30 and 50 MHz riometers at the Douglas observatories (80° magnetic latitude). Measured absorption is proportional to the square root of the particle intensity.

I Introduction

The Douglas Antarctic Geophysical Observatory (77°51′S 166°43′E) at McMurdo Sound began operation in February 1962. The magnetically conjugate Arctic observatory (68°49′N 93°26′W) at Shepherd Bay, N.W.T., Canada, began operation in August 1963. These stations, at a magnetic latitude of 80°, are located inside the polar-cap regions, removed poleward from the auroral zones to minimize auroral interference and geomagnetic cut-off effects.

Radio techniques are used which allow effects taking place at altitudes from 30 to 90 kilometers to be observed with ground-based equipment.

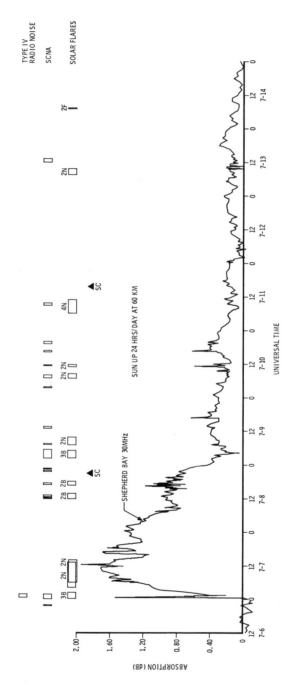

Fig. 1   The 30 MHz riometer absorption at Shepherd Bay is shown for the 7 July 1966 event. The initial sharp increase is sudden cosmic-noise absorption due to solar X-rays. Particle absorption began to dominate at 0120 on 7 July and continued for a week. Shepherd Bay was in continuous sunlight during this period. Related solar and geophysical data are also shown.

Riometers are operated which measure the signal strength of galactic radio noise at 30 and 50 MHz. The ionization produced by the interaction of the charged particles with the atmosphere increases the electron density so that radio waves passing through the ionosphere are significantly absorbed. The absorption of the radio waves at a given frequency is proportional to the square root of the intensity of charged particles for a fixed energy spectrum. This technique is sensitive to protons from about 5 to 100 MeV.

2 Discussion

The 7 July 1966 event was related to a 3B flare (34°N 45°W) beginning at 0022 on 6 July 1966. The event was observed in continuous daylight at Shepherd Bay while McMurdo was in continuous darkness. The Shepherd Bay absorption due to particles, which was already in progress, began to dominate the decreasing sudden cosmic-noise absorption at about 0120 on 7 July (see Fig. 1). This represents the earliest ground-based observation of the onset of this event (Hakura 1968) and is in good agreement with satellite observations.

The absorption profile during the SCNA, due to solar X-rays, follows closely the X-ray observations on Explorer 33 (Van Allen 1968), the start time and the time of maximum intensity agreeing to within a few minutes. The absorption due to particles increased to a maximum of nearly 2 dB at 1220 UT on 7 July 1966 then decayed to 0.3 dB during the next 36 hours and stayed near this level for several days. A maximum absorption of 0.5 dB was observed at McMurdo in continuous darkness. Because the sensitivity of the riometer technique is considerably reduced during darkness, these data are not useful in following the intensity as a function of time during small events such as this one. The absorption due to charged particles observed after 0120 UT at Shepherd Bay is consistent with protons as observed by Kahler and Lin (1968) and Heristchi *et al.* (1968) with a small contribution from electrons.

Acknowledgments

This research was sponsored by the National Science Foundation and the Douglas Independent Research and Development Program.

References

HAKURA, Y., 1968, The polar-cap absorption on 7–10 July 1966, *Ann. IQSY*, this volume, Paper 45.

HERISTCHI, DJ., J. KANGAS, G. KREMSER, J. P. LEGRAND, P. MASSE, M. PALOUS, G. PFOTZER, W. RIEDLER, and K. WILHELM, 1968, Balloon measurements of solar protons in Northern Scandinavia on 7 July 1966, *Ann. IQSY*, this volume, Paper 38.

KAHLER, S. W., and R. P. LIN, 1968, Spatial gradients of energetic protons and electrons observed after the 7 July 1966 solar flare, *Ann. IQSY*, this volume, Paper 42.

VAN ALLEN, J. A., 1968, The solar X-ray flare of 7 July 1966, *Ann. IQSY*, this volume, Paper 30.

47

Very Low Radio Frequency Observations of the Solar Flare and Polar-Cap Absorption Event of 7 July 1966

J. H. Crary and D. D. Crombie

Institute for Telecommunication Sciences and Aeronomy, Environmental Science Services Administration, Boulder, Colorado, USA

Abstract

The solar flare of 7 July 1966 produced normal sudden phase anomalies and amplitude increases on very low frequency (VLF) signals received over sunlit paths, while identifiable effects of the resulting polar-cap event were observed on two northern polar-cap paths, namely Criggion to Anchorage and Seattle to Frankfurt. No effects of comparable magnitude were observed on the polar path from Hawaii to Frankfurt. The presence or absence of disturbances on these and other paths is used to define the area in which the polar-cap event caused VLF effects.

After making assumptions as to the actual length of the Seattle to Frankfurt path which was affected, it was deduced that the mean change in effective height of reflection was between 13 km and 27 km. Although it is not possible to trace the return of the height of reflection to its normal value, the attenuation on this path did not return to normal until about 30 hours after the onset of the polar-cap event.

I Introduction

A solar flare occurred at approximately 0025 UT on 7 July 1966, which was accompanied about an hour later by a small polar-cap event (PCE). The solar flare produced a sudden phase anomaly (SPA) on many paths monitored by or for the Ionospheric Telecommunications Laboratory of the Institute for

Table I   Sudden Phase Anomalies at about 0030 UT, 7 July 1966

Path	f (kHz)	Start (UT)	Max. (UT)	$\Delta\phi$ (cycles)	Ampl. Change (dB)	Remarks
Ottawa–Boulder	80	0030	0043	0.08	+12	End masked by sunset.
Annapolis–Boulder	88	0029	0043	0.11	+6	NSS End masked by sunset.
	21.4	0028	0043	0.06	+3	End masked by sunset.
Hawaii–Boulder	26.1	0026	0042	0.41	+3	NPM
	13.6	0027	0043	0.43	0	Haiku
	10.2		0053	0.47	−6	Haiku
Canal Zone–Boulder	24.0	0029	0033	0.05	?	NBA Confused by sunset.
Seattle–Boulder	18.6	0026	?	?	+6	NPG Evidence of mode interference.
Seattle–New Orleans	18.6	0025	0040	0.16	0	NPG
Seattle–Manila	18.6	0025	0041	0.85	+3	NPG
Hawaii–Anchorage	26.1	0025	0041	0.39	+8	NPM
Ft. Collins–Anchorage	20.0	0026	0042	0.17	+6	WWVL
	19.9	0028	0042	0.19	0	WWVL
Annapolis–Anchorage	21.4	0027	0043	0.2	+2	NSS
Criggion–Frankfurt	19.6	no effects		—	—	GBZ Path in darkness.
Canal Zone–Frankfurt	24.0	no effects		—	—	NBA Path in darkness.
Hawaii–Frankfurt	26.1	0026	0044	0.58	+10	NPM No PCPA.
Seattle–Frankfurt	18.6	0028	0044	0.2	+1	NPG
	18.6	0120	0230	0.5	0	Further slow increase of 0.15 cycle to 0430. Amplitude after 0430 is −3 dB for rest of day.
Criggion–Anchorage	19.6	0022	0047	0.4	+1	GBZ Lost signal lock before PCPA.

Telecommunication Sciences and Aeronomy (ITSA), Boulder, Colorado. Twenty of the observations, for which the actual recordings are available, are summarized in Table 1. The largest phase anomaly was observed on the path from Seattle to Manila. This path, about 10,700 km long, was fully sunlit.

The size of the phase anomaly is a poor indication of the relative effects of the solar flare on the ionosphere because size depends on path length, frequency, and the average zenith angle along the path. The effects of path length and frequency can be eliminated by assuming that the significant effect of a solar flare is to lower the effective height of reflection by an amount Δh which is the same at all illuminated points along the path and by assuming that only one waveguide mode is present. The value of Δh can be estimated then by the methods described by Wait (1962). The assumption that Δh is constant along the path is incorrect of course, but the assumption does yield a reasonable average value of Δh, provided that the sun's zenith angle is not too great.

This procedure has been used for some of the paths of interest for which it is appropriate. The results are shown in Table 2. Although the apparent value of Δh depends significantly on frequency, its mean value is about 11 km, which is quite large. For example, only one out of the 37 flares observed in 1961 (reported by Chilton *et al.* 1964) showed a larger value of Δh.

Table 2   Decrease Δh in Mean Effective Height of Reflection during the Solar Flare

Path	f (kHz)	Path Length (km)	$\Delta\phi$ (cycles)	Δh (km)
Hawaii–Boulder	26.1	5400	0.41	9
	13.6	5400	0.43	13
Hawaii–Anchorage	26.1	4500	0.39	10.5
Seattle–Manila	18.6	10800	0.85	11.4

2   Prompt PCE Effects

Only one path shows phase variations which can be definitely associated with the PCE at 0120 UT following the flare.[1] This is the path from Seattle, Washington (NPG), to Frankfurt, Germany. After the initial SPA maximum was reached the phase began to return to normal. At about 0120 UT, however, a further phase advance commenced (Fig. 1). The phase had advanced about 0.5 cycle by 0230 and there was a further slow increase of 0.15 cycle

[1] In what follows, phase anomalies associated with polar-cap events will be called polar-cap phase anomalies (PCPA).

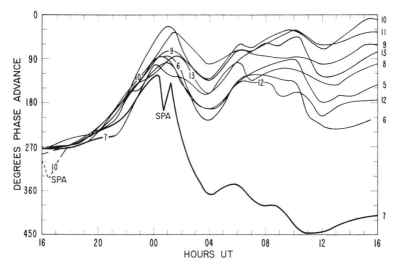

Fig. 1   Relative phase of NPG (Seattle, Wash., 18.6 kHz) at Frankfurt 4 July 1600 UT–
13 July 1800 UT 1966.

until 0400 UT. At about 0200 UT the amplitude decreased significantly and
remained about 6 dB less than usual for the next 36 hours (Fig. 2).

It is significant that another high-latitude path from Hawaii to Frankfurt
showed no phase change which could be attributed to the PCE, although the
solar flare SPA was clearly shown.

Observations on another polar path, from Criggion, Wales, (19.6 kHz) to
Anchorage, Alaska, are also available. These records show the SPA caused
by the flare, but the receiving equipment lost synchronization at about 0110
UT because of a normal decrease in signal level. As a result, it is not definite
that a prompt PCPA occurred on this path, although there is some evidence

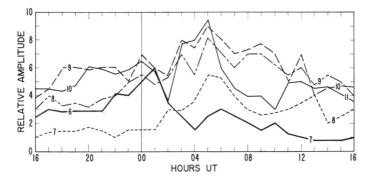

Fig. 2   Relative amplitude of NPG (Seattle, Wash., 18.6 kHz) at Frankfurt between
6 July 1600 UT, and 10 July 1600 UT 1966.

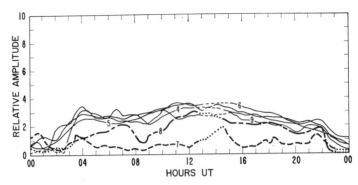

Fig. 3   Relative amplitude of GBZ (Criggion, Wales, 19.6 kHz) at Anchorage, 4–9 July 1966.

that it did. The amplitude of the signal along this path (Fig. 3) appears to have dropped about 10 dB below normal at about 0400 UT and did not recover until 1100 UT the next day. Data[2] for the Criggion–Boulder path indicate that neither the phase nor the amplitude on this path was observably affected.

These paths are shown on a gnomonic projection of the north polar area in Fig. 4 which also shows magnetic L shells for $L \leqslant 7$ and the sunrise line for 0120 UT at D-region heights. It will be seen that the four paths are essentially sunlit within the $L = 3$ shell. Also plotted in Fig. 4 is the path from Annapolis, Maryland (NSS), to Anchorage, Alaska, which shows no effect due to PCE.

These observations define outer limits for the area affected by the PCE. Since the Seattle–Frankfurt path was the most affected, the PCE area must be concentrated close to this path. The fact that the Criggion–Anchorage path was at least somewhat affected, while the Hawaii–Frankfurt path was not affected, indicates that the PCE was south of the latter and was, therefore, concentrated east of the intersection of the two paths. The outer southern and eastern extremities of the affected area are defined by the Criggion–Boulder and Annapolis–Frankfurt paths, which were not significantly affected. Finally, the western limit of the affected area is defined by the Annapolis–Anchorage path.

If the length of the path affected by the PCE is known, the mean change in the effective height of reflection along this part of the path can be estimated by a procedure similar to that mentioned earlier and applied to the SPA. This procedure is admittedly only an approximation and assumes that the height of the ionosphere changes slowly along the path. It neglects the possible generation of higher order modes, but this is considered to be legitimate since such modes would be highly attenuated in the long daytime

[2] Kindly provided by B. E. Blair of the Radio Standards Laboratory, NBS, Boulder, Colorado.

portion of the path. The length of a given path which is affected depends on the shape of the affected area and its position with respect to the path.

For the Seattle–Frankfurt path the maximum length affected by the PCE is that distance between the intersection of this path with the Annapolis–Anchorage path and the receiver at Frankfurt, or approximately 6000 km. If it is assumed, however, that the PCE was circular, then the largest circle which can be drawn between the Hawaii–Frankfurt and Criggion–Boulder paths, enclosing part of the Criggion–Anchorage path, is about 2500 km in diameter and is centered over Greenland. The two estimates, 6000 km and 2500 km, of the length of path affected appear to represent a reasonable

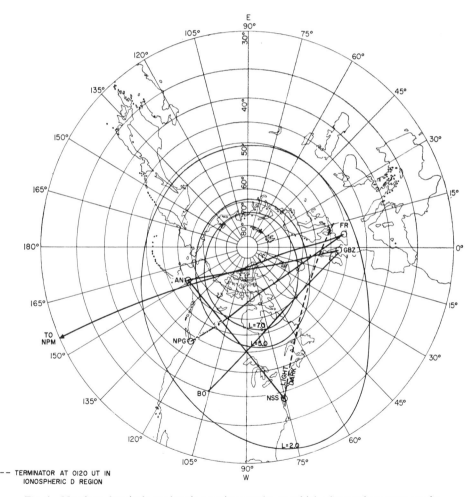

---- TERMINATOR AT 0120 UT IN
     IONOSPHERIC D REGION

Fig. 4   Northern hemisphere showing various paths on which observations were made, and *L* shells.

range of values and will be used to estimate the effective decrease in height of reflection during the PCPA.

Thus, if the length of path affected was 6000 km, the observed PCPA may be produced by a reduction of 13 km in the mean effective height of reflection. If the length of the path affected was only 2500 km, the corresponding reduction in height is about 27 km. Both these estimates assume that the phase angle of the reflection coefficient of the ionosphere does not change during the event.

The assumption that 6000 km of the path was affected is an extreme one and could only result from a fortuitous set of circumstances. On the other hand, 2500 km is possibly an underestimate of the size of the affected area. Because the affected area was in daylight, however, even the smaller decrease in reflection height is rather large, while the larger value seems excessive. Nevertheless, it seems comparable with other PCPA observations which have been summarized by Crombie (1965).

These tentative conclusions on the size and general position of the area causing the observed effects rest heavily on the absence of observed effects on the Hawaii–Frankfurt path. It should be remembered, however, that the signals on that path are appreciably higher in frequency (26.1 kHz) than the other signals (NPG 18.6 kHz, GBZ 19.6 kHz) which show PCPA effects. There is, however, no simple quantitative explanation to indicate that the difference in frequencies is of such importance.

The area affected by the PCE could have been of any shape. Our data suggest only that the affected region lay within the area bounded by the unaffected paths. For example, if the affected area had been extended along the higher value L-shells, it could have produced the observed effects. It could be a ring-shaped area covering a complete L-shell. In this case, it would pass across the Hawaii–Frankfurt and Criggion–Anchorage paths only in two narrow bands. By comparison with the observed effect on the Seattle–Frankfurt path, it is estimated that such a ring could be only about 100–125 km thick without producing phase effects larger than the background effects present on the recorded signals. In addition, this would require that the area just happened to appear along the L-shell which extends along the Seattle–Frankfurt path, but it seems fortuitous. The shape, size, and position of future PCE's could be defined much more closely by making observations on other paths, preferably those oriented N and S. Suitable paths would be those from Seattle, Boulder, and Annapolis to either Thule, Greenland, or Spitzbergen.

Because the data reported here are only for the area between longitudes of 0° and 150°W, it is not known whether corresponding PCE's occurred at other longitudes. If so, the affected areas were not contiguous with those discussed here. Observations on paths crossing the Arctic Ocean would be useful in this context.

3   Antarctic Data

Observations of the transmissions from Criggion, Annapolis, and Seattle were made at Byrd Station, Antarctica, during this event. These data indicate that the paths from Criggion and Annapolis were not affected either during the event or the next day. The records of transmissions from Seattle during this period were not usable. Similar observations were also made at Plateau Station (80°S 40.5°E), but the original data are not yet available.

4   Some Riometer Observations

Some riometer data are available from College and Barter Island, Alaska, from Great Whale River, Manitoba, Canada, and from Thule, Greenland. These indicate (Leinbach, private communication) that the PCA seen by the riometer is essentially uniform over a greater area than that indicated by the VLF data. This may indicate that the two methods of measurement are affected by different parts of the D region, or that the mechanisms responsible for the VLF and riometer effects are entirely different. A difference in the two effects is also noted because the riometer method is relatively insensitive to PCE at night, while the VLF method is sensitive during both night and day (Crombie 1965).

5   Duration of the Polar Cap Events

Unlike the effects of X-rays emitted by solar flares, D-region effects due to PCE's may last for several days. This is the behavior observed during this event, and it is particularly evident in the amplitude records. Figure 2 shows the relative amplitude of the signals from NPG recorded at Frankfurt, from 1600 UT on 6 July to 1600 UT on 11 July. The amplitude drops at about 0100 UT on 7 July and continues 6–8 dB below normal until about 1300 UT on 8 July.

Similarly, the relative amplitude of GBZ recorded at Anchorage, as shown in Fig. 3, is about 10 dB below normal from 0400 UT on 6 July until 1100 UT on 8 July.

The phase record of NPG recorded at Frankfurt for the period 1600 UT on 4 July until 1600 UT on 13 July is shown in Fig. 1. The curves for each day have been superimposed in the region of 16–22 hours UT for easy comparison. The SPA and PCPA on 7 July are readily visible. It might be expected that the recovery from the PCPA could also be seen on these curves. The curves for the first few days after 7 July show an increased upward drift, in comparison with the curves for the 4–6 July, which might represent such a recovery. On 12 July the diurnal drift is back to the value of 5 and 6 July, which could be considered normal. On 13 July, however, it has increased to the value typical of the period following the PCPA. It is not definite whether or not the recovery is shown. The difficulties may be due to the instability of the oscillators at the transmitter and receiver, since the curves in Fig. 1 include these instabilities as well as variations due to propagation. For example, a uniform difference between the two oscillators of 5 in 10^{11} per day would produce an accumulated phase change of about 0.7 cycle in three days. This demonstrates the difficulty of observing a slow recovery. Both the transmitter and receiver had crystal oscillators and it is possible, therefore, that the apparent recovery shown between 7 and 12 July is due to differences in the oscillator frequencies rather than a movement of the ionosphere.

6 Conclusions

On the basis of the observations reported in this paper it may be concluded that

1. The area in which polar-cap VLF effects occurred was quite restricted in size and the outer limits of its size are defined by the observations discussed. Moreover, reasonable deductions can be made about its shape. In particular, the fact that no effects were seen on the Hawaii–Frankfurt path, whereas the almost contiguous path from Criggion to Anchorage was probably affected, indicates that if the affected area was circular in shape then it must have been over or east of Greenland.

2. The absence of observations over the other half of the polar cap precludes any conclusion about affected areas there, except that, if present, they were not contiguous with those discussed.

3. The fact that available riometer observations indicate an essentially uniform effect in an area larger than that indicated by the VLF effects may mean that the two methods are affected by different parts of the D region, or by entirely different mechanisms. This should not be surprising in view of the known difference in the effect of PCE's on VLF propagation and riometer observation at night.

4. The PCPA observed on the NPG–Frankfurt path and the limited extent of the disturbance, suggest that the effective height of reflection of the ionosphere was lowered by as much as 25 km from the previous daytime level. This decrease in height seems excessive and may result from the use of an overly simple model of the lower ionosphere. Such models yield reasonable results for the SPA's due to solar-flare X-rays, however.

5. Although it is not possible to be certain about the duration of the period for which the effective height of reflection was reduced, there is no doubt that the attenuation rate along two paths was greatly increased for about 30 hours after the PCA event. To be certain of observing the slow recovery of phase following a PCPA, oscillator stabilities of about 1 part in 10^{11} per day or better are needed at both transmitter and receiver.

6. Observations along other paths (such as those from Seattle, Boulder, and Annapolis to Thule or Spitzbergen) could be used to define more closely the area affected during a polar-cap event.

Acknowledgments

The data from Anchorage were provided by the Space Disturbance Monitoring Station of ITSA under the supervision of Dr. H. J. A. Chivers. The Frankfurt data were provided by Dr. Eitzenberger of the Battelle Research Institute. The data from Manila were obtained by the Manila Observatory under the supervision of Father Richard A. Miller.

The Antarctic data were recorded for ITSA by Chung Park and R. Sefton of Stanford University at Byrd Station and by R. Flint, of Stanford University, at Plateau Station.

The work was supported in part by the National Science Foundation under Grant GA 232 and by the Advanced Research Project Agency under Order 183.

References

CHILTON, C. J., F. K. STEELE, and D. D. CROMBIE, 1964, An atlas of solar flare effects observed on long VLF paths during 1961, *NBS Tech. Note, No. 210*, 13 March 1964 (National Bureau of Standards, Washington D.C.).

CROMBIE, D. D., 1965, On the use of VLF measurements for obtaining information on the lower ionosphere, *Proc. Inst. Elect. Electron. Engrs*, **53**, 2027–2034.

WAIT, J. R., 1962, Comments on a paper by W. D. Westfall, *J. Geophys. Res.*, **67**, 916–917.

48

Observations of the Interplanetary Magnetic Field, 4–12 July 1966

N. F. Ness and H. E. Taylor*

Laboratory for Space Sciences, NASA–Goddard Space Flight Center, Greenbelt, Maryland, USA

Abstract

Simultaneous interplanetary magnetic field measurements by geo-centric satellites Explorer 33 and IMP-3 have been made of the magneto-hydrodynamic shock wave associated with the sudden commencement storm at 2102 on 8 July 1966. Detailed analysis of the arrival time and orientation of the shock surface and shock normals show that the surface was not perpendicular to the sun–earth line and velocity had decreased so that at 1 AU it was less than 710 km s^{-1} compared with the average velocity of 950 km s^{-1} computed from the transit time from the parent solar flare class 2B on 7 July 1966.

1 Introduction

This note discusses simultaneous observations of the interplanetary magnetic field by three widely separated satellites: Explorers 28, 33, and Pioneer 6 during 4–12 July 1966. These data establish the general macrostructure of the field in cislunar space and include the microstructural feature of the shock wave associated with the geomagnetic sudden commencement (ssc) at 2102 on 8 July 1966. Preliminary results and analyses reveal a remarkable corre-spondence of the measurements by the geocentric satellites Explorers 28 and 33. The very limited data coverage by Pioneer 6 precludes a similar compari-son but is included because the satellite was separated in heliocentric longi-tude by $+44°$ (with respect to the earth). Thus it provides unique data relative

* NAS-NRC Postdoctoral Resident Research Associate.

to the region on the sun (34°N 45°W) where a class 2B flare occurred on 7 July at 0022. Van Allen and Ness (1967) have presented an analysis of the simultaneous energetic particle and magnetic field observations of the interplanetary shock wave detected on 8 July by Explorer 33.

2 Satellites and Instrumentation

The NASA satellite Explorer 28 (IMP-3) was launched on 29 May 1965 into a highly eccentric earth orbit with an initial apogee of approximately 42 R_e (earth radius = 6378.2 km) and an orbital period of 5.8 days. A single monoaxial fluxgate magnetometer on the spin stabilized spacecraft measures the vector magnetic field once every 40.96 seconds with an accuracy to ± 1 gamma. The instrumentation and analysis of the data is similar to that of the earlier IMP-1 (Ness *et al.* 1964) and IMP-2 (Fairfield and Ness 1967). During the period of interest the IMP-3 apogee for orbits 69, 70, and 71 was approximately 90° east of the sun ($\phi_{se} = 90°$). Thus the measurements obtained correspond to a local time of 1800.

The NASA satellite Explorer 33 was launched into an extremely high apogee–high perigee orbit on 1 July 1966. The initial apogee of 70 R_e was beyond the moon (60 R_e) and occurred on 7 July at a solar ecliptic longitude (ϕ_{se}) of 242°, corresponding to a local time of 0400. The orbital period of the satellite is approximately 14 days so that during the period of interest the satellite is at least 40 R_e or more from the earth. A triaxial fluxgate magnetometer on the spin stabilized spacecraft measures the vector magnetic field every 5.12 seconds with an accuracy to ± 0.25 gamma. The NASA–GSFC experiment and initial results detecting the earth's magnetic tail and neutral sheet at distances up to 80 R_e on subsequent orbits has been reported by Ness *et al.* (1967) and Behannon (1968).

The NASA deep space probe Pioneer 6 was launched on 16 December 1965 into a heliocentric orbit with perihelion of 0.81 AU and aphelion of 1.01 AU. A monoaxial fluxgate magnetometer measures the vector magnetic field approximately once every 1.5 seconds (dependent upon telemetry bit rate) with an accuracy to ± 0.25 gamma. The experiment and early results revealing the filamentary nature of the interplanetary magnetic field have been presented by Ness *et al.* (1966). Simultaneous data with IMP-3 (Ness 1966) gave evidence for the spatial uniformity of the interplanetary magnetic field on a cislunar distance scale and also the co-rotation of the interplanetary magnetic field on larger distance scales. During early July 1966 Pioneer 6 was located approximately 44° ahead of the earth in heliocentric longitude and 0.83 AU from the sun. The earth–Pioneer 6 distance ranged between 1.04 and 1.10 $\times$ 10⁸ km while the earth–sun–probe angle ranged between 42.7 and 45.1°. The theoretical co-rotation time for such macrostructure features as sector boundaries (Wilcox and Ness 1965) is 2.8 days assuming a steady solar wind velocity of 400 km s⁻¹.

3 Data Presentation

Each of the experiments on the three satellites measures the magnetic field at a different rate dependent upon the telemetry format and bit rate. The data presented in this note represent hourly averages computed from the original data as follows. The three orthogonal components of the vector field are linearly averaged for 5.46 minutes for Explorer 28 (6 samples), 81.9 seconds for Explorer 33 (16 samples) and 30 seconds for Pioneer 6 (20 samples). The component averages are then used to construct an average field magnitude and direction. If the magnetic field varies appreciably during these basic time intervals then the average field is not necessarily a good representation of the instantaneous field.

The hourly averages are computed in a similar fashion, linearly averaging the average components (10–11 for Explorer 28, 43–44 for Explorer 33, and 120 for Pioneer 6). These are then used to construct an average magnetic field for the hour interval. In addition to the magnitude computed from the component averages, a linear average of the basic magnitudes is also computed. The difference in these two manners of computing magnitudes depends on the level of fluctuations. If the direction changes frequently during the hour, then there will be a large difference between the two magnitudes. If the direction is very steady, then the two magnitudes will be approximately the same.

The data contained in this note illustrate this point very clearly. In the figures both magnitudes are plotted and the region between them is shaded so that the existence of an interval of fluctuating magnetic field is readily detected. During those times the average direction is not always a good representation of the instantaneous field direction.

4 Observations

The magnetic field as observed by Explorer 28 during 4–12 July 1966 is presented in Fig. 1. Since the satellite is in a geocentric orbit, it continuously monitors the interplanetary field only when it is outside the earth's bow shock; 100 per cent interplanetary data is presented as a solid curve. On the basis of a study by Fairfield (1967), the average field in the magnetosheath is found to be closely aligned in direction with the interplanetary field. Thus magnetosheath field directions can be used to indicate the direction of the interplanetary field. Figure 1 includes magnetosheath field directions to provide as continuous a set of measurements as possible with this satellite.

The tendency of the interplanetary field direction to parallel closely the average spiral directions ($\phi_{se} = 135°$, $315°$) and be divided into intervals of constant sense is evident in these data. Two sector boundaries are observed during this period, one corresponding to a change from $-$ to $+$ polarity of field sense ($+$ out of sun) at 1600 on 4 July and an accompanying one from $+$

to — at about 0500 on 8 July. The + sector thus extends in time for about 4 days. The flare occurs at a time when the interplanetary field of 4 gamma at 1 AU is directed along the general Archimedean spiral in a sense away from the sun ($\phi \sim 135°$). The characteristic increased field magnitude following a sector boundary (Wilcox and Ness 1965) is observed where the field rises from 5 gamma to 15 gamma. The ssc associated shock wave produces increased fields at 2100 on 8 July.

The corresponding observations for Explorer 33 are shown in Fig. 2. Here the data coverage is more continuous and provides an improved monitor of the interplanetary field during and following the flare event on 7 July. Note

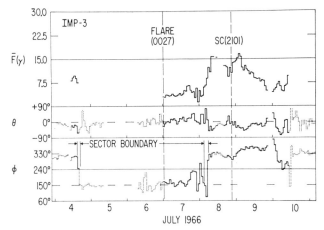

Fig. 1   Geocentric solar ecliptic hourly averages of the interplanetary magnetic field and magnetosheath field (dotted) as observed by Explorer 28 (IMP-3) on orbits number 69, 70, and 71 during 4–12 July 1966. Gaps in data correspond to the satellite being located within the magnetosphere. Dotted portions are magnetosheath measurements.

that the sector boundary (− to +) observed on 4 July in the interplanetary medium by Explorer 28 when 37 R_e east of the earth–sun line is clearly observed in the magnetosheath by Explorer 33 while it is 60 R_e west of the sun–earth line. Fluctuating fields are observed near the sector boundary and following the shock wave and are identified by the large differences (up to 5 gamma) in the two magnitudes presented. In general all the macrostructural features observed by Explorer 28 are simultaneously detected by Explorer 33. Indeed a direct overlay of Figs. 1 and 2 reveals a remarkable agreement to within a gamma in magnitude and 5–10° in direction at most times. The agreement of the field in these data shows that the interplanetary magnetic field is generally uniform on cislunar distance scales, i.e. < 0.01 AU. However, in the case of microstructural features such as the shock wave observed at 8 July 0210 there appear to be significant differences, as will be discussed shortly.

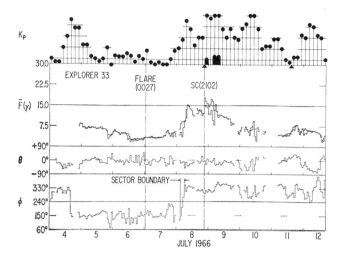

Fig. 2   Geocentric solar ecliptic hourly averages of the interplanetary magnetic field as observed by Explorer 33 on orbit number 1 during 5–12 July 1966. Gaps in data correspond to poor quality data reception. Dotted portions are magneto-sheath measurements. *Kp* is plotted at the top.

The limited data obtained by Pioneer 6 are presented in Fig. 3. Unfortu-nately the telemetry acquisition by DSIF ground stations at this time was very poor, and extended data gaps exist. This precludes any direct comparison of the macrostructural features of sectors. From the data it appears that a sector boundary (from − to +) is observed on 9 July at about 1600. How-ever, the delay time for co-rotation of a stationary sector pattern from the

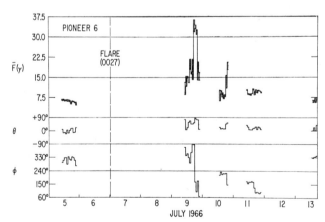

Fig. 3   Spacecraft-centered solar ecliptic hourly averages of the interplanetary magnetic field as observed intermittently by the heliocentric satellite Pioneer 6 at about 1.05×10^8 km distance from the earth during 5–12 July 1966. Gaps in data correspond to failure of terrestrial ground antenna stations to receive the transmitted telemetry signal.

earth to Pioneer 6 is about 3 days dependent upon solar wind velocity. This yields a predicted sector boundary at 7 July 1600. The extended 3-day data gap in Pioneer 6 includes this time ± 1.5 days. The nature of the apparent sector boundary, as analyzed in a finer time scale for Pioneer 6, shows that there appear to be several filaments close to the boundary because the field switches polarity back and forth (from $+$ to $-$ and $-$ to $+$) several times. Since θ is very large and ϕ is far from the ideal spiral angles of $130°$ and $310°$, this may not be a real sector boundary but only a complex interplanetary structure.

5   The Interplanetary Shock

The shock wave associated with the sudden commencement (ssc) on earth at 2102 on 8 July was observed at IMP-3 and Explorer 33 simultaneously (within the resolution of the instruments). The actual times were: IMP-3, 2106 ± 20.5 seconds; Explorer 33, 2105.42 ± 6 seconds. Thus at that time the line between the two satellites lay in the plane of the shock surface. The geometry is shown in Fig. 4.

The observed field changes were essentially identical at the two satellites. The magnitude discontinuously increased from 12 gamma to 21 gamma. The directional changes were relatively small, being from $\theta = -6°$, $\phi = 305°$ to

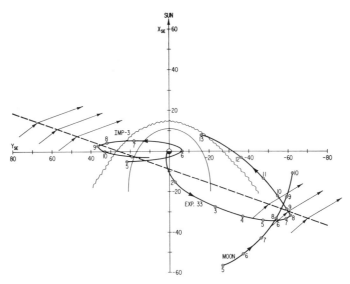

Fig. 4   Projection on the ecliptic plane of trajectories of Explorers 28 and 33 during early July 1966 and average magnetopause and shock wave positions as observed by Explorer 28. Superimposed are the pre- and post-shock wave interplanetary magnetic field directions and the trace of the shock-wave surface associated with the geomagnetic sudden commencement storm beginning at 8 July 2102.

$\theta = 0°$, $\phi = 293°$ for IMP-3, and from $\theta = -10°$, $\phi = 310°$ to $\theta = -18°$, $\phi = 300°$ for Explorer 33.

Using the fact that the component of the field vector **B** normal to the discontinuity surface must be conserved so that the change vector, $\Delta\mathbf{B}(=\mathbf{B}_1 - \mathbf{B}_2)$, must also lie in the plane of the discontinuity, we can calculate the surface normal. The results in geocentric solar ecliptic coordinates are as follows: IMP-3, $\theta = +16°$, $\phi = 160°$; Explorer 33, $\theta = -47°$, $\phi = 163°$. Normals computed using the coplanarity theorem (valid in the case of a true shock wave) give similar results: IMP-3, $\theta = 24°$, $\phi = 158°$; Explorer 33, $\theta = -27°$, $\phi = 182°$. The discrepancy in θ appears to be real and may be a consequence

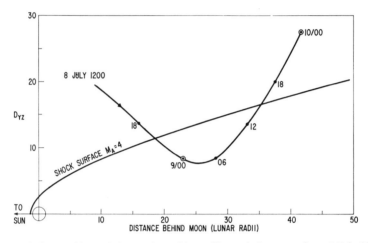

Fig. 5   Relative position of the Explorer 33 satellite and the moon from 8 July 1200 to 10 July 0000 during which time the ssc-associated shock wave was observed. A theoretical bow shock wave trace for an Alfvénic Mach Number (M_A) = 4 is included for comparison. The quantity D_{YZ} represents the distance, measured in lunar radii, of the satellite to the extended moon–sun line.

of the fact that Explorer 33 was located behind the moon relative to the sun (see Fig. 5). A negative change in the latitude angle of the normal is what would be expected if the shock motion were impeded by the presence of the moon since Explorer 33 is 9.4 R_m (R_m = 1738 km) "above" the moon. (Its position relative to the moon in selenocentric solar ecliptic coordinates is $X_{sse} = -19.6\ R_m$, $Y_{sse} = -5.1\ R_m$, $Z_{sse} = +9.4\ R_m$.)

A knowledge of the orientation of the shock then allows a refined calculation of its velocity in the vicinity of the earth. If it is assumed that the onset time of the ssc at the earth corresponded to the passage of the shock at the earth the velocity is

$$v' = \frac{5.4 \times 10^4 \text{ km}}{210 \text{ s}} = 250 \pm 40 \text{ km s}^{-1}.$$

Because this is less than the solar wind velocity, it appears that the propagation velocities through the magnetosphere and magnetosheath are significantly different from the interplanetary value. An upper limit on the velocity may be estimated by assuming that the onset time of the ssc at earth corresponded to the arrival of the shock at the bow shock. This assumption yields

$$v < \frac{1.5 \times 10^5 \text{ km}}{210 \text{ s}} = 710 \pm 50 \text{ km s}^{-1}$$

In any event, the velocity of the shock by the time it reaches the earth is clearly less than the average velocity of the shock out from the sun which was 950 km s^{-1} (see Van Allen and Ness 1967). A knowledge of plasma velocities and densities on both sides of the shock would enable one to calculate the shock velocity unambiguously.

The most prominent event which we can tentatively identify as a shock in the Pioneer 6 records occurred at 1822 on 10 July. At this time the field magnitude increased from 9 gamma to 22 gamma and the direction changed by about 10° from $\theta = 48°$, $\phi = 270°$ to $\theta = 41°$, $\phi = 61°$ in spacecraft-centered solar ecliptic coordinates. The outward shock normal calculated using the coplanarity theorem was $\theta = 40°$, $\phi = 204°$. It is not clear whether this shock was associated with the flare of 7 July or not. It is of interest to note that, viewed from Pioneer, this flare was located less than 5° from the central meridian of the sun. Although there were no other flares of comparable (or greater) importance observed during the days from 7 through 10 July, it is not impossible that Pioneer observed the effects of flares invisible to observers on the earth, since it is separated significantly in heliocentric longitude.

6 Summary and Conclusions

During the period of 4 to 12 July 1966, two sector boundaries and a flare associated shock wave were observed by the magnetometers on IMP-3, Explorer 33 and Pioneer 6. In the preceding 27 days, IMP-3 measured two other sector boundaries so that the interplanetary sector structure at the time of the flare on 7 July can be deduced to be as shown in Fig. 6 (400 km s^{-1} steady solar wind is assumed). There were four distinct sectors with sizes 1/7, 2/7, 2/7, 2/7 solar rotation as found in the earlier study by Wilcox and Ness (1965).

The flare apparently occurred near the + to − sector boundary which passed the earth on 8 July. A possible configuration of the shock generated by the flare is sketched in Fig. 6b. This sketch conforms with the shock normals deduced from the measured fields both at IMP-3 and Explorer 33 near earth and also at Pioneer 6. Although the gaps in the data coverage on Pioneer preclude an unambiguous association of the 10 July shock at Pioneer 6 with the 8 July ssc at earth, such an association seems plausible. This then

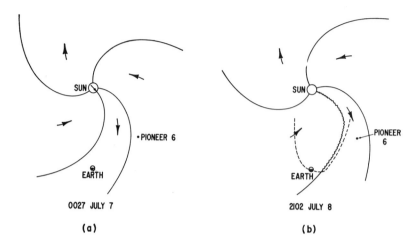

Fig. 6   The interplanetary sector structure:
(*a*) The interplanetary sector structure at the time of the 7 July flare as deduced from the preceding 27 days of IMP-3 measurements. The longitude of the flare on the sun is marked by an arrow.
(*b*) A possible configuration of the interplanetary shock (dashed curve) and sector structure at the time of the 8 July ssc at the earth. The sector boundary is shown distorted in the way one might expect following a sudden increase in a localized area of solar wind flux (both density and velocity).

implies that the shock propagated more rapidly out along the spiral magnetic field (and the sector boundary) than transverse to it. It is hoped that the reason for this behavior will become clear in future studies when both the plasma and the magnetic field data can be studied together.

References

BEHANNON, K. W., 1968, Mapping of the earth's bow shock and magnetic tail by Explorer 33, *J. Geophys. Res.*, **73**, 907–930.

FAIRFIELD, D. H., 1967, The ordered field of the magnetosheath, *J. Geophys. Res.*, **72**, 5865–5877.

FAIRFIELD, D. H., and N. F. NESS, 1967, Magnetic field measurements with the IMP-2 Satellite, *J. Geophys. Res.*, **72**, 2379–2402.

NESS, N. F., 1966, Simultaneous measurements of the interplanetary magnetic field, *J. Geophys. Res.*, **71**, 3315–3318.

NESS, N. F., K. W. BEHANNON, S. C. CANTARANO, and C. S. SCEARCE, 1967, Observations of the earth's magnetic tail and neutral sheet at 510,000 km by Explorer 33, *J. Geophys. Res.*, **72**, 927–933.

NESS, N. F., C. S. SCEARCE, and S. C. CANTARANO, 1966, Preliminary results from the Pioneer 6 Magnetic Field Experiment, *J. Geophys. Res.*, **71**, 3305–3313.

NESS, N. F., C. S. SCEARCE, and J. B. SEEK, 1964, Initial results of the IMP-1 magnetic field experiment, *J. Geophys. Res.*, **69**, 3531–3569.

VAN ALLEN, J. A., and N. F. NESS, 1967, Observed particle effects of an interplanetary shock wave on July 8, 1966, *J. Geophys. Res.*, **72**, 934–943.

WILCOX, J. M., and N. F. NESS, 1965, A quasi-stationary co-rotating structure in the interplanetary medium, *J. Geophys. Res.*, **70**, 5793–5806.

49

Observed Particle Effects of an Interplanetary Shock Wave on 8 July 1966

J. A. Van Allen* and N. F. Ness†
* University of Iowa, Iowa City, Iowa, USA
† NASA–Goddard Space Flight Center, Greenbelt, Maryland, USA

Abstract

"At 2106 UT on 8 July 1966, a distinctive, discontinuous drop in the intensities of solar protons $E_p \sim 0.5$ MeV was observed by Explorer 33 in interplanetary space at 187,000 km in the antisolar direction from the earth. The protons had been emitted by the sun in a flare whose onset time was 0027 UT on 7 July. The intensity drop is attributed to the effects of an interplanetary shock wave whose detailed structure was observed by a triaxial flux gate magnetometer on the same satellite."

Published in full in *J. Geophys. Res.*, 1967, **72**, 935–942.

50

The Forbush Decrease associated with the Proton Event of 7 July 1966 as recorded by Neutron Monitors

H. Carmichael

Deep River Laboratory, Atomic Energy of Canada, Ltd., Chalk River, Ontario, Canada

Abstract

Observations of cosmic-ray intensity variations in different directions in space were made by neutron monitors at a number of stations, and are presented graphically. The two north- and south-pointing stations showed a 3 per cent intensity decrease almost simultaneously; decreases at other stations were not simultaneous indicating anisotropic flux.

Observations were contributed by 34 neutron monitor stations (for graphs see Carmichael 1968, this volume, Paper 36). The variations of galactic cosmic radiation in July 1966 are very complex, indicating a changeable and highly anisotropic flux. At the two north- and south-pointing stations the intensity decreased about 3 per cent in 3 hours starting at 2300 UT at Alert and at 2400 UT at McMurdo on 8 July. This may be considered to be the classic Forbush decrease. Most of the other stations look nearly in the plane of the ecliptic and they did not experience a simultaneous decrease. Some had a transient decrease starting about 0600 UT on 8 July followed by a main decrease starting at 0600 UT on 9 July. The variations in ecliptic directions in space as a function of time are depicted graphically and related to the earth–sun direction in Fig. 1.

Acknowledgment

We thank Jon Ables, Dallas, for the basic computer program and John Steljes, Deep River, for the addition of the contour map and the isometric diagram.

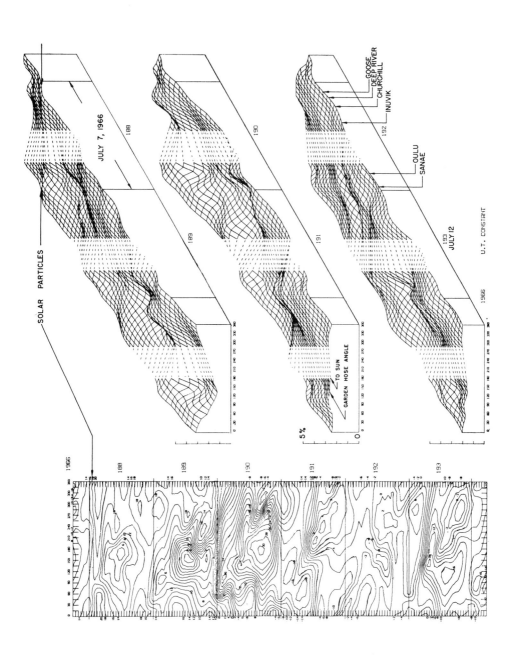

51

Observations of the Interplanetary Plasma subsequent to the 7 July 1966 Proton Flare

A. J. Lazarus and J. H. Binsack

Department of Physics and Laboratory for Nuclear Science, Massachusetts Institute of Technology, Cambridge, Massachusetts, USA

Abstract

Changes in plasma conditions subsequent to the 7 July 1966 flare were monitored by detectors on the space probe Pioneer 6 and on the earth satellite Explorer 33. During the period of observations, Pioneer 6 was located 0.84 AU from the sun at a heliocentric longitude of 45° relative to earth. Thus, the 7 July flare was close to central meridian for Pioneer 6. Explorer 33 was beyond the bow shock, and monitored interplanetary conditions in the vicinity of the earth. A comparison is made of the changes in plasma properties observed on these two satellites during the post-flare period.

1 Introduction

In this note we report preliminary results from observations of the interplanetary plasma during a time period that includes the class 2 solar flare of 7 July 1966. The plasma conditions were measured by two spacecraft that were widely separated in solar longitude: Explorer 33, which was in the interplanetary medium in the vicinity of the earth, and Pioneer 6, which was approximately 45° to the west as well as being closer to the sun. Figure 1 shows the relative positions of the two spacecraft at the time of the flare. The 7 July flare occurred 48° west of central meridian as viewed from the earth and therefore was almost at central meridian as seen by Pioneer 6. Also shown in Fig. 1 is a magnetic field sector boundary which will play an important role in our later discussion.

378

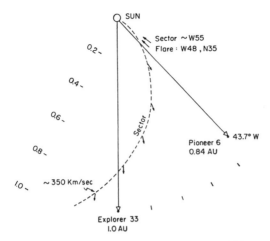

Fig. 1   The relative ecliptic plane positions of Explorer 33 and Pioneer 6 at the time of the 7 July flare. A magnetic field sector boundary is shown based on observations of solar wind speeds at Explorer 33 at the time the boundary passed that spacecraft. The outward radial motion of the boundary is indicated at arrows.

The instruments used to measure the plasma were of the M.I.T. Faraday cup type and have been described in detail by Lazarus, Bridge, and Davis (1966).

2   Explorer 33 Measurements

Figure 2 shows the position of Explorer 33 with respect to the earth. Throughout the time interval discussed in this paper, Explorer 33 was outside the earth's bow shock, and we shall assume that the plasma parameters it measured were characteristic of the interplanetary solar wind. There is a chance that the moon may have had some influence on the plasma, but we shall tentatively assume that it did not.

Hourly averages of plasma parameters as measured by Explorer 33 in the period from 6 through 12 July are shown in Fig. 3. The main features which we wish to point out are that (*a*) the bulk velocity remains relatively constant until it takes a sudden jump near the time of a sudden commencement (as observed on the earth) on 8 July, (*b*) after the velocity does increase it remains at a high value for about three days, and (*c*) there is a period of high density on 8 July which we attribute to the passage of a magnetic sector boundary (Ness and Taylor 1968).

Figure 4 shows the data in more detail for the period we wish to discuss. Note again the period of high density. The magnetic field data of Ness and Taylor (1968) show that a sector boundary passed by the Explorer 33 spacecraft during the period from 0400 to 0740 on 8 July. During the passage of the boundary the field direction (which had been along the spiral direction

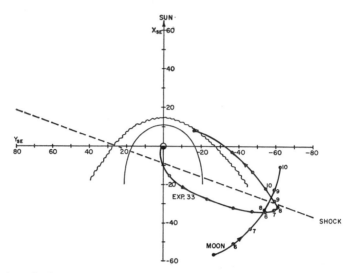

Fig. 2   A projection on to the ecliptic plane of the orbit of Explorer 33 and the moon. Numbers on the orbits indicate dates in July 1966. The trace of the shock-wave surface determined by Ness and Taylor (1968) is indicated by a dashed line. The reader is referred to their paper, from which this figure is taken.

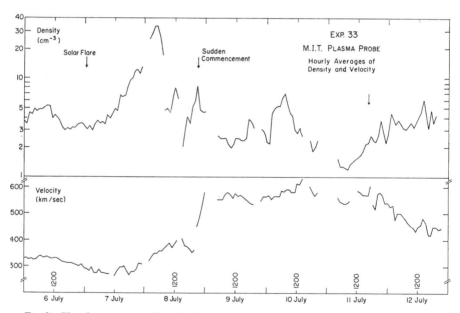

Fig. 3   Hourly averages of preliminary values of plasma parameters measured at Explorer 33. The large density on 8 July is probably associated with the passage of a magnetic sector boundary. The velocity increase on 8 July corresponds to the passage of the shock. Note that the solar wind velocity stays high for several days afterwards.

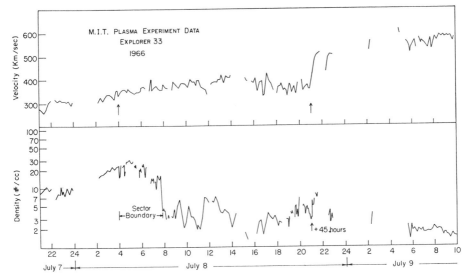

Fig. 4   Detailed plot of plasma data from Explorer 33. The vertical arrow at 2106 on
8 July indicates the time of the shock passage, 45 hours after the optical observation of the flare.

pointing *away* from the sun) varied considerably. Detailed magnetic field
data show that the abrupt drop in density which occurred at about 0740
coincided with the last major change in field direction. After that time, the
field was generally along the spiral direction but pointing *toward* the sun.
Note that no significant change in velocity was observed.

A large increase in velocity occurred at 8 July 2106 UT and was coincident
with an increase of density. This jump in velocity and density occurred at the
time of the shock passage reported by Van Allen and Ness (1967) and is
roughly 45 hours after the occurrence of the flare. The detailed changes in
plasma parameters are shown in Table 1, which also includes data from
Pioneer 6 which will be discussed shortly. In Table 1 we have also included

Table I   Approximate Plasma Parameters at Shocks

	Velocity (km s^{-1})		Density (particles cm^{-3})		Shock Speed (km s^{-1})
	Before	After	Before	After	
Explorer 33					
8 July 2106 UT	~350	~550	~3	~6	~750
Pioneer 6					
9 July 0940 UT	~340	~460	~12	~70	~500
10 July ~1800 UT	~500	~700	~2	~5	~830

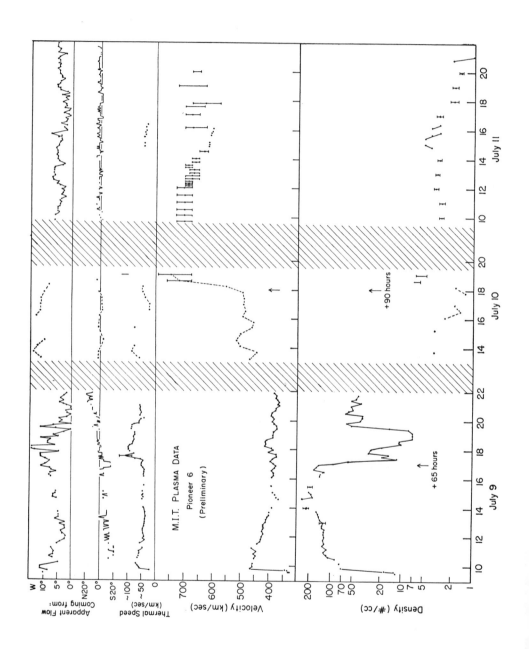

M.I.T. PLASMA DATA
Pioneer 6
(Preliminary)

estimates of the shock speed obtained by demanding continuity of mass flow across the shock. In all cases we assumed that the shock normal lay in the ecliptic along a radial line from the sun.

The sudden commencement associated with the Explorer 33 shock observation was observed at 2102 UT on the earth. Ness and Taylor report simultaneous observation of the shock by IMP-3 and Explorer 33 and thereby establish the trace of the shock on the ecliptic plane as shown in Fig. 2. If we use that trace and in addition assume that the shock front normal lies in the ecliptic plane, the shock normal is 20° to a radial line. Our estimate of shock speed is then reduced to approximately 700 km s^{-1}, which is consistent with the estimate of Ness and Taylor. It must be pointed out that our estimates of velocities are preliminary, and although the relative velocities are reasonably good, the absolute values may be low by as much as 20 per cent.

Thus, our tentative interpretation of the solar-wind parameter changes during the period shown in Fig. 3 is as follows: (*a*) the initial increasing density during the late hours of 7 July and early hours of 8 July is probably primarily associated with the passage of the magnetic sector boundary rather than being related to the flare; such increases in density are not unusual (Wilcox and Ness 1965) although the sharp drop in density is unusual; (*b*) the jump in velocity and density at 2106 UT is a moderate shock; (*c*) the high velocity plasma following the shock is probably the "pusher" gas emitted by the flare itself.

3   Pioneer 6 Observations

The Pioneer 6 plasma instrument measures the positive ion energy spectrum from approximately 100 to 9500 eV in 30 seconds. The spectrum is then stored and transmitted at a data rate chosen by command from the receiving station. Thus the data points represent a measurement taken in a relatively short time, but the time between spectra may be as long as 20 minutes.

The plasma parameters determined at Pioneer 6 are shown in Fig. 5. The spacecraft was tracked irregularly, and no data are available from the time of the optical observation of the flare until 9 July 0935 UT. On 9 July one spectrum is transmitted every 5 minutes.

Fig. 5   Plasma data observed from Pioneer 6. The cross-hatched areas are times during which no data are available. The lines connecting the data points are linear interpolations and are dashed on 10 July to indicate the long time between measurements. The last data points on 10 July were obtained by hand-processing of fractional spectra, and error bars are included to show the uncertainty in the parameters. On 11 July the plasma is relatively cold and falls almost completely into one energy channel of the detector. The thermal speeds are most probable speeds assuming an isotropic, Maxwellian velocity distribution in a frame of reference moving with the plasma. Angular measurements north and south of the ecliptic plane are roughly quantized to 5° intervals. Angular measurements in the ecliptic are uncertain within ±1°. No correction for aberration has been made.

The first two spectra on 9 July indicate a plasma of moderate density and low velocity. Then a dramatic rise in both velocity and density takes place. (The changes in plasma parameters are given in Table 1.) A period of extremely high density follows and is terminated by a sharp drop in density, approximately 65 hours after the sighting of the optical flare. Other abrupt changes in density are clearly evident although the velocity remains nearly constant, implying passage of contact surfaces rather than shocks. The period of fairly high density continues until the end of the tracking period. When tracking is again resumed on 10 July, the velocity has increased and the density is low. (The data rate is lower on this day and a spectrum is transmitted only every 20 minutes). The last two spectra of the day (approximately 90 hours after the optical flare) show a sudden rise in both density and velocity. The velocity is still at its high value when tracking resumes on 11 July and remains at a high level throughout that tracking period.

Thus we tentatively interpret the Pioneer 6 observations as follows: (a) the initial rise on 9 July appears to be a strong shock; (b) the large variations in density during the remainder of the day are not accompanied by velocity changes and would appear to be contact surfaces; (c) the rise in density and velocity on 10 July appears to be a weaker shock than that of 7 July, and the event appears to represent the arrival of flare particles.

4 Discussion

Other than the details of the shocks themselves, which will have to await more careful study, the intriguing question is whether the shock observed on Pioneer 6, 90 hours after the optical flare, could be associated with the observations at Explorer 33, 45 hours after the optical flare. The flare is on central meridian for Pioneer 6 and the spacecraft is closer to the sun; the flare material should have arrived well before it did at the earth. But the fact that the velocity observed at Pioneer 6 became large only after 10 July, combined with the long period of observation of high-velocity plasma after the shock of 8 July at Explorer 33, tends to argue that the flare material was not missed because of the poor tracking coverage.

A short period of magnetic field observation before the strong shock on 9 July shows that the field was pointing along the spiral direction *away* from the sun (Taylor, private communication). Thus it is consistent with Explorer 33 observations *before* the passage of the sector boundary. After the period of high density, the field appears to point away from the sun (Ness and Taylor 1968) and is *not* consistent with conditions after the shock passage seen on Explorer 33.

If the various features arrived at Pioneer 6 by co-rotation, they should be delayed by approximately 70 hours from those seen on Explorer 33. The time delay for the high-velocity plasma was 45 hours. Thus even *lower* values of bulk velocity would be needed to explain the results.

Referring to Fig. 1, it would appear possible that the resolution of the problem might be along the following general lines: The flare material was able to travel relatively freely to Explorer 33, perhaps pushing on the denser region of plasma only near 1 AU. In order to reach Pioneer 6 the situation was quite different. The flare particles were forced to push on the denser plasma contained in the sector boundary. A shock was formed which arrived at Pioneer 6 in the forefront of the dense material. The flare particles, delayed by the interaction with the dense plasma in the sector boundary did not arrive until 10 July.

An additional intriguing change in plasma characteristics observed at Pioneer 6 occurred on 11 July. The proton component was relatively cold and the alpha-particle component appears clearly separated. During that day the number density ratio of alpha particles to protons was approximately 0.12, an unusually high value. Unfortunately the Explorer 33 instrument did not have sufficient energy range to detect alpha particles when the velocity was high, but we hope that we shall be able to look at this aspect in data from other flares.

Acknowledgments

This work has been supported in part by the National Aeronautics and Space Administration under Contract NAS 2-3793 administered by the Ames Research Center.

References

LAZARUS, A. J., H. S. BRIDGE, and J. DAVIS, 1966, Preliminary results from the Pioneer 6 M.I.T. plasma experiment, *J. Geophys. Res.*, **71**, 3787–3790.

NESS, N. F., and H. E. TAYLOR, 1968, Observations of the interplanetary magnetic field 4–12 July 1966, *Ann. IQSY*, this volume, Paper 48.

VAN ALLEN, J. A., and N. F. NESS, 1967, Observed particle effects of an interplanetary shock wave on July 8, 1966, *J. Geophys. Res.*, **72**, 935–942.

WILCOX, J. M., and N. F. NESS, 1965, Quasi-stationary corotating structure in the interplanetary medium, *J. Geophys. Res.*, **70**, 5793–5805.

52

Perturbations décelées dans la magnétosphère, au moyen des sifflements radioélectriques, à la suite de l'événement à proton du 7 juillet 1966

Y. Corcuff

Laboratoire de Physique de la Haute Atmosphère, Faculté des Sciences de Poitiers, France

Sommaire

L'analyse des sifflements reçus aux moyennes latitudes et à Byrd Station, en Antarctique, du 6 au 14 juillet 1966, fournit quelques informations magnétosphériques. Un mouvement important de la plasmapause vers la terre se produit le 8 juillet entre 02 et 14 TU: la distance géocentrique de cette région de transition voisine de 5,5 R_e les 6 et 7 juillet, n'est que de 3 à 4 R_e du 9 au 14 juillet. La densité électronique de la plasmasphère thermique, partie de la magnétosphère limitée vers l'extérieur par la plasmapause, tend à augmenter dans la nuit du 8 au 9 juillet. Cette contraction de la plasmasphère, qui semble précéder l'orage magnétique débutant le 8 juillet à 2102 TU, a également été mise en évidence par le satellite OGO-3 le 9 juillet.

L'étude des sifflements radioélectriques a montré, jusqu'ici, que la densité électronique N de la magnétosphère peut varier considérablement au cours d'un orage magnétique dans des proportions très variables avec l'intensité de l'orage et l'altitude géocentrique (Carpenter 1963a, Corcuff 1965). A celles comprises entre 2 et 2,5 R_e dans le plan équatorial, sondées par les sifflements reçus à Poitiers, N diminue souvent dans un rapport de 2 à 9 au cours des orages les plus intenses; pour d'autres, de moindre intensité, N est inchangé ou tend à augmenter.

Bien que les sifflements enregistrés à Poitiers (46°34′N 0°21′E géog.) du 6 au 12 juillet 1966 soient peu nombreux et se prêtent mal à des mesures précises de densité électronique, leur analyse, complétée par celle des sifflements enregistrés à Prague (50°32′N 14°34′E géog.) par F. Jiricek, permet de dire qu'aucune diminution de l'ionisation ne s'est produite entre 2 et 2,5 R_e les 7, 8, 9 et 11 juillet. Les valeurs de N semblent même relativement élevées dans la nuit du 8 au 9 juillet.

Par ailleurs, grâce à la collaboration de D. L. Carpenter et Chung Park, de Stanford, qui ont analysé avec un soin tout particulier les sifflements enregistrés à Byrd Station (80°S 120°W géog.) en Antarctique du 6 au 14 juillet, il est possible de préciser la position approximative de la plasmapause au cours de cette période.

En effet, rappelons que les sifflements reçus notamment à Byrd Station sont généralement des "knee-whistlers" qui, selon Carpenter (1963b), ne peuvent s'expliquer que si la densité d'ionisation de la magnétosphère ne décroît pas régulièrement avec l'altitude mais présente une discontinuité brutale à une distance de l'ordre de 3 à 5 R_e dans le plan équatorial, se traduisant par une faille dans le profil d'ionisation. L'altitude géocentrique de cette discontinuité qui serait un phénomène permanent de la magnétosphère diminue quand l'activité magnétique augmente: elle est de l'ordre de 6 à 7 R_e pour $Kp = 0$ à 1 et de 4 R_e pour $Kp = 2$ à 4 (Carpenter 1967). L'étude de la variation diurne de sa position a permis en outre à Carpenter (1966) de décrire un modèle tridimensionnel de l'ionisation thermique de la magnétosphère. Il comprend deux régions: l'une interne, la plasmasphère, où N est de l'ordre de 100 électrons cm^{-3}, l'autre externe où N ne dépasse pas quelques électrons cm^{-3} et qui s'étend jusqu'à la magnétopause. Ces deux régions sont séparées par la plasmapause, limite ayant la configuration d'une coquille magnétique dont l'épaisseur dans le plan équatorial n'excéderait pas 0,15 R_e. Les mesures directes de concentrations en ions thermiques H^+ et He^+ obtenues par les spectromètres de masse ioniques installés à bord des satellites OGO (Taylor, Brinton et Smith 1965) confirment ces résultats.

Les 6 et 7 juillet 1966, la variation diurne de la position de la plasmapause est caractéristique des journées calmes: L est minimum et de l'ordre de 5 entre 04 et 06 TML, maximum et de l'ordre de 5,7 en fin d'après midi.

Le 8 juillet, alors que le Kp augmente et atteint une valeur de 4+ entre 06 et 09 TU, la diminution de L qui précède le minimum du matin est plus accentuée que les jours précédents: L décroît de 5,5 à 3,5 environ entre 02 et 14 TU, soit entre 18 TML le 7 et 06 TML le 8 juillet. A 18 TU le 8 juillet, la plasmapause se situe à 4 R_e. L'absence de données ne permet pas de la localiser de 19 TU à 04 TU le 9 juillet, période où un début brusque d'orage eut lieu le 8 à 2102 TU.

Ensuite, et jusqu'au 14 juillet, l'altitude géocentrique de la plasmapause n'excède jamais 4 R_e et l'amplitude des variations reste faible. Principalement le 10 juillet, la variation diurne est celle des journées perturbées: elle est caractérisée par un mouvement de la plasmapause vers la terre du côté éclairé de celle-ci, contrairement à la tendance générale observée quand les conditions magnétiques sont modérément perturbées et stables. Un minimum très étalé a lieu entre 12 et 00 TU (04 et 16 TML); il se situe à $L = 3,2$.

Les 11, 12 et 13 juillet, L varie peu et reste compris entre 3 et 4. Un retour complet à des conditions calmes se produit vers le 16 juillet.

Bien que le comportement dynamique de la plasmapause soit mal connu, *les quelques résultats précédents mettent en évidence un mouvement important de cette région de transition vers la terre entre 02 et 14 TU le 8 juillet*, donc avant le début brusque de l'orage qui eut lieu à 2102 TU. L'altitude géocentrique de la plasmapause, voisine de 5,5 R_e les 6 et 7 juillet, n'est que de 3 à 4 R_e du 9 au 14 juillet. Enfin, aucune diminution de l'ionisation n'a été décelée du 6 au 12 juillet entre 2 et 2,5 R_e, aux longitudes 0° et 15°E géographique. Il est intéressant de noter qu'une contraction semblable de la plasmasphère thermique a également été mise en évidence le 9 juillet par le satellite OGO-3 (Taylor, Brinton et Pharo 1968).

Les renseignements concernant la position de la plasmapause, inclus dans cette note, m'ont été aimablement fournis par D. L. Carpenter et Chung Park; qu'ils en soient, ici, vivement remerciés.

Bibliographie

CARPENTER, D. L., 1963a, The magnetosphere during magnetic storms; a whistler analysis, *Tech. Rep. 62-059*, Stanford Electronics Laboratories.
—— 1963b, Whistler evidence of a knee in the magnetospheric ionization density profile, *J. Geophys. Res.*, **68**, 1675–1682.
—— 1966, Whistler studies of the plasmapause in the magnetosphere: 1. Temporal variations in the position of the knee and some evidence on plasma motions near the knee, *J. Geophys. Res.*, **71**, 693–709.
—— 1967, Relations between the dawn minimum in the equatorial radius of the plasmapause and D_{st}, K_p and local K at Byrd Station, *J. Geophys. Res.*, **72**, 2969–2971.
CORCUFF, Y., 1965, Etude de la magnétosphère au moyen des sifflements radioélectriques, *Thèse de Doctorat d'Etat*, Poitiers (Edition du CNRS).
TAYLOR, H. A., JR, H. C. BRINTON, et C. R. SMITH, 1965, Positive ion composition in the magnetoionosphere obtained from OGO-A satellite, *J. Geophys. Res.*, **70**, 5769–5781.
TAYLOR, H. A., JR, H. C. BRINTON, et M. W. PHARO III, 1968, Evidence of contraction of the earth's thermal plasmasphere subsequent to the solar flare events of 7 and 9 July 1966, *Ann. IQSY*, this volume, Paper 53.

53

Evidence of Contraction of the Earth's Thermal Plasmasphere subsequent to the Solar Flare Events of 7 and 9 July 1966

H. A. Taylor, Jr., H. C. Brinton, and M. W. Pharo III

Aeronomy Branch, NASA–Goddard Space Flight Center, Greenbelt, Maryland, USA

Abstract

Direct measurements of thermal H^+ and He^+ in the magnetosphere have been obtained from ion mass spectrometers on Orbiting Geophysical Observatories (OGO) 1 and 3. Typical H^+ profiles exhibit a gradual decrease in concentration with altitude within the plasmasphere, while the outer boundary of the plasmasphere is characterized by an abrupt decrease in concentration to 5 ions cm^{-3} or less. This boundary, the plasmapause, is observed to move inward and outward in an inverse correlation with the magnetic activity index Kp. The magnetosphere was disturbed during the solar flare period 7–9 July 1966, and on 9 July the plasmapause was observed to be unusually low, at $L = 3.3$. This observation contrasted with measurements of the plasmapause on both preceding and succeeding orbits, when in the absence of flares and magnetic disturbance the H^+ boundary was observed to expand to L values as high as 6. These measurements correlate well with "knee" whistler observations of the plasmapause.

1 Introduction

1.1 Background

The high-altitude distributions of the positive ions of hydrogen and helium have been observed directly by ion mass spectrometers aboard the OGO-1 and 3 satellites. Measurements during 1964 and 1965 from OGO-1 (Taylor,

389

Brinton, and Smith 1965, Brinton, Pickett, and Taylor 1968) and during 1966 from OGO-3 (Taylor, Brinton, and Pharo 1968) show that above 1000 kilometers hydrogen and helium ion concentrations fall off slowly with increasing altitude until the occurrence of the plasmapause, characterized by a sudden decrease in the ion number density to 5 ions cm^{-3} or less. A primary characteristic of the plasmapause is its observed inward and outward displacement, which appears to be inversely related to magnetic disturbance. This paper will describe the behavior of the plasmapause during the important solar flare period of 7–9 July 1966.

1.2 The Experiment

The Bennett radio-frequency spectrometers flown on OGO 1 and 3 measure ambient thermal ions between 1 and 45 amu. The instruments used on the two flights are identical and provide a dynamic sensitivity range of approximately 5×10^0 to 1×10^6 ions cm^{-3}, with a resolution of 1 in 20 amu. The time between successive samples of each ion is 64 seconds. The instrumentation is described in detail by Taylor et al. (1965).

1.3 Location of Observations

During June and July 1966 the OGO-3 orbit was inclined at 31 degrees, with a perigee of about 316 kilometers and an apogee of 122,100 kilometers. In July the inbound passes occurred near local midnight, while the outbound passes were near dusk. In the region of interest, above $L = 3$, the rate of change of local time with respect to L is reasonably low, so that L or altitude is likely to be the primary variable observed in the data. The orbital period was nearly 48 hours, making comparative spatial observations possible at two-day intervals.

2 Results

2.1 Typical Undisturbed Profile

The data to be discussed were obtained during June and July 1966, when the attitude control system of OGO-3 permitted optimum data acquisition. An example of the high-altitude ion profiles is shown in Fig. 1. The concentrations of H^+ and He^+ have been plotted against L rather than altitude because the data so strongly suggest geomagnetic control of the ion distributions. The limiting sensitivity which can be realized with machine data processing is 5 ions cm^{-3}; accordingly, the upper portions of the profiles terminate at this concentration. The profiles do not extend below $L = 2.7$ because of gaps in the data processed to date.

The plasmapause is defined by the sharp decrease in H^+ occurring at

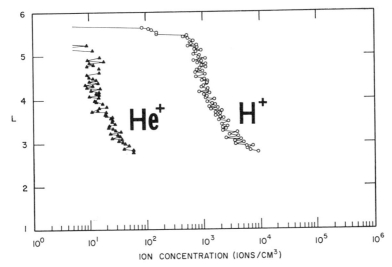

Fig. 1   Variations of hydrogen and helium ion concentration with L, showing typical plasmapause for events observed on inbound pass, 19 July 1966; $Kp_m = 2\,o$. The notation Kp_m refers to the maximum value of the magnetic activity index Kp recorded during the 24-hour interval prior to the time of plasmapause observation.

approximately $L = 5.7$. These profiles are typical of the OGO-3 data obtained during periods of low disturbance, and are also representative of data obtained during 1964 from OGO-1 (Taylor *et al.* 1965).

2.2   Correlation between Displacement of Plasmapause and Magnetic Activity

In order better to establish a basis for the comparison of undisturbed data with the distributions obtained during proton flare events, all of the passes available during June and July 1966 which exhibit a sharp boundary have been examined. It was found that for profiles obtained on outbound passes in the dusk quadrant of the magnetosphere the plasmapause occurs at appreciably higher L positions than on inbound, midnight passes. This local-time asymmetry in the plasmasphere has been observed in whistler data (Carpenter 1966) and predicted by Nishida (1966) and Brice (1967). As a result of this asymmetry we have chosen to examine the correlation of plasmapause position with magnetic activity only in the data obtained in the midnight local time quadrant.

The result of examining 18 inbound H^+ profiles is shown in Fig. 2. The points represent observed steep gradients which are clear examples of the plasmapause. The L coordinates of the plasmapause events are plotted against the maximum value of the planetary magnetic activity index Kp recorded in the 24-hour period prior to the plasmapause observation. We call this maximum value Kp_m. These measurements occurred between 2245 hours and

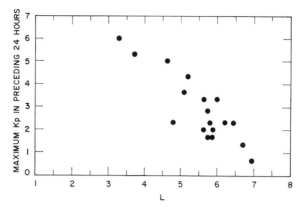

Fig. 2   Positions in L of observed H^+ plasmapause, plotted against Kp_m. Only events observed on inbound passes near local midnight are shown.

0115 hours local time and in the geomagnetic latitude interval -16 to $+14$ degrees. The inverse relationship between L and Kp is evident, with the extremes in magnetic activity correlating with the extreme positions of the plasmapause. This relationship is similar to that determined from whistler data for the period June–August 1963 (Carpenter 1967).

2.3   Effects of Solar Flare Events

The magnetosphere was disturbed during the period 7–9 July 1966, with importance 2 solar flares occurring on 7, 8, and 9 July resulting in a sudden commencement of an extensive magnetic storm at 2103 GMT on 8 July. During the week prior to this period the magnetic activity was comparatively low. The nearest pre-storm data now available were obtained on 3 July 1966, when $Kp_m = 2+$. The H^+ distribution on this date was typical of the distributions seen during low activity, the plasmapause being at $L = 6.4$.

The H^+ profiles shown in Fig. 3 illustrate the strong inward displacement of the plasmapause during the storm period. In this figure only the H^+ distributions are shown; in each case the minor component He^+ profiles closely parallel the H^+ profiles as shown in Fig. 1. On 9 July the plasmapause moved inward to $L = 3.3$; this observation occurred approximately six hours after the highest magnetic activity of the period was recorded, $Kp = 6o$. On 11 July the plasmapause recovered partially, to $L = 4.7$. This observation occurred approximately 24 hours after the secondary maximum in the storm, when $Kp = 5$ at about 0900 hours on 10 July. Finally, on 13 July the plasmapause recovered to approximately $L = 6.3$. It may be noted that although the H^+ profile of 13 July indicates significant recovery from the intense portion of the storm, a comparison with the H^+ profile of 19 July suggests that the recovery is not yet complete.

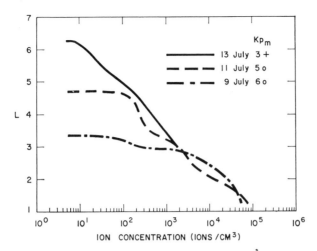

Fig. 3   Smoothed hydrogen ion profiles from OGO-3 inbound
passes showing inward displacement and subsequent
recovery of plasmapause during proton flare period. Data
sampling rate required smoothing of raw profiles which
are otherwise identical with those shown in Fig. 1.

3   Discussion: The Plasmasphere and Magnetic Activity

It is evident from these data that the envelope of light ions surrounding the
earth expands and contracts in a manner that correlates with important
changes in geomagnetic activity. This phenomenon has been observed repeatedly in whistler data (Carpenter 1967) and in plasmapause observations
made with the MIT Faraday cup experiment (Binsack 1967). It is significant
that the L coordinate of several of the plasmapause events detected by OGO-3
agree with simultaneous ground based and satellite VLF observations
(Carpenter, private communication). This evidence seems particularly important in light of the study made by Carpenter and Stone (1967) of the
behavior of the plasmasphere during a polar substorm. The whistler data
showed that on the night side of the earth rapid inward motions of the
plasmapause occurred, of the order of 0.4 R_e/hour, which were closely associated with depressed magnetic field levels recorded at the earth's surface
during polar substorms.

Other evidence relating to plasma motions is found in the observations by
Cahill and Bailey (1967) of field distortions which are attributed to inflation
of the magnetosphere by low-energy particle ring currents detected by Frank
(1966). An inflation of the magnetosphere was detected by Cahill[1] on
17 June 1967, when the plasmasphere was observed to be greatly compressed.

[1] Reported by L. J. Cahill, Jr., in a paper entitled "Inflation and compression of the
magnetosphere," presented at the Conjugate Point Symposium, Boulder, Colorado,
June 1967.

This appears to relate directly to the OGO 3 observations by Frank (1967) of low-energy protons and electrons during July 1966. On 9 July Frank observed a strong enhancement of protons in the $31 \leqslant E \leqslant 49$ keV range, which appears to coincide exactly with the location of the H^+ plasmapause observed from the same satellite. Assuming that the bunching of these particles into ring currents results in magnetic field depressions and attendant plasmasphere compressions, these independent energetic and thermal particle observations may prove quite consistent.

The picture of energetic particles penetrating the magnetosphere to a level which coincides with the observed discontinuity in the thermal ion distributions is intriguing. This further suggests the strong influence of the magnetic field on the distribution of the exospheric plasma and will stimulate new studies in this area.

References

BINSACK, J. H., 1967, Plasmapause observations with the M.I.T. experiment on IMP-2, *J. Geophys. Res.*, **72**, 5231–5237.

BRICE, N. M., 1967, Bulk motion of the magnetosphere, *J. Geophys. Res.*, **72**, 5193–5211.

BRINTON, H. C., R. A. PICKETT, and H. A. TAYLOR, JR, 1968, Thermal ion structure of the plasmasphere, *Planet. Space Sci.*, in press.

CAHILL, L. J., JR, and D. H. BAILEY, 1967, Distortion of the magnetosphere during a magnetic storm on September 30, 1961, *J. Geophys. Res.*, **72**, 159–169.

CARPENTER, D. L., 1966, Whistler studies of the plasmapause in the magnetosphere: I, *J. Geophys. Res.*, **71**, 693–709.

—— 1967, Relations between the dawn minimum in the equatorial radius of the plasmapause and D_{st}, K_p, and local K at Byrd Station, *J. Geophys. Res.*, **72**, 2969–2971.

CARPENTER, D. L., and KEPPLER STONE, 1967, Direct detection by a whistler method of the magnetospheric electric field associated with a polar substorm, *Planet. Space Sci.*, **15**, 395–397.

FRANK, L. A., 1966, Explorer 12 observations of the temporal variations of low-energy electron intensities in the outer radiation zone during geomagnetic storms, *J. Geophys. Res.*, **71**, 4631–4639.

—— 1967, On the extraterrestrial ring current during geomagnetic storms, University of Iowa Report No. 67–9, February 1967 (University of Iowa, Iowa).

NISHIDA, A., 1966, Formation of the plasmapause, or magnetospheric plasma knee, by the combined action of magnetospheric convection and plasma escape from the tail, *J. Geophys. Res.*, **71**, 5669–5679.

TAYLOR, H. A., JR., H. C. BRINTON, and C. R. SMITH, 1965, Positive ion composition in the magnetoionosphere obtained from the OGO-A satellite, *J. Geophys. Res.*, **70**, 5769–5781.

TAYLOR, H. A., JR., H. C. BRINTON, and M. W. PHARO III, 1968, Contraction of the plasmasphere during geomagnetically disturbed periods, *J. Geophys. Res.*, **73**, 961–968.

54

Solar Particle Observations inside the Magnetosphere during the 7 July 1966 Proton Flare Event

S. M. Krimigis, J. A. Van Allen, and T. P. Armstrong

Department of Physics and Astronomy, The University of Iowa, Iowa City, Iowa, USA

Abstract

Observations of protons emitted by the 7 July 1966 solar flare at 34°N 47°W with the low-altitude–high-latitude University of Iowa satellite Injun 4 show the following: (a) High energy ($E_p \sim 27$ MeV) protons arrive promptly over the earth's polar caps and decay in a manner consistent with diffusive propagation. (b) The counting rate due to protons in the interval $0.52 \leqslant E_p \leqslant 4$ MeV and moving normal to the magnetic vector shows a *double plateau* as the satellite moves over the polar caps. (c) The position of the "knee" for protons in the above energy interval varies from $L \sim 7.5$ to $L \sim 6.3$ at magnetic local times of about 04.5 hours and 11.5 hours, respectively. (d) After the sudden commencement the latitude gap between trapped protons and solar protons disappears, suggesting that some solar protons may become trapped in the earth's radiation belts. (e) Simultaneous observations with similar detectors inside the magnetosphere (Injun 4) and outside the magnetosphere (Explorer 33) show that low-energy (~ 0.5 MeV) protons have essentially immediate access from the interplanetary space to the polar caps of the earth. Finally, the theoretical implications of these results are discussed.

I Introduction

We report herein observations of protons emitted in the 7 July 1966 solar flare, obtained inside the magnetosphere from 7 to 10 July 1966. These observations were made with detectors on board the University of Iowa satellite Injun 4 which was launched on 21 November 1964 into a nearly polar orbit of 81° inclination, with initial apogee altitude of 2502 kilometers and perigee altitude of 527 kilometers. Data are analyzed during that portion of the satellite orbit for which $L \gtrsim 4$, and the dependence of the counting rate on universal time, invariant latitude, and magnetic local time is examined. Energy spectra for protons and alpha particles at selected times are computed, and the particle fluxes are compared with those outside the magnetosphere observed simultaneously with Explorer 33. Finally, a comparison of the results with proposed theoretical models is given.

2   The Detector

The Injun 4 detector relevant to these observations is a totally depleted silicon surface barrier in the form of a thin circular disk, whose thickness is 25 micrometers and whose frontal area is 1.75 ± 0.2 mm^2 (Nuclear Diodes, Inc.). The detector is located inside a conical collimator with a full vertex angle of 40° and is otherwise shielded by a minimum of 10.2 g cm^{-2} of brass, which corresponds to the range of 95 MeV protons. To shield against sunlight a nickel foil whose thickness is 0.21 mg cm^2 of air equivalent for α particles is placed in front of the detector. Four electronic discrimination levels are provided. The first two (channels A and B) are sensitive to protons and heavier nuclei and the last two (channels C and D) are sensitive only to particles heavier than deuterons (Table 1). The thin detector, coupled with a double-delay line clipped pulse of 200 nanoseconds full width, renders the detector insensitive to electrons of any energy. The electron insensitivity and the calibration methods that have been used are identical with those described in detail elsewhere (Krimigis and Armstrong 1966). The satellite is equipped with a permanent magnet and energy-dissipating hysteresis rods so that it will maintain a particular axis continuously aligned with the local geomagnetic field vector. Thus, for the low-energy proton observations reported here, the axis of the detector collimator was maintained continuously perpendicular ($\pm 10°$) to the local geomagnetic field vector so that the detector was receiving particles whose pitch angles were 90° $\pm$ 30°.

In addition to the solid-state detector, the Injun 4 instrumentation includes a shielded GM-tube whose threshold for protons is approximately 27 MeV. This detector has been described previously (Krimigis and Van Allen 1967).

3   Observations

3.1   Energetic Protons

In Fig. 1 is plotted the counting rate of the shielded GM tube for the period 7–10 July 1966, averaged over the polar cap for $L \gtrsim 8$. It is observed that during the pass which ended at 7 July 0050 UT, the detector counting rate was accurately equal to the pre-event cosmic-ray background rate.

Table 1   Characteristics of the Injun 4 Detectors

Detector†	Unidirectional Geometric Factor (cm² sr)	Omnidirectional Geometric Factor (cm²)	Particles to which Sensitive	Dynamic Range
A	0.0064 ± 0.0007	—	Protons: $0.52 \leqslant E_p \leqslant 4$* MeV Electrons: None	From inflight source to 10^6 Hz
B	0.0064 ± 0.0007	—	Protons: $0.90 \leqslant E_p \leqslant 1.8$* MeV Electrons: None	,,
C	0.0064 ± 0.0007	—	α-Particles: $2.09 \leqslant E_\alpha \leqslant 15$* MeV	,,
D	0.0064 ± 0.0007	—	α-Particles: $3.89 \leqslant E_\alpha \leqslant 7.6$* MeV	,,
112-GM	—	8.9‡	Protons: $E_p \gtrsim 27$§ MeV Electrons: Insensitive except via bremsstrahlung for $E_e \gtrsim 1$ MeV	From galactic cosmic ray rate of 30 to 10^5 Hz

* Upper limit for vertical incidence only; the corresponding limits for incidence at 20° to the collimator axis are 4.2, 1.9, 18, and 8 MeV for A, B, C, and D, respectively.

† A, B, C, D correspond to different electronic discrimination levels in the same basic detector.

‡ If exposed in free space; effective geometric factor is smaller by approximately 30% as actually mounted in the satellite.

§ This threshold corresponds to protons incident perpendicular to the axis of the cylindrical-type tube. For protons incident at an angle of 60° to the axis, the threshold is approximately 40 MeV.

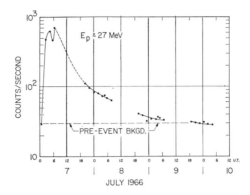

Fig. 1   Time history of protons $E_p \gtrsim 27$ MeV
as observed over the earth's polar caps
with Injun 4.

Hence the arrival of particles at the earth, due to a flare on the sun, whose onset was at 0023 UT (Van Allen 1968) took place after 0050 UT. On the following satellite pass at approximately 0234 UT the counting rate had already approached its maximum value. It subsequently decreased until, at about 9 July 1800 UT, it was indistinguishable from the cosmic-ray background. The intensity–time profile is reminiscent of several such events during the previous solar cycle, in that it has a rapid increase to the maximum and a slow nonexponential decay of 2–3 days. Such a time behavior may be accounted for in terms of diffusion in the interplanetary medium (cf. Krimigis 1965). More complete observations of the present event have shown that this is indeed the case (Heristchi *et al.* 1968).

3.2   Low-Energy Protons

Figure 2 shows the counting rate of the solid-state detector, due to protons in the energy interval $0.52 \leqslant E_p \leqslant 4$ MeV, during a northbound Injun 4 pass over the polar cap. We observe the following: (*a*) solar protons in the quoted energy interval do not have access to regions where $L < 5.5$, independently of magnetic local time; (*b*) the counting rate shows a *double* plateau as the satellite moves from a magnetic local time (MLT) of about 4 hours to MLT of about 11 hours; (*c*) the position of the knee for protons in this energy interval is at $L \sim 7.5$ (at 50 per cent of the plateau counting rates) at MLT ~ 4.5 hours and at $L \sim 6.3$ at MLT ~ 11.5 hours.

The double plateau is found to be a persistent feature of all polar-cap passes of the satellite, prior to the occurrence of the sudden commencement at 8 July 2102 UT. To investigate further this effect, four such passes are shown in Fig. 3, along with a polar plot of the satellite trajectory for these

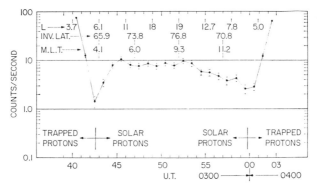

Fig. 2   A characteristic pass of Injun 4 over the polar cap, prior to the sudden commencement. Note the well-defined boundary between solar protons and trapped protons.

passes in invariant latitude and MLT. We observe that all four passes show the double-plateau feature at several points in local time. Comparison of the data with the simultaneous measurements of Explorer 33 (see Sec. 5 of this paper) shows that the variation in the counting rate is *not* due to time variations in the intensity of the primary proton beam.

3.3   Energy Spectra of Protons and Alpha Particles

The ratios A/B and C/D of the counting rates of proton and alpha detectors, respectively, may be used to determine the energy spectra. During the time interval 0330 to 0540 UT on 8 July, the intensity remained relatively constant and the ratios were as follows:

$$\frac{A}{B} = 2.14 \pm 0.1, \quad \text{protons}; \qquad \frac{C}{D} = 2.70 \pm 0.5, \quad \alpha \text{ particles}$$

If one assumed a differential energy spectrum

$$\frac{dj}{dE} = \frac{K}{E_0} \exp\left(-\frac{E}{E_0}\right)$$

for $E_p \gtrsim 0.52$ and $E_\alpha \gtrsim 2.1$ MeV, then the values of E_0 for protons and alpha particles are $E_{0p} \sim 0.8$ MeV and $E_{0\alpha} \sim 2$ MeV, respectively. It is noted that the simultaneous ratio of two proton channels comparable with A and B on Explorer 33, which was located outside the magnetosphere, is given by

$$\frac{P2}{P3} = 2.0 \pm 0.01 \quad \text{protons on Explorer 33}$$

resulting in a comparable value of E_{0p} (Armstrong *et al.* 1968).

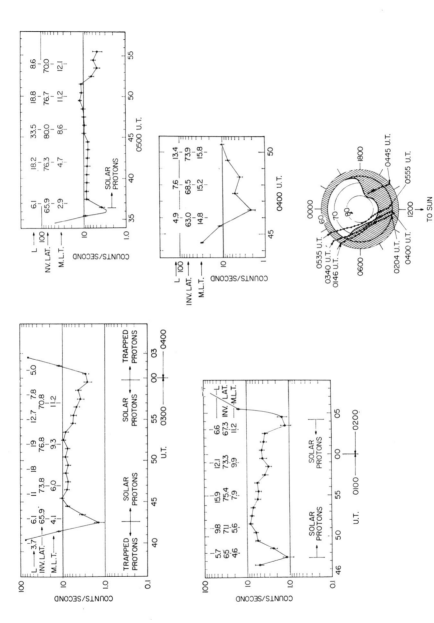

Fig. 3   Data from four Injun 4 passes over the polar caps on 8 July 1966. The satellite trajectory for each pass is shown at the lower right-hand corner in invariant latitude and MLT coordinates. $0.516 \leqslant E_p \leqslant 4$ MeV.

4   Remarks on the Low-Energy Protons

In the preceding section we pointed out the double-plateau feature of the counting-rate profile on a polar pass. Although it has been known for some time that the entrance of low-energy protons onto the earth's polar caps is not adequately explained by Störmer theory, no adequate theories have been proposed to explain the experimental data of Pieper *et al.* (1962), Stone (1964), and Harding (1966, M.S. Thesis, Univ. Iowa, unpublished). Recently Taylor (1967) has made a calculation using the Taylor–Hones model of the geomagnetic field and finds that the polar plateau is an irregularly shaped region with full accessibility to incoming low-energy (~ 1.2 MeV) solar protons in some parts and limited or no accessibility in others. The polar plot in Fig. 3 is shown in more detail in Fig. 4 where the shaded area for

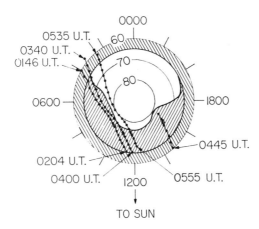

Fig. 4   Detail of Fig. 3 showing the satellite trajectory. Points on the trajectory are one minute apart and the corresponding UT is given for the first and last points. The region in a given trajectory where the second plateau was observed is marked with cross-hatching. The irregularly shaped contour is the result of Taylor's calculation.

$\Lambda \gtrsim 65°$ is a region of limited accessibility, while the open area is accessible to particles of all pitch angles. Our experimental data show that there is qualitative agreement between Taylor's predictions and the observations. It does appear, however, that the boundary of the region with limited accessibility is at a consistently lower latitude than that predicted by Taylor. It may be possible to use the experimental data to determine more accurately the parameters involved in the calculation.

At this point the question arises as to whether the double plateau persists after the occurrence of the sudden commencement. Figure 5 shows a pass taken at about 2125 UT, approximately 20 minutes after the sudden commencement. It is observed that the depressed plateau at about 11 hours MLT

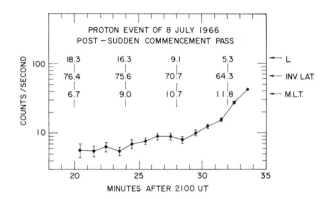

Fig. 5   A post-sudden commencement pass. Note the merging of trapped protons and solar protons.

is no longer present; in addition, the latitude gap between trapped protons and solar protons has disappeared and the distinction between solar and trapped protons is no longer apparent. It is suggested that low-energy solar protons can enter the relatively ordered region of the magnetic field at high latitudes at values of $L \sim 6$ and become permanently trapped in the geomagnetic field, although their contribution to trapped proton intensities at comparable energies may not be important.

5   Simultaneous Observations inside and outside the Magnetosphere

Recently, Krimigis and Van Allen (1967) have reported simultaneous observations with Injun 4 near the earth and Mariner 4 (the latter located about 23×10^6 km downstream from the earth and near the sun–earth line) and have concluded that the observed delay in arrival time for 0.5 MeV solar protons between the two spacecraft is 0 ± 2 hrs.

The present measurements make possible a much improved examination of the question of access of particles to the earth through the magnetosphere by use of simultaneous measurements between Explorer 33 and Injun 4 for the following reasons: (*a*) Explorer 33 is in the immediate astronomical vicinity of the earth, but clearly outside of the earth's magnetosphere (Fig. 6); (*b*) the event of 7 July 1966 is of sufficiently high intensity that the statistical accuracy of the Injun 4 counting rates is superior to those reported earlier by Krimigis and Van Allen (1967, see also Williams and Bostrom 1967); and (*c*) the intensity–time structure is rich in detail, thus making possible a refined search for time delays. Because of (*a*) above, any dissimilarities in the intensity–time profiles between the two spacecraft cannot be attributed to large scale ($\sim 10^6$ km) inhomogeneities in the interplanetary medium, as might have been the case for the Mariner 4 and Injun 4 comparison.

The University of Iowa detector complement on Explorer 33 is virtually identical to the Injun 4 detector (Armstrong and Krimigis 1968) with discrimination levels set to count protons in the energy ranges $0.3 \leqslant E_p \leqslant 10$ MeV, $0.5 \leqslant E_p \leqslant 4$ MeV, and $0.82 \leqslant E_p \leqslant 1.9$ MeV. The conical collimator of the detector has a half-angle of 30°, and the spacecraft is spinning at the rate of approximately 26 rev min^{-1}. The absolute value of the unidirectional geometric factor is 0.082 ± 0.003 cm^2 sr.

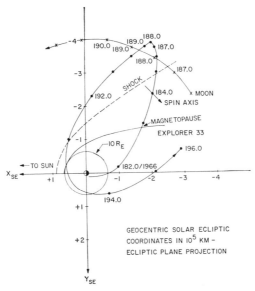

Fig. 6   Ecliptic plane projection of the first orbit of Explorer 33 and a segment of the orbit of the moon, both in geocentric solar ecliptic coordinates. The numbers on the orbit correspond to decimal day of the year, with 0000 UT on 1 January denoted by 0.0 days. Note that during the period of observations Explorer 33 was on the sunward side of the shock front (shock front and magnetopause locations by courtesy of K. W. Behannon and N. F. Ness).

Figure 7 shows the (counting rate, time) profile of the $0.5 \leqslant E_p \leqslant 4$ MeV channel from Explorer 33 (solid curve) and the (counting rate, time) profile of the equivalent channel from Injun 4 (plotted points) obtained while the latter satellite (orbital inclination 81°) was moving over the earth's polar caps at an altitude ranging from 1500 to 2000 km. The solid curve was drawn by using half-hour averages of the counting rate, while the plotted points represent 8–16 minute averages of the Injun 4 counting rate over the polar caps. Since the unidirectional geometric factors of the two detectors differ by approximately a factor of 10 (within 25 per cent), the Injun 4 points were moved up one decade in the logarithmic scale so that the absolute values of the intensity at the positions of the two satellites can be compared directly. It is seen that *a.* The absolute intensities of protons in identical energy channels are essentially the same moment-by-moment (within the uncertainties in the geometric factors and the statistics), in interplanetary space and over the polar caps of the earth, during the entire 4-day period of simultaneous observations.

b. There are statistically significant differences in only two or three instances (e.g., about 9 July 1800 UT), which are attributed tentatively to marked anisotropies in the interplanetary intensity and/or to strong polar magnetic storms.

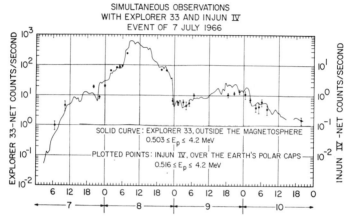

Fig. 7   Simultaneous observations of directional intensities of solar protons with Explorer 33 and Injun 4. The smooth curve is drawn through half-hour averaged counting rates of Explorer 33. Each plotted point represents a polar-cap averaged counting rate for Injun 4. The respective sets of data are superimposed on the same absolute intensity basis (to within 25%) by displacing the counting-rate scale of Injun 4 data upward by one decade.

We therefore conclude that, on the whole, low-energy (~ 0.5 MeV) solar protons have full access to the earth's polar caps from the interplanetary medium, with a delay of 0.5 hour or less. Simultaneous observations of 0.90 MeV protons and 2.1 MeV alpha particles have also been compared and lead to the same conclusion.

Of particular interest is the abrupt decrease in the intensity at about 2300 UT on 8 July. A more detailed plot of this period shows that while the counting rate at the position of Explorer 33 is still decreasing, the rate at Injun 4 has already decreased to the new level. We infer from this observation that the decrease in intensity at Injun 4 *preceded* that at Explorer 33 by at least 8 minutes, in crude agreement with the concept of a plasma cloud moving radially outward from the sun past the earth and past Explorer 33, in that order, carrying the energetic particles with it.

6   Remarks on Simultaneous Observations

Although it has been established that the earth's magnetospheric boundary is greatly distorted by the flow of the solar wind, there is essential disagreement regarding the topology of the magnetic field at the boundary between the magnetosphere and the interplanetary medium. Figure 8 illustrates two contrasting models. The model shown in Fig. 8a envisages considerable merging (Dungey 1961, Levy *et al.* 1964, Axford *et al.* 1965) between the geomagnetic and interplanetary magnetic fields, such that charged particles

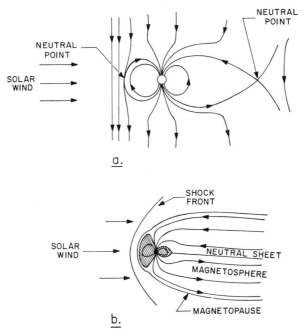

Fig. 8   (*a*) Magnetospheric model that envisages merging between the geomagnetic and interplanetary fields (Dungey 1961, Levy *et al.* 1964). (*b*) Magnetospheric model in which merging of lines of force does not occur (Dessler 1964, Michel and Dessler 1965).

approaching the earth on an interplanetary magnetic field line have immediate access to points over the earth's polar caps.

The model shown in Fig. 8b envisages no merging between the geomagnetic and interplanetary fields (Dessler 1964, Michel and Dessler 1965) near the earth. Proponents of this model suggest that solar-emitted protons having $E_p \lesssim 5$ MeV must diffuse into the very long tail of the magnetosphere and spread slowly from the auroral zone over the polar caps after a delay or "diffusion time" which is a function of, among other parameters, the length of the tail and the energy per unit charge of the particle. For example, applying Eq. 4 of Michel and Dessler (1965), wherein E_q is energy per unit charge

(Michel and Dessler 1967), to a 0.5-MeV proton and a magnetospheric tail length of 1 AU one calculates a delay time of 30 hours between the arrival of protons in the vicinity of the earth but outside of the magnetosphere and their arrival over the polar caps at the earth. Tail lengths considerably longer than 1 AU (and hence longer delay times) are advocated by Michel and Dessler.

It is seen from Fig. 6 that Explorer 33 was located clearly outside the shock front (data on shock-front location by courtesy of K. W. Behannon and N. F. Ness, GSFC). Hence, our observations (a) provide a specific test of the diffusion calculation (Michel and Dessler 1965) for solar protons made in the context of a long-tail model of the magnetosphere (Dessler 1964) (Fig. 8b) and are in drastic disagreement with its predictions; and (b) appear to favor an "open" magnetospheric model of the sort depicted in Fig. 8a (Van Allen 1965, 1966, Dessler 1966).

It may be remarked, however, that the foregoing conclusions are based on the concept of noninteracting particles moving in a quasi-stationary magnetic field, and that collective (plasma) phenomena have been ignored. Transport of a fully ionized plasma across a magnetic field at a rate much faster than that attributable to single-particle diffusion has been observed in the laboratory. This phenomenon of anomalous diffusion was investigated theoretically by Spitzer (1960) and more recently by Stix (1967), and shown to be due to electric fields. Thus, it may be that interconnection between magnetic lines of force of the interplanetary and geomagnetic fields is not necessary for access of low-energy protons to the earth's polar caps, if such particles are only a minor component of a much more dense plasma cloud, and theoretical discussions on the subject of interconnection of lines of force may be irrelevant to this matter.

Acknowledgments

The authors thank Dr. L. A. Frank and Messrs. H. K. Hills and J. D. Craven for making the Injun 4 GM-tube data available prior to publication. We are indebted to Messrs. W. A. Whelpley of the University of Iowa and C. W. Coffee of Langley Research Center, as well as many University of Iowa and LRC personnel, who contributed to making Injun 4 a success. Messrs. D. C. Enemark, E. W. Strein, R. Ganfield, and B. Randall assisted in various phases of the design, fabrication, and calibrations of the Injun 4 solid-state detector. We also appreciate the assistance of E. W. Strein, D. R. Camp, and B. Randall of the University of Iowa and Dr. N. F. Ness and Paul Marcotte of Goddard Space Flight Center in executing the Explorer 33 experiment. Messrs. R. L. Brechwald, C. Wong, and C. M. Tsai assisted in the reduction of data at the University of Iowa.

Development and construction of the University of Iowa satellite Injun 4 was supported under contract NAS1-2973 with the National Aeronautics and

Space Administration/Langley Research Center. The Explorer 33 experiment was developed under contract NAS5-9076 with National Aeronautics and Space Administration. Analysis and publication of the data have been supported in part by NASA grant NsG 233-62 and Office of Naval Research contract Nonr-1509(06).

Figures 6–8 are reproduced with permission of *Physical Review Letters*, **18**, 1204.

References

ARMSTRONG, T. P., and S. M. KRIMIGIS, 1968, Observations of protons in the magnetosphere and magnetotail with Explorer 33, *J. Geophys. Res.*, **73**, 143–152.

ARMSTRONG, T. P., S. M. KRIMIGIS, and J. A. VAN ALLEN, 1968, Observations of the solar particle event of 7 July 1966 with University of Iowa Detectors, *Ann. IQSY*, this volume, Paper 43.

AXFORD, W. I., H. E. PETSCHEK, and G. L. SISCOE, 1965, The tail of the magnetosphere, *J. Geophys. Res.*, **70**, 1231–1236.

DESSLER, A. J., 1964, Length of magnetospheric tail, *J. Geophys. Res.*, **69**, 3913–3918.

—— 1966, Discussion of Letter by J. A. Van Allen, 'Further remarks on the absence of a very extended magnetospheric tail', *J. Geophys. Res.*, **71**, 2408–2410.

DUNGEY, J. W., 1961, Interplanetary magnetic field and the auroral zones, *Phys. Rev. Lett.*, **6**, 47–48.

HERISTCHI, DJ., J. KANGAS, G. KREMSER, J. P. LEGRAND, P. MASSE, M. PALOUS, G. PFOTZER, W. RIEDLER, and K. WILHELM, 1968, Balloon measurements of solar protons in Northern Scandinavia on 7 July 1966, *Ann. IQSY*, this volume, Paper 38.

KRIMIGIS, S. M., 1965, Interplanetary diffusion model for the time behavior of intensity in a solar cosmic ray event, *J. Geophys. Res.*, **70**, 2943–2960.

KRIMIGIS, S. M., and T. P. ARMSTRONG, 1966, Observations of protons in the magnetosphere with Mariner 4, *J. Geophys. Res.*, **71**, 4641–4650.

KRIMIGIS, S. M., and J. A. VAN ALLEN, 1967, Observations of the February 5–12, 1965, solar particle event with Mariner 4 and Injun 4, *J. Geophys. Res.*, **72**, 4471–4486.

LEVY, R. H., H. E. PETSCHEK, and G. L. SISCOE, 1964, Aerodynamic aspects of the magnetosphere flow, *Amer. Inst. Aeronaut. Astronaut. J.*, **2**, 2065–2076.

MICHEL, F. C., and A. J. DESSLER, 1965, Physical significance of inhomogeneities in polar cap absorption events, *J. Geophys. Res.*, **70**, 4305–4311.

—— 1967, Correction to paper by F. C. Michel and A. J. Dessler, 'Physical significance of inhomogeneities in polar cap absorption events', *J. Geophys. Res.*, **72**, 2979.

PIEPER, G. F., A. J. ZMUDA, C. O. BOSTROM, and B. J. O'BRIEN, 1962, Solar protons and magnetic storms in July 1961, *J. Geophys. Res.*, **67**, 4959–4981.

SPITZER, LYMAN, JR., 1960, Particle diffusion across a magnetic field, *Phys. Fluids*, **3**, 659–661.

STIX, T. H., 1967, Resonant diffusion of plasma across a magnetic field, *MATT*-460, *Plasma Physics Laboratory Research Report* (Princeton University Press, Princeton, N.J.).

STONE, E. C., 1964, Local time dependence of non-Störmer cutoff for 1.5 MeV protons in quiet geomagnetic field. *J. Geophys. Res.*, **69**, 3577–3582.

TAYLOR, H. E., 1967, Latitude–local time dependence of low-energy cosmic-ray cutoffs in a realistic geomagnetic field, *J. Geophys. Res.*, **72**, 4467–4470.

VAN ALLEN, J. A., 1965, Absence of 40-keV electrons in the earth's magnetospheric tail at 3300 earth radii, *J. Geophys. Res.*, **70**, 4731–4739.

—— 1966, Further remarks on the absence of a very extended magnetospheric tail, *J. Geophys. Res.*, **71**, 2406–2407.

—— 1968, The solar X-ray flare of 7 July 1966, *Ann. IQSY*, this volume, Paper 30.

WILLIAMS, D. J., and C. O. BOSTROM, 1967, The February 5, 1965, solar flare event: 2. Low energy proton observations and their relation to the magnetosphere, *J. Geophys. Res.*, **72**, 4497–4506.

55

Preliminary Analysis of Micropulsations of the Earth's Electromagnetic Field in connection with the Proton Flare of 7 July 1966

E. T. Matveeva and V. A. Troitskaya

Academy of Sciences of the USSR, Moscow, USSR

Abstract

The results of analysis of the behaviour of micropulsations at 12 observatories located in polar caps, auroral zones and middle latitudes are given for the first half of July 1966.

It is revealed that there are some peculiarities in the occurrence of pearls before and after the flare. Before the flare only pulsations with periods greater than 3 sec are observed and only in high latitudes. After the flare world-wide generation of pearls with periods less than 3 sec was traced. It is suggested that their occurrence is an indication of penetration of energetic particles in the magnetosphere.

To study peculiarities in the behaviour of micropulsations during the time intervals before and after the solar flare of 7 July 1966, the data of 12 observatories located in polar caps, auroral zones and middle latitudes were used. Table 1 gives the names of the stations, and the time scales of the processed records.

The analysis was conducted for the first half of July, separately for records with time scale 90 mm/hour and for records with time scale 30 mm/min. This procedure allowed the whole range of micropulsations to be divided into two parts. One contained the whole family of continuous pulsations beginning from Pc3 and including Pc4, Pc5 and Pi2. The other consisted of the shortest periodic micropulsations, namely Pc1, Pc2, Pi1, and the IPDP.

The analysis of the records with the time scale 90 mm/hour (Pc3 and

Table I   Observing Stations and Time Scales of their Records

Station	Time Scales of Processed Records	
M'Bour	30 mm/min	360 mm/hour
Alma–Ata	30 mm/min	90 mm/hour
Irkutsk	30 mm/min	90 mm/hour
Petropavlovsk	30 mm/min	90 mm/hour
Borok	30 mm/min	90 mm/hour
Sogra	30 mm/min	—
Tixi	30 mm/min	90 mm/hour
Lovozero	30 mm/min	—
Novolazarevskaya	30 mm/min	20 mm/hour
Heiss	30 mm/min	90 mm/hour
Mirny	30 mm/min	90 mm/hour
Vostok	30 mm/min	300 mm/hour

pulsations with longer periods) has not given any specific results which could be associated with the proton flare of 7 July. The behaviour of these pulsations showed the usual dependence on magnetic activity, that is, their periods augmented with the diminishing of Kp and vice versa.

An example of the occurrence of micropulsations in the shortest periodic range is given in Fig. 1. Together with the regularities in the occurrence of micropulsations there are given the changes in Kp and in polar-cap absorption at three stations. The most interesting feature of the behaviour of micropulsations after the solar flare of 7 July is the world-wide occurrence of "pearls" with periods less than 2 seconds in the time interval from 2 to 4 hours GMT on 8 July on practically all analysed records. The generation of these pearls precedes the magnetic storm by about 19 hours. This result is most interesting, especially if we take into account that during the first week of July no other cases of world-wide generation of pearls with periods less than two seconds were observed without significant time delays at stations separated by more than 140° in longitude (for instance Novolazarevskaya and Petropavlovsk). The period before the proton flare was in general relatively quiet as regards the generation of pearls of period less than 3 seconds. On all days the periods of pearls were around 3–4 seconds and they occurred only at high latitude stations.[1] In the period after the solar flare the generation of pearls was observed in both high and middle latitudes especially in the time interval 8–11 July and on 14 July. The preferred occurrence of pearls on the days following the storm was established earlier (Wentworth 1964, Plyasova-Bakunina and Matveeva 1968). Table 2 gives the picture of the day-to-day

---

[1] There are many morphological and probably physical reasons for separating the pearls with periods more than 2.5–3 seconds and less than this value (Troitskaya *et al.* 1967).

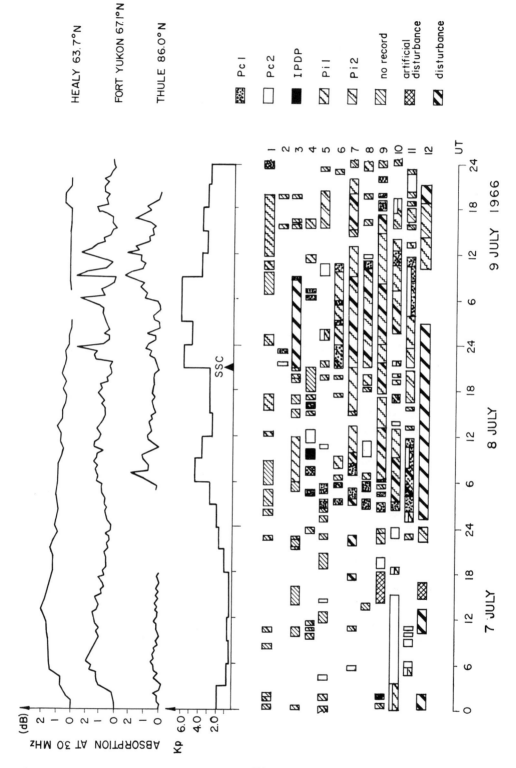

Table 2*   Day to Day Generation of Pearls

Date July 1966	Polar Cap		Auroral Zone		Middle Latitudes	
	N	S	N	S	W	E
1	⊕	—	—	—	—	—
2	⊕	—	—	⊕	—	—
3	⊕	⊕	⊕	⊕	—	—
4	⊕	⊕	⊕	⊕	—	—
5	—	—	—	—	—	—
6	⊕	⊕	—	⊕	—	—
7	—	—	—	—	—	—
8	+	+	+	+	+	+
9	+	+	+	+	—	+
10	+	+	—	+	+	+
11	—	+	+	+	+	+
12	—	—	⊕	—	—	—
13	—	—	+⊕	no record	—	⊕+
14	+	⊕+	+	+	+	⊕
15	⊕	—	⊕+	—	+—	—

* The data were taken from the records of stations listed in Table 1.
Symbols: pearls lasting not less than 1 hour with periods greater than 3 sec ⊕, with periods less than 3 sec +.

generation of pearls at stations located in polar caps, auroral zones and middle latitudes. From this table following conclusions can be drawn:

1. The period before the proton flare was relatively quiet as regards the generation of pearls, especially with period less than 3 seconds.

2. 25.5 hours after the proton flare and 19 hours before the sudden storm commencement there occurred an exceptional case of pearl generation on a world-wide scale, with almost the same periods at all stations (~ 1.8–2 sec).

3. In the week following the proton flare the occurrence of pearls of different periods was systematically observed day after day in different regions.

There are some other interesting features of the behaviour of micropulsations during the period analysed, and first of all the occurrence of IPDP on

Fig. 1   Example of regularities in the occurrence of micropulsations on 7–9 July 1966. In the lower part of the figure are given in a specific code the times of occurrence of different types of pulsations; in the upper part of the figure are given the variations of polar-cap absorption at three stations and the changes of *Kp*.

Lower part: 1 M'Bour   7 Tixi
2 Alma Ata   8 Lovozero
3 Irkutsk   9 Novolazarevskaya
4 Petropavlovsk   10 Heiss
5 Borok   11 Mirny
6 Sogra   12 Vostok

8 July must be stressed. This phenomenon, as was shown earlier (Troitskaya, Bolshakova, and Matveeva 1966), is connected with variations of intensity in the radiation belts. It is interesting that this event occurs before the magnetic storm (see Fig. 1).

As a consequence of modern conceptions of the mechanism of the generation of pearls (e.g. Tverskoy 1967) we can suggest that after the proton flare of 7 July energetic particles have penetrated the magnetosphere before the main bulk of the corpuscular stream causing the magnetic storm has reached the surroundings of the earth. These particles have generated the world-wide pearls of 8 July. The global excitation of pearls may be due either to the intensity of the event, and the dimensions of the source, or to conditions in the ionospheric waveguide, permitting Pc1 world-wide propagation.

The systematic occurrence of pearls in the week following the flare may be interpreted as an indication of long lasting penetration or existence of energetic particles in the earth's magnetosphere after the flare.

References

HAKURA, Y., 1968, The polar cap absorption on 7–10 July 1966, *Ann. IQSY*, this volume, Paper 45.

PLYASOVA-BAKUNINA, T. A., and E. T. MATVEEVA, 1968, Connection of type Pc1 pulsations with magnetic storms, *Geomagn. i Aeronomiya*, **8**, in press.

TROITSKAYA, V. A., O. V. BOLSHAKOVA, and E. T. MATVEEVA, 1966, Rapid variations of electromagnetic field as indicator of a state of radiation belts and magnetosphere of the earth, *Geomagn. i Aeronomiya*, **6**, 533–540.

TVERSKOY, B. A., 1967, Position of radiation belts of the earth, *Geomagn. i Aeronomiya*, **7**, 226–242.

WENTWORTH, R. C., 1964, Enhancement of hydromagnetic emissions after geomagnetic storms, *J. Geophys. Res.*, **69**, 2291–2298.

56

The Variations of the Geomagnetic Field in Middle and High Latitudes during the Proton Flare Event of July 1966

A. Best, G. Fanselau, A. Grafe, H.-R. Lehmann, and Chr.-Ulr. Wagner

Geomagnetic Institute of the German Academy of Sciences, Potsdam, German Democratic Republic

Abstract

The present summary gives in its beginning a general survey of magnetic activity. The magnetic records indicate that a general rather than a sudden increase of ultra-violet radiation is associated with the proton flare. The *Dst* component for a geomagnetic latitude of about 51.5°N and the current systems at the polar cap and the auroral zone are given and discussed for different times of the geomagnetic disturbance following the proton flare. Also discussed are the period spectra and the energy spectra of the variations occurring during the main phase of the storm for observatories in different latitudes.

I Magnetic Activity (June to September 1966)

A survey of the *Kp* indices (Fig. 1) shows that during the month of June and the first days of July there are no important magnetic disturbances. The magnetic disturbance from 8 to 10 July which followed the proton flare of 7 July was the first violent disturbance after a long quiet epoch. The 2nd, 3rd, and 13th days of July can even be looked upon as magnetically quiet days. Also 7 July, the proton flare day, was a quiet day until about 2200 UT (indicated by a *Kp* index of 0.1). After the decrease of the disturbance the activity fell during the following days of July.

Figure 1 demonstrates clearly that the disturbance of the epoch 8 to 10 July originated from a solar zone of activity, showing intense activity after two

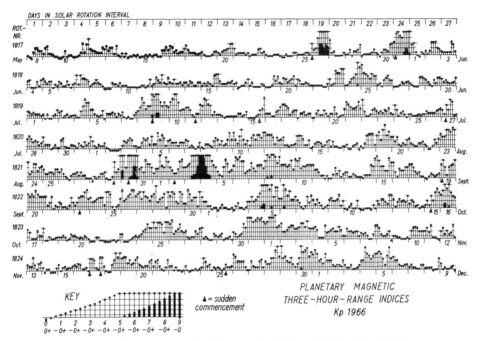

Fig. 1   Planetary magnetic 3-hour range indices *Kp* May–Nov. 1966.

successive solar rotations as can be seen from the 27-day recurrence diagram. This zone of activity appeared during the first days of July in the region of 25°N heliographic latitude and 184° heliographic longitude, and caused two new proton flares on 28 August at 1523 UT and on 2 September at 0542 UT.

2   Geomagnetic Variations on 7 July 1966

As the proton flare occurred during a day which had, with the exception of the nocturnal hours, been a quiet one we attempted to obtain results as to a possible effect by an analysis of geomagnetic *Sq* variations.

A geomagnetic effect on the *Sq* variations can be produced by an increase of the intensity of ionizing wave radiation or by incoming high-energy particles.

Since in Europe and in the main part of America the proton flare occurred during the night-time, we have investigated the magnetic variations of the Asian station Srednikan to discover whether the proton flare was accompanied by a sudden increase of ionizing radiation. Such a sudden increase, however, had not been detected by the station mentioned.

To obtain some knowledge about the slow increase of the wave radiation and about the intrusion of very fast particles, we have evaluated records of geomagnetic observatories situated in the region 38° to 62°N and 10° to 15°E. These are listed in Table 1. Based upon these measurements the *Sq*

Table I List of the Observatories Used for Evaluation

Name	Symbol	Geomagnetic Lat. (Φ)	Geomagnetic Long. (Λ)	Geographic Lat. (ϕ)	Geographic Long. (λ)
Honolulu*	HO	21.1°	266.5°	21°18′	−158°06′
L'Aquila*	AQ	42.9°	92.9°	42°23′	13°19′
Boulder	BD	48.9°	316.4°	40°03′	−105°18′
Fredericksburg	FR	49.6°	349.8°	38°12′	−77°22′
Moscow	KP	50.8°	120.5°	55°29′	37°19′
Yakutsk	YA	51.0°	193.8°	62°01′	129°40′
Niemegk*	NI	52.2°	96.6°	52°04′	12°40′
Srednikan	SR	53.2°	210.6°	62°26′	152°19′
Victoria*	VI	54.3°	292.7°	48°31′	−123°25′
Rude Skov	RS	55.8°	98.5°	55°51′	18°27′
Nurmijärvi	NU	57.8°	112.5°	60°30′	24°39′
Lovö	LO	58.1°	105.8°	59°21′	17°50′
Eskdalemuir	ES	58.5°	82.9°	55°19′	−03°12′
Sitka*	SI	60.0°	275.4°	57°04′	−135°20′
Tixie Bay	TI	60.1°	191.1°	71°34′	128°54′
Cape Wellen	WE	61.0°	237.0°	66°10′	−170°11′
Dombas*	DO	62.3°	100.1°	57°03′	− 09°07′
Lerwick	LE	62.5°	88.6°	60°08′	− 01°11′
Dixon Island	DI	63.0°	161.4°	73°32′	80°33′
Sodankylä	SO	63.8°	120.0°	67°22′	26°39′
Loparskaya	LY	64.1°	126.5°	68°57′	33°03′
College	CO	64.6°	256.6°	64°52′	−147°50′
Kiruna	KI	65.3°	115.9°	67°50′	20°25′
Cape Chelyuskin	CC	65.9°	177.5°	77°43′	104°17′
Abisko	AI	66.0°	115.0°	68°21′	18°49′
Tromsö	TR	67.2°	116.8°	69°40′	18°57′
Point Barrow	PB	68.6°	241.2°	71°18′	−156°45′
Fort Churchill	CHR	68.8°	322.5°	58°48′	−94°06′
Tikhaya Bay	TB	70.9°	156.5°	80°37′	18°15′
Baker Lake	BL	73.9°	314.8°	64°20′	−96°02′
Godhavn	GO	79.9°	32.5°	69°14′	−53°31′
Resolute Bay*	RB	83.0°	289.6°	74°42′	−94°54′
Alert	AT	85.9°	168.2°	82°30′	−62°30′
Thule Village	TH	88.9°	357.8°	77°29′	−69°10′

* Observatories used for calculation of power spectra.

variations were calculated. For the same observatories the *Sq* variations of the quiet days (28 June, 2, 3, and 13 July) were determined. For comparison and as a reference level the *Sq* variations of five observatories calculated for 7 July are shown in Fig. 2. If there had been a strong intensity increase of wave radiation after the proton flare the amplitude of the *Sq* variations should have been larger on 7 July than on the remaining quiet days. It was found that the totalled ranges of variation of all the stations on 7 July was larger than on other days, which demonstrates a general increase of the radiation intensity. Figure 2 proves that the magnetic records give no evidence of incoming

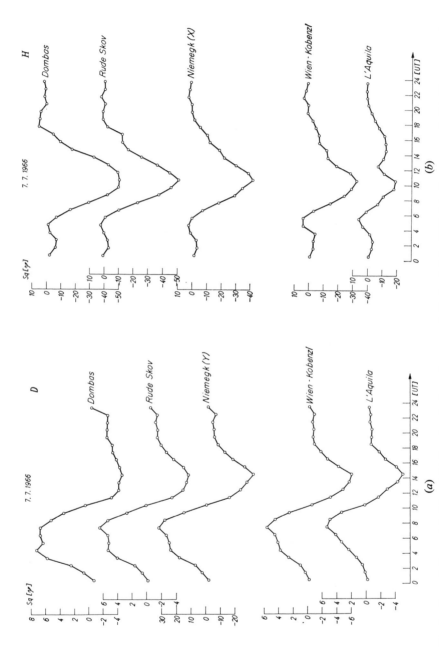

Fig. 2   Sq variation related to night-time level: dependence on latitude, 7 July 1966. (a), D component; (b), H component.

high-energy particles in middle latitudes. At higher latitudes disturbances on 7 July occurred at about 2200 UT (see, for example, College records, Fig. 3).

3 Magnetically Disturbed Conditions from 8 to I0 July 1966

Strong disturbances in high geomagnetic latitudes occurred on 8 July, and the *Kp* index reached the value of 4+ (see Fig. 1). Magnetograms of the stations Alert, College, Baker Lake, and Niemegk are reproduced in Fig. 3. The disturbances observed at the single polar stations exhibit different pictures in their variation with time (compare College with Alert and Baker Lake), but there are hardly any marked disturbances in middle latitudes.

3.I The Sudden Commencement

The main disturbance begins with a sudden storm commencement on 8 July at 2103 UT. This ssc can only be made out as such for middle-latitude

Table 2   Sudden Storm Commencement Amplitude in Different Latitudes

Station	Horizontal Disturbance Vector ΔH (γ)	ssc Amplitude		Remarks
		ΔY (γ)	ΔX (γ)	
Honolulu	14	0	14	
L'Aquila	30	-11	27	
Boulder	50	25	43	
Fredericksburg	49	7	49	
Moscow	33	-8	32	
Niemegk	36	-11	34	
Srednikan	55	39	-39	
Victoria	39	-11	37	
Nurmijärvi	22	-8	20	
Lovö				ssc determination not exactly practicable
Eskdalemuir	45	-17	42	
Sitka	42	-21	36	
Dombas				see Lovö
Lerwick	21	-13	16	
Sodankylä	207	-156	-133	
College	167	-166	15	
Kiruna	314	172	-262	
Abisko	361	294	-210	
Tromsö	188	-181	51	
Point Barrow	411	-410	32	ssc not fully discernible due to great disturbances
Fort Churchill	53	-40	-34	
Baker Lake	211	-101	-185	
Resolute Bay	204	78	-188	
Alert	221	88	-203	

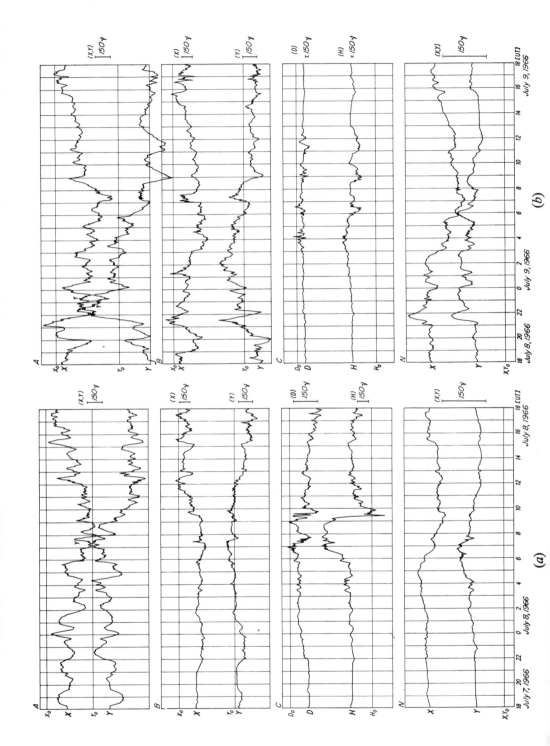

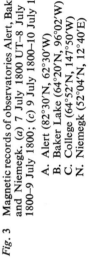

Fig. 3 Magnetic records of observatories Alert, Baker Lake, College, and Niemegk. (*a*) 7 July 1800 UT–8 July 1800; (*b*) 8 July 1800–9 July 1800; (*c*) 9 July 1800–10 July 1800.

    A. Alert (82°30′N, 62°30′W)
    B. Baker Lake (64°20′N, 96°02′W)
    C. College (64°52′N, 147°50′W)
    N. Niemegk (52°04′N, 12°40′E)

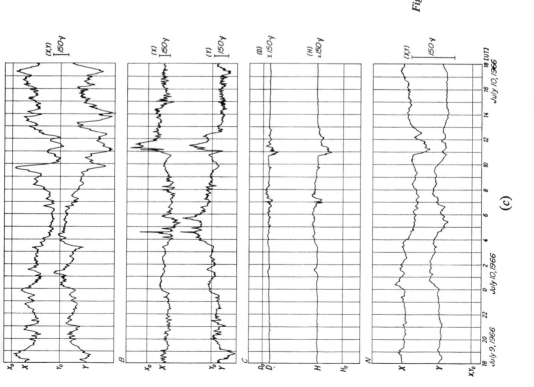

stations. Table 2 shows the ssc amplitude in the D or Y and H or X component respectively, and the horizontal vector of the disturbance resulting from this is also given. In higher latitudes violent disturbances had been occurring during the period of the ssc, and the determination of the ssc amplitude is difficult and uncertain, as can clearly be seen in the records of Alert and Baker Lake. It can also be noticed that the disturbance intensity at the polar stations does not increase or only unimportantly so, and is different in behaviour at the single polar stations (Fig. 3).

In Fig. 3d this ssc is shown according to the record of the Niemegk observatory, where there is a recording for the geomagnetic east component η (Fanselau and Grafe 1968). As can be seen from Fig. 3d, in the horizontal

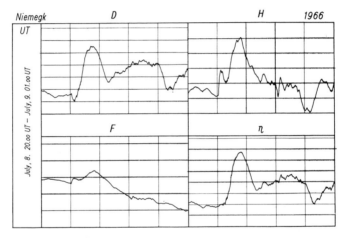

Fig. 3d Record of ssc, east component, Niemegk (unit of ordinates 20γ).

component the ssc has a positive deviation only. The geomagnetic east component does not show any deviations. This proves that the ssc has no variations of the type Ds but of the type Dst only.

3.2   The Dst Component

Figure 4 shows the Dst component for the middle latitudes 51.5° over the period 8 July 1200 UT to 10 July 1500 UT. For calculation we used the Dst-variation records of the observatories Boulder, Fredericksburg, Moscow, Niemegk, Srednikan, and Victoria. The values were obtained as deviations between the half-hourly instantaneous values and the instantaneous value at 2100 UT on 8 July. The slow falling off of the Dst variation to the maximum amplitude was typical of this storm. These conditions are characteristic of storms of low activity. The main phase of the storm began at about 0100 UT on 9 July. The maximum of the Dst phase was reached on 9 July at 0730 UT with -60γ. We can also see clearly the recurring falling-off of the Dst

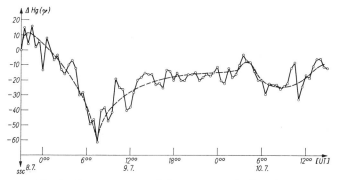

Fig. 4   *Dst* component of the geomagnetic disturbance.

variation to -30γ on 10 July during the interval 0400 to 1300 UT. Simultaneous new disturbances after a quiet period were recorded at the College observatory.

3.3   Current Systems of the DP Component

A further aim was the calculation and drawing of current systems in northern middle and high latitudes for different times. Figure 5 represents the current systems in geomagnetic coordinates for 8 to 9 July 1966, for the eight times 2300, 0000, 0100, 0300, 0400, 0500, 0700, and 1000 UT. The current line density was obtained approximately from the local gradients of the magnetic disturbance vectors. For some observatories no vector could be given for certain times since the copy of the magnetogram was illegible.

Figure 5a shows the current system at 2300 UT on 8 July, i.e. two hours after the beginning of the storm. A current with an east–west direction clearly occurs in the European–Asiatic area and is closed over the polar cap. The centre of the current vortex was near the Tromsö observatory. Figure 5b, which shows the current system one hour later, is almost identical with Fig. 5a, with only the current-line density being somewhat increased. The two figures are very similar to the representation of the current system of a "polar magnetic substorm" given by Akasofu, Chapman, and Meng (1965). The current system in the two instances is eccentric relative to the geomagnetic pole; with the systems depicted in Figs. 5a and b only the centre of the current systems is shifted towards south. The current system for 0100 UT has been drawn in Fig. 5c. There is a further increase of the current-line density in the European–Asiatic area. The splitting-off of a second current system with its centre near the polar cap is particularly interesting. The current in this system flows from west to east. In Fig. 5d the current system exhibits two current systems about equally strong. There are again very strong local gradients of the geomagnetic vectors in the European area. The second current system with its centre near the Alert observatory is already fully

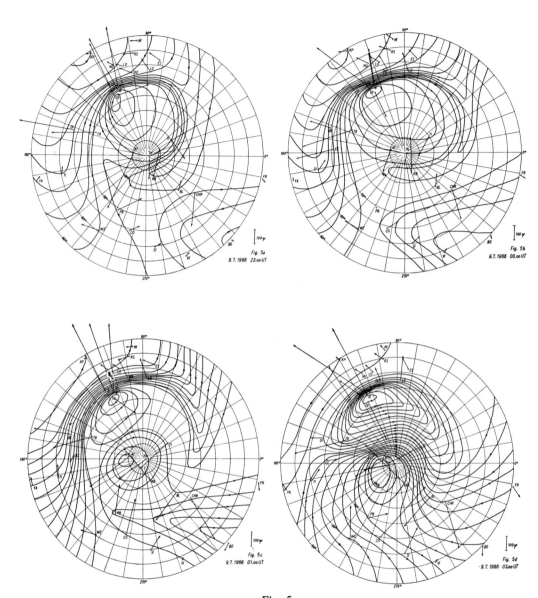

Fig. 5a
8.7.1966 23.00 UT

Fig. 5b
9.7.1966 00.00 UT

Fig. 5c
9.7.1966 01.00 UT

Fig. 5d
9.7.1966 03.00 UT

Fig. 5

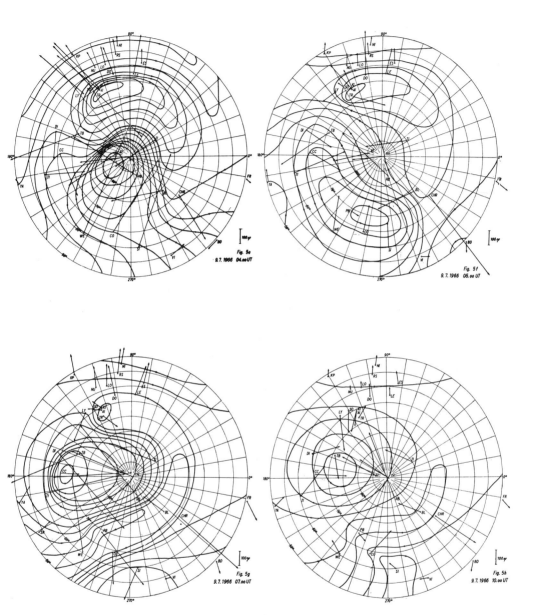

Fig. 5 Current systems for middle and high latitudes in the northern hemisphere 8–9 July 1966: *a*, 8 July 1966, 2300 UT; *b*, 9 July 1966, 0000 UT; *c*, 0100; *d*, 0300; *e*, 0400; *f*, 0500; *g*, 0700; *h*, 1000 UT.

developed at 0300 UT. The shape of these two current systems is more similar to the one during a "polar magnetic substorm" as given by Nagata and Kokubun (1960). The current-line densities are less marked at 0400 UT (Fig. 5*e*), but there are comparatively strong disturbance amplitudes in the Far East area, in Western America and in the polar-cap region. The gradients in the two current systems have become smooth in middle latitudes. The following can be seen for the current system at 0500 UT (Fig. 5*f*): The current system in Europe is slowly dissolving, and the centre of the second current system has shifted towards the south. The current direction in Resolute Bay, however, cannot be made to agree with the given current flow. But all other measurements correspond to the current flow given. In the further course of the disturbance the current centre moves westward. At 0700 UT (Fig. 5*g*) it is near the Cape Chelyuskin observatory. The reversal of the current direction in Baker Lake is typical: whereas the direction of the current in the previous hours had been south to north, it flows from west to east at 0700 UT. At 0700 UT there are also the strongest disturbance amplitudes in Asia, America, and at the polar cap. Towards 1000 UT (Fig. 5*h*), i.e. when the strongest disturbances had come to an end, the current system which had been present at the beginning of the storm has completely disappeared in Europe. The second current system, however, is still in full existence.

3.4 Frequency and Energy Spectra of the Geomagnetic Variations during the Main Phase of the Disturbance

The geomagnetic storm shows only a low intensity (weak storm).

To obtain a summarizing picture of the frequency behaviour for the disturbances as a function of latitude, the power spectra were calculated for the interval 8 July 1966, 2100 UT, to 10 July 1500 UT for different observatories (marked by an asterisk in Table 1). The variations of the X and Y component or the H and D component respectively were analysed on the basis of 5-minute mean values for the periods from 20 to 120 minutes. The interpretation of the spectra of the different components yielded information on the frequencies and the mean magnetic energy density of the variations.

The power spectra are not very conspicuous at the southern stations L'Aquila and Honolulu (Fig. 6). For Honolulu we have obtained a maximum of the spectral density for periods 60 and 90 minutes for the two components. For stations situated farther to the north higher frequencies are typical, whereas in middle latitudes (Niemegk, Boulder, Fredericksburg) the maximum of spectral density lies at about 50 to 60 minutes. We find for stations of the highest latitudes an additional maximum at 40 and 30 minutes (see Resolute Bay) for the two components.

The average trend of the spectra of the energy density of the variations is a decrease from slow to higher periods for the interval investigated here. The

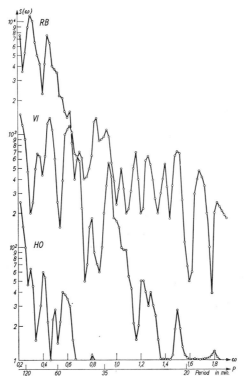

Fig. 6   Power spectra of X component for Resolute Bay, H components for Victoria and Honolulu, 8 July 2100 to 10 July 1966, 1500 UT.

amplitude of the spectra depends on the intensity of the disturbance. While the intensity of disturbance of this storm is small in southern and middle latitudes, the observatories in higher latitudes show a violent activity during the period investigated, i.e. the mean level of the magnetic energy density increases steadily with increasing latitude.

Acknowledgments

We should like to express our gratitude to all observatories listed in Table 1 for making their magnetograms available.

References

AKASOFU, S.-I., S. CHAPMAN, and J. MENG, 1965, The polar electrojet, *J. Atmos. Terr. Phys.*, **27**, 1275–1305.

FANSELAU, G., and A. GRAFE, 1968, Die Registrierung der geomagnetischen Ost–West-Komponente und ihre Bedeutung für die ssc-Morphologie, *Gerlands Beitr. Geophys.*, **77**, 82–86.

NAGATA, T., and S. KOKUBUN, 1960, On the earth storm: IV. Polar magnetic storm with special reference to relations between geomagnetic disturbances in the northern and southern auroral zone, *Rep. Ionosph. Space Res. Japan*, **14**, 273–290.

57

Ionospheric Conditions following the Proton Flare of 7 July 1966 as deduced from Topside Soundings

L. Herzberg and G. L. Nelms

Radio Physics Laboratory, Defence Research Telecommunications Establishment, Ottawa, Ontario, Canada

Abstract

Following the solar proton flare of 7 July 1966, two unusual conditions of the ionosphere were observed with the topside sounders of the Alouette satellites: (1) the G condition, a phenomenon observed on earlier occasions during magnetic storms, where, from the topside, the F1 layer becomes visible below the F2 layer; (2) a new condition, provisionally named Σ condition, whose presence is recognized by the occurrence of narrow dark bands, crossing the reflection trace of Alouette 2 ionograms at low frequencies where the frequency resolution is relatively large. The bands are tentatively interpreted as narrow vertical regions of electron density depletion ("minitroughs"), possibly connected with a stationary hydromagnetic wave. The correlation of the sounder results with particle counter and plasma probe data is discussed.

I Introduction

During the solar flare event of 7 July 1966 the satellites Alouette 1 and Alouette 2 which carry sweep-frequency radio sounders were in operation. Both satellites are in polar orbits, with 80° inclination. The orbit of Alouette 1 is near circular at about 1000 km height, that of Alouette 2 elliptical with about 500 km perigee and about 3000 km apogee. In early July 1966 Alouette 2 was at apogee over the north polar region.

Although not all the observations during the days in question have been processed so far, there is sufficient material from the northern hemisphere available to show the sporadic occurrence at high northern latitudes of two unusual ionospheric conditions which appear to be connected with the proton event: the G condition, which has been observed on other occasions, and a second condition which we have provisionally named Σ condition and which is apparently new, at least in the form in which it manifests itself in topside soundings.

2 G Condition

The G condition has been designated as such by URSI. It is observed in bottomside soundings at high latitudes during magnetically disturbed conditions and is characterized by a decrease in the F2 layer penetration frequency until the F2 layer becomes masked by the F1 layer. In other words, there is a decrease in the electron density of the F2 layer, while that of the F1 layer remains more or less constant. From the topside of the ionosphere the condition has first been observed by Nelms and Warren (1965).

Figure 1 shows three electron-density profiles derived (by G. E. K. Lockwood) from Alouette 1 ionograms obtained during a northerly satellite pass

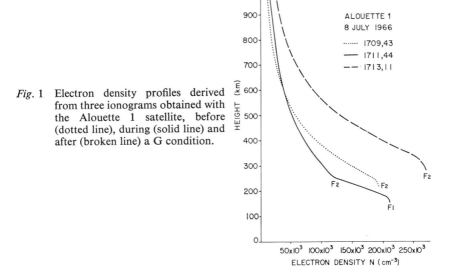

Fig. 1 Electron density profiles derived from three ionograms obtained with the Alouette 1 satellite, before (dotted line), during (solid line) and after (broken line) a G condition.

after the proton flare: the dotted line is the profile just before the G condition was encountered, the solid line is that during the G condition, and the broken line that obtained 2 minutes after the time when the G condition was observed, and, it should be noted, at a satellite position nearly 1000 km farther north. The diagram shows clearly the decrease during the G condition of the electron density in the F2 layer (200–400 km), revealing the F1 layer. The electron density in the F1 layer (140–200 km) remained more or less constant during the time that it could be observed. After the G condition, the recovery began characteristically in the lower part of the F2 layer.

Figure 2 illustrates essentially the same effect. We show here, along a whole pass in which the G condition occurs and, for comparison, also along a pass

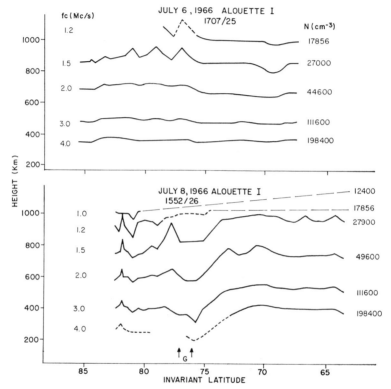

Fig. 2   Altitudes of constant frequency of reflection or constant electron density for a satellite pass before the proton flare and for a pass after the flare, which shows occurrence of the G condition. Time runs from left to right in the diagram. (Times indicated are the starting times of the satellite passes.)

before the flare event (at approximately the same latitude) the altitudes at which given frequencies are reflected, i.e. the altitudes at which the electron density has a certain value. As we enter the region where the G condition exists, the levels with relatively high electron density descend considerably, those with lower electron density rise slightly. The main effect is a downward movement of the maximum electron density and a later rise (and increase), actually to above the original altitude.

Figure 3 gives an (Alouette 2) ionogram of the type obtained during a G condition. The characteristic loops at the high-frequency end of the reflection traces correspond to an unusual change in the gradient of the electron density (for further details see caption of Fig. 3). Figure 4 gives the electron densities computed from this ionogram (full line), from one recorded 1 minute earlier (dotted line), and from one recorded $1\frac{1}{2}$ minutes later (broken line).

This series of electron density profiles differs from that shown in Fig. 1 in an important point: there is, apart from a slight decrease in electron density in the F2 region (near 300 km), during the G condition a significant increase in electron density in the F1 and E regions. There is a shift of the electron

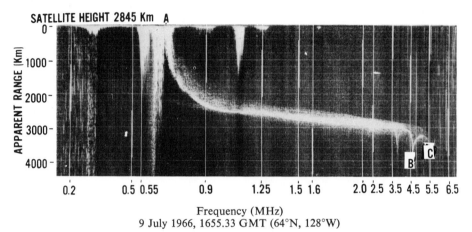

Frequency (MHz)
9 July 1966, 1655.33 GMT (64°N, 128°W)

Fig. 3   Ionogram obtained with the Alouette 2 satellite. The abscissa gives the frequencies of successive radio-wave pulses transmitted from the satellite, the ordinate the delay time of the reflected signals in terms of the radar range of the reflecting layer. The traces AB and AC, the so-called reflection traces, are the successive reflected signals propagated with the two possible directions of polarization, returning from successively lower levels of the ionosphere with successively higher electron density. B and C give the critical or penetration frequencies corresponding to the maximum of the electron density. The loops at the high-frequency end of the reflection traces correspond to an unusual change in the gradient of the electron density.

density maximum from $N = 185 \times 10^3$ cm^{-3} at an altitude $h = 220$ km to $N = 255 \times 10^3$ cm^{-3} at $h \simeq 95$ km. This means that in this case the sounder "sees" into the ionosphere to below 100 km. After the occurrence of the G condition, or beyond the region where the G condition is present, the enhancement of the F1 and E region disappears, while we have the usual "filling in" of the electron density profile in the F2 region with a slight all-over increase of the electron density, compared with the condition before the onset of the disturbance, and an upward movement (and increase) of the electron density maximum.

It appears therefore that there are two different conditions which produce topside ionograms of the same general type: the classical G condition as defined by URSI in which the electron density in the F1 layer remains more or less constant, and a G' condition in which there is a significant increase in electron density in the F1 and even in the E layer. Careful scaling of the ionograms will make it possible to distinguish between the two conditions, and work in this direction is now in progress. In the present paper, however, no distinction could yet be made between the G and G' conditions, and both will be treated together as "G condition".

We have observed the G condition on a number of occasions on the second to the fifth day after the proton flare (days 189 to 192). The geographical distribution of the observed incidences is shown in Fig. 5a. The G condition seems to occur more or less randomly over the polar cap, at geographical

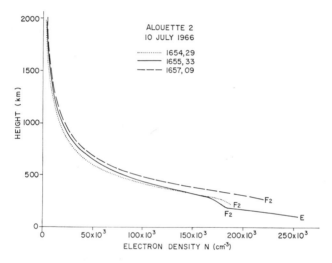

Fig. 4   Electron density profiles corresponding to the ionogram shown in Fig. 3 (solid line) and to one obtained slightly earlier (dotted line) and one slightly later (broken line).

latitudes above 60°, although the distribution pattern appears to be centered on the magnetic pole. There is some indication of a southward expansion of the area of incidence after the sudden commencement of the magnetic storm (ssc). The G condition has been observed at all local times with a slight bias towards the "day" hours (during this polar summer event).

Area and duration of a single occurrence of the G condition are difficult to judge on the basis of the satellite observations: the satellite observations are obtained only from a narrow region beneath the satellite orbit and it is also in many cases not easy to decide, by inspection of the ionograms alone and without detailed scaling, whether or not a G condition is present in successive ionograms. However, after studying all the ionograms obtained during the event, it seems safe to say that the linear extent of the G condition, as observed, was of the order of 1000 km. There is some indication that the condition was present roughly in the same area at the same local time on succeeding days. (This has definitely been observed to be so during the 24 June 1966 magnetic storm.)

We have no good physical interpretation of the G condition. For the classical G condition a simple expansion, perhaps due to heating, of the upper ionosphere has been suggested. For what we call the G′ condition, one may think of a sudden enhancement of ionization in the lower ionosphere over a narrow region, perhaps due to particle precipitation, followed by readjustment through diffusion, apart from recombination processes. We have so far

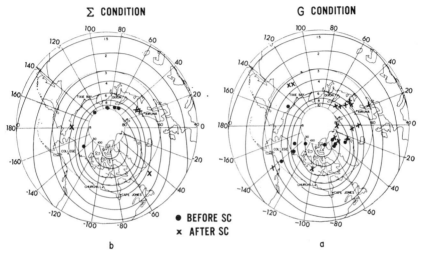

Fig. 5   Geographical distribution after the solar proton flare of 7 July 1966 of (*a*) the G condition; (*b*) the Σ condition.

(see below) not found a good correlation between the occurrences of the G condition and the quality of the incident radiation. Perhaps the separate analysis of the classical G and the new G′ condition as to their latitude and time dependence and their possible correlation with particle data will give some clue as to the underlying physical process.

3 Σ Condition

The other unusual condition of the ionosphere which we have observed in the course of the 7 July 1966 event, the Σ condition, is characterized in the ionograms by the presence of sharp, narrow vertical bands or spikes, at low frequencies, which cross the reflection trace. An example is shown in Fig. 6. The spikes extend generally to both sides of the reflection trace but only rarely, and only at very low frequencies, do they reach the height of the satellite. The ionogram here reproduced is our best example. It is one of the two or three cases where the spikes form a fairly regular sequence. In most cases the spikes follow each other without any recognizable law and may be single, like the single spike at $\omega = 1.2$ MHz in the example reproduced.

A model for the Σ condition which we find rather attractive is the presence of what we have named "minitroughs". We picture a minitrough as a narrow cylinder of diminished electron density from whose rough walls signals are reflected back to the satellite. The travel time of these obliquely reflected signals may be shorter or longer than that of the signal of the same frequency which would have been reflected from the undisturbed ionosphere. Such a

Frequency (MHz)

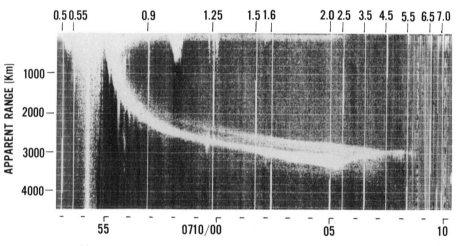

Alouette 2, 10 July 1966. Satellite height 2945 km, 72°N 29°E.

Fig. 6   Ionogram showing the Σ condition. The short horizontal lines below the iono-gram are second markers.

mechanism will produce a band of signals on both sides of the reflection trace, as observed. The sharp definition of the "spikes" could be understood as the effect of the fast passage of the satellite in and out of the minitroughs.

If we make the assumption that the minitroughs are stationary, their width can be determined from the known flight velocity (c. 8 km s^{-1}) of the satellite and their width on the ionogram in seconds. (The horizontal dashes below the ionogram are second markers.) We find the width of the minitroughs (from density maximum to density maximum) to be about 2 km. If, as we are tempted to do on the basis of the sometimes occurring regular series of mini-troughs, we interpret the observations as a hydromagnetic oscillation we obtain for it a period of the order of 0.2 sec.

A scale length of a few kilometers is not unreasonable, considering the fact that the Debye length is of the order of 10 cm. Also the width of the ducts in which Alouette 1 signals have been observed to propagate is of the order of a kilometer (Muldrew 1963).

It should be noted that the disturbance in electron-density distribution discussed here as the Σ condition is not identical with other disturbances recognized so far. It is different from "spread F", an example of which is seen on the ionogram of Fig. 6 at satellite height near 0.8 MHz; this condition looks diffuse on the ionogram and is due to randomly distributed irregularities of the size of some meters. The Σ condition also appears to be different from certain irregularities of 10 to 15 km size which produce on the ionograms a scalloped appearance of the reflection trace.

Figure 5*b* gives the geographical distribution of the Σ condition. While, as said before, the incidences of the G condition appear to be rather randomly distributed over the polar cap, the Σ condition seems to be tied to definite L shells: the incidences before the ssc are roughly at $L = 11$ (for ground level), those after the ssc at $L = 6$.

There is also a difference in the two conditions with respect to their distribution in local time. Whereas the G condition (during this polar summer event) is observed at all local times though perhaps slightly more frequently during the "day", the Σ condition is observed only between 09 and 17 hours local time, that is only on the sunward side of the earth. There is also a gap in the occurrence of the Σ condition around noon, between 1130 and 1530, but since we have altogether rather few observations, this latter effect may well be spurious.

There can be little doubt that there is a close connection between the shape of the earth's magnetic field and the distribution of the Σ condition, if not also of the G condition. It is well known that during a proton flare event there is a displacement of the magnetic field pattern away from the poles after the ssc. Correspondingly, the location of the Σ and probably also of the G condition moves farther south after the ssc.

As mentioned above, the G condition has been known for some time to occur during magnetically disturbed periods which do not have to be connected with a solar proton flare event, and has been observed from the topside with both the Alouette 1 and the Alouette 2 satellite. In contrast, the Σ condition has for the first and so far only time been observed during the days after the 7 July 1966 proton flare, and then only with the Alouette 2 satellite. We have carefully examined all the ionograms obtained with Alouette 2 from 1 January 1966 to 7 July 1966 at Ottawa and at College, that is from northern passes of the satellite. Though there were a number of incidences of the G condition, especially during the magnetic storm of 24 June, not a single occurrence of the Σ condition was found.

From our experience so far, we are inclined to think that the Σ condition occurs only in connection with a proton flare event (and the 7 July event was the first important polar flare event of 1966), and further, that it can be observed only with the Alouette 2 and not with the Alouette 1 topside sounder. The relevant difference in the sounders of the two satellites appears to be the frequency resolution below 2 MHz where the effect is observed. The Alouette 1 sounder pulses have about 15 kHz frequency separation and are swept with a repetition frequency of about 60 Hz. The corresponding figures for Alouette 2 (below 2 MHz) are a frequency separation of about 4 kHz and pulse repetition frequency of about 30 Hz. Since the two satellites travel with approximately the same velocity, this means that the reflection level of successive pulses from Alouette 2 falls about 7 times less steeply with distance

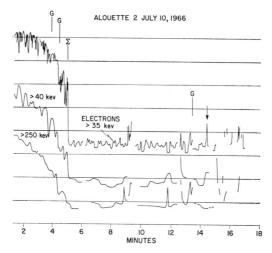

Fig. 7   Part of an energetic particle record obtained with the Alouette 2 satellite. (By courtesy of I. B. McDiarmid and J. R. Burrows.) Times of occurrence of the G and the Σ condition are indicated.

along the pass than the reflection level for the Alouette 1 pulses. A periodic disturbance which is stationary (horizontal standing wave) or propagates only very slowly would be more easily observed by the Alouette 2 sounder; with a more nearly horizontal plane of reflection, successive maxima and minima in space will be more clearly resolved.

I. B. McDiarmid and J. R. Burrows of Ottawa have kindly made available to us the results of energetic particle measurements made with the Alouette 2 satellite at times when we have found unusual conditions in the ionosphere. Figure 7 shows part of such a record. The traces correspond to the intensities (on a logarithmic scale) of electrons with energies above 35 keV, 40 keV, and 250 keV respectively. (The short period alternation of the intensity is due to the spin of the satellite.) This is trapped radiation of the outer Van Allen belt. In Fig. 7 at 1105 there is an abrupt decrease of the radiation as the satellite exits from the Van Allen belt. Exactly at this instant we observe a Σ condition. A G condition is observed shortly before the exit and also somewhat later in the pass.

Looking over the particle records of the passes in which the Σ or the G condition occur and for which we have particle data, we can say that the Σ condition occurs always at an abrupt change in the intensity of the electrons of energy greater than 35 keV. The abrupt change does not necessarily have to be the limit of the Van Allen belt proper, as in the example shown; it may also be some sudden short-time intensification (spike), like the one marked with an arrow (between 14 and 16 min) in Fig. 7. We have also never observed the Σ condition while the satellite was within the Van Allen belt.

We observe the Σ condition only in comparatively few instances of all those where a sudden change in the intensity of the > 35 keV electrons occurs. This must mean that either the occurrence of the Σ condition depends on additional factors not recognized or that it can be observed only when the experimental conditions are especially favorable, for instance when the antennae are in a specific direction with respect to the earth's magnetic field.

The occurrence of the G condition seems to be less dependent on a sudden change in the electron intensity above 35 keV, though it frequently occurs at such times. In fact, we have not found a significant correlation between any recorded particle radiation and the G condition. In contrast to the case of the Σ condition, we have observed the G condition occasionally when the satellite was inside the Van Allen belt.

Very recently, in co-operation with L. H. Brace and J. A. Findlay of Goddard Space Flight Center, we have collated some of our minitrough observations with results obtained by them with the plasma probe carried on Alouette 2. Whereas the sounder measures the electron density at the satellite only once every 30 seconds, the plasma probe measures concentrations and temperatures of electrons and positive ions in the immediate neighbourhood of the satellite at a much faster rate, essentially at fraction-of-a-second intervals. A preliminary survey has disclosed several occasions where minitroughs and electron density decreases at the satellite are observed simultaneously by the two experiments. Two facts stand out: (a) sometimes, for instance in the case of the strongest vertical bands on the ionogram shown in Fig. 6 (at 0709,55.4 and 0709,59.2 sec), decreases in the electron density at the satellite of about 40 per cent are recorded within a fraction of a second of the observation of the minitroughs; (b) decreases in the electron density at the satellite are often observed in quasi-periodic sequences with a period of the same order of magnitude as that observed for series of minitroughs (~ 0.2 sec).

We propose to do more detailed work on the correlation of sounder and plasma probe data. We hope that thereby our concept of the minitroughs as of narrow cylindrical regions of electron density decrease, or of a wavelike disturbance of the electron density, will be strengthened, and that we will be able to show that the narrow regions of electron depletion at times reach from the height of reflection, 100 km or more below the satellite, upward to, at least, the altitude of the spacecraft.

Note added in proof: Further study of topside ionograms has revealed incidences of the Σ condition during ionospheric disturbances which did not include proton flares. The latter therefore are not necessary for the occurrence of the Σ condition.

Acknowledgments

We wish to thank Drs. I. B. McDiarmid and J. R. Burrows for supplying us with their energetic particle measurements and Dr. L. H. Brace and Mr. J. A. Findlay for the use of their plasma probe observations.

References

MULDREW, D. B., 1963, Radio propagation along magnetic field-aligned sheets of ionization observed by the Alouette topside sounder, *J. Geophys. Res.*, **68**, 5355–5370.
NELMS, G. L., and E. S. WARREN, 1965, Some irregular variations of the electron density in the topside of the ionosphere, *Space Research V*, Ed. D. G. King-Hele, P. Müller and G. Righini (North-Holland Publ. Co., Amsterdam), pp. 637–638.

58

Ionospheric Conditions following the Proton Flare Event of 7 July 1966 as measured at Ground-based Stations
I. Low-Energy Particle Effects in the Lower Ionosphere at Medium Latitudes

R. Knuth and E. A. Lauter
Observatory for Ionospheric Research, Kühlungsborn, German Democratic Republic

Abstract

The results of the particle effects in medium latitudes in the lower ionosphere during the storm-time period following the proton flare event was a small but detectable event which follows the normal behaviour, i.e. a sudden increase of absorption during the primary magnetic storm effect (decrease in H), lasting a few hours, followed by a small but significant after-effect arising from temporary trapping processes in the outer radiation belt.

The behaviour of the lower ionosphere during the period following the July 1966 proton flare event has been studied on the basis of the results of an A3 absorption network on high, medium and low frequencies established in Middle Europe by the cooperation of several ionospheric observatories. Intensity variations in D-region absorption may be used as an indicator for (*a*) enhancements of X-ray fluxes from the sun, especially if noon values of absorption are used, (*b*) the presence of direct incoming high-energy protons and electrons, and (*c*) precipitation of electrons from the radiation belts.

The high-energy particle fluxes are mainly detectable at low frequencies during the sunset and sunrise periods. The photodetachment processes, most effective at solar zenith angles above 85°, are able to produce an excessive ionization during times of enhanced corpuscular fluxes, which can be detected by means of absorption measurements on low frequencies at steep incidence ($i \simeq 45°$) (Lauter 1966). Fluxes somewhat less than 100 electrons cm^{-2} s^{-1} may be detected by this method.

For the proton event period July 1966 a survey of such absorption measurements is presented in Fig. 1. The absorption for sunrise and sunset periods and for night-time is given for three frequencies, and in addition the noon absorption at a medium frequency. It may be seen that during the period 30 June to 6 July the noon absorption was slightly lower than its monthly median value, but it was enhanced during the period 7–12 July by about

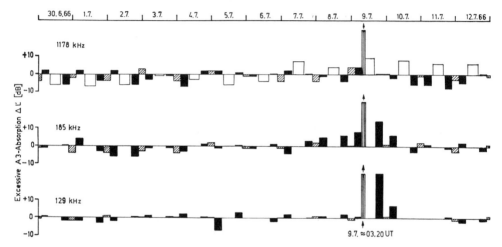

Fig. 1   Mean behaviour of ionospheric absorption during the period of the July 1966 proton flare event. (Deviations $\Delta L'$(dB) from the monthly median values of A3 absorption). Solid blocks, sunset and sunrise; hatched blocks, night; open blocks, noon; vertical hatching, event of 9 July 1966.

6 dB. This may be an effect of a general increase of the solar ionizing radiation after the proton flare event.

The absorption during the night and at solar zenith angles $\chi = 90°$ (full and hatched blocks in Fig. 1) shows no significant deviations from the mean value up to 8 July, so that we may conclude that, at least at medium geomagnetic latitudes $\Phi \leqslant 55°$ in the European sector, there were no incoming particles immediately following the proton flare. This may be especially seen from the night-time and morning measurements of 6–7 July at various frequencies between 2614 and 129 kHz in Fig. 2, where no remarkable deviations from normal behaviour are detectable.

Contrary to the proton flare period itself there was a very significant period of high absorption connected with the magnetic disturbances in the early hours of 9 July, which is thought to be related to the plasma cloud of the flare.

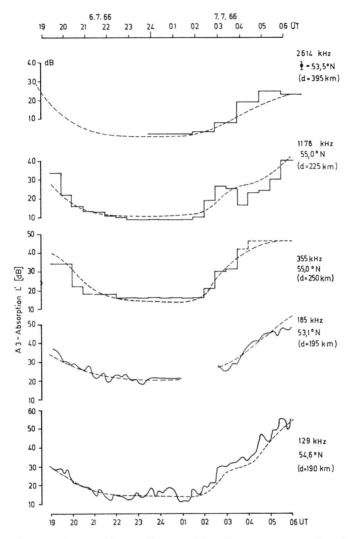

Fig. 2   A3 absorption in high-, medium-, and low-frequency propagation during the
night 6–7 July 1966.

In Middle Europe this event started at about 0320 UT, just after sunrise, in
the ionospheric D region. This increase of absorption means that the start of
a particle event in the lower ionosphere happened at a time when the magnetic
field was remarkably lowered (e.g. the horizontal component of the Observatory Niemegk decreased by 100 γ). Such connections between decreases of
H and an excessive absorption caused by extra ionization due to high-
energy particles have been observed quite often in our latitude (Lauter and
Knuth 1967). This is the well-known effect of the shift of the auroral zone

towards lower latitudes during a geomagnetic storm. The conclusions of Stoffregen, that the high-energy part of the incoming particles is centred somewhat southwards of the auroral belt, may be in agreement with our observation described above as well as with the suggestion that high-energy particles from the outer radiation belt may be precipitated during the main phase of a geomagnetic storm. Whether we refer to the first or the second mechanism, moderate-energy protons or high-energy electrons may be responsible for the observed excessive ionization in the height range between 70 and 100 km. Referring to the ionospheric vertical sounding data during

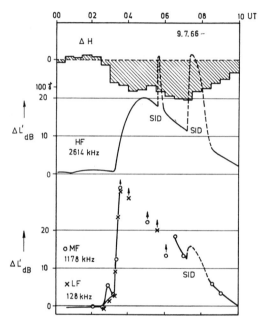

Fig. 3   Excessive A3 absorption ($\Phi \simeq 55°$N) on high, medium, and low frequencies by incoming solar particles during decrease of geomagnetic horizontal intensity.

this period, it must be stated that in northern latitude stations high absorption was present some hours earlier (cf. Part II, following paper), so that the southward shifting mechanism gives the better interpretation of this behaviour. The sudden increase of excessive absorption on 9 July is shown in Fig. 3. The peak of excessive absorption was reached somewhat before 0500 UT with an increase of about 20 dB on high frequencies and more than 30 dB on medium and low frequencies. As may be seen from the daily variations of absorption on different frequencies (Fig. 4) the period of excessive absorption lasted till noon, coinciding with the magnetic deviation ΔH. This excessive absorption had superimposed upon it two sudden ionospheric disturbance (SID) events (see Fig. 3) which have been omitted in the general review of Fig. 4. (It may be mentioned that small enhancements of absorption have been observed prior to the sudden increase on medium and low frequencies. As indicated in Fig. 3, this small enhancement, for which the significance can not be established, started at about 0245 UT.)

From earlier investigations (Lauter 1950, Bracewell *et al.* 1951) on low-frequency propagation, it was established that pronounced after-effects exist

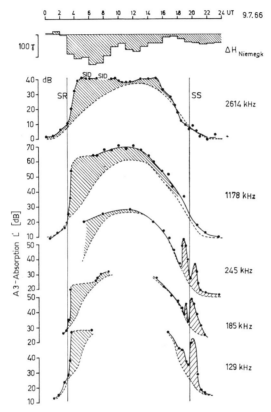

Fig. 4 Trend of A3 absorption during the low energy particle event of 9 July 1966:
⬚ primary effect during decrease of magnetic horizontal component at about 0320 UT.
▨ secondary precipitation effect during sunset period on low frequencies.

in lower ionospheric ionization following such primary storm effects. It is suggested (Lauter 1961) that during such storm-time periods storage of high-energy particles occurs in the outer radiation belt, an effect which has been actually observed by means of satellites. A leakage of these trapped particles after normalization of the geomagnetic field causes an additional particle flux of low intensity into the lower ionosphere in the areas corresponding to the radiation belt horns. The resulting weak excessive ionization may be detected only on low and very low frequency propagation paths, in latitudes of about 55°. The excessive ionization observed during sunset conditions on 9 July may be explained by such a mechanism. As can be seen from Fig. 4, this excessive absorption was not detectable on high and medium frequencies, but was well pronounced on the lower frequencies. The fluctuations of the absorption during this period are typical for this kind of precipitation event. This after-effect in absorption was fairly short and not very intense. Normally, such after-effects last up to 10 days after severe storms, but for the event analysed there are only indications that the precipitation (which was too small to affect the night-time absorption) may have lasted till sunrise the next morning (10 July).

References

Bracewell, R. N., K. G. Budden, et al., 1951, The ionospheric propagation of low- and very-low-frequency radio waves over distances less than 1000 km, Proc. Instn Elect. Engrs, 98, 221–236.

Lauter, E. A., 1950, Zur Statistik der nächtlichen abnormalen E-Schicht, Z. Met., 4, 234–240.

—— 1961, Die exzessive Ionisation in der unteren Ionosphäre und Instabilitäten im äusseren Strahlungsgürtel, Naturwissenschaften, 13, 473–474.

—— 1966, A survey of A3-absorption measurements at low and medium frequencies, Annls Géophys., 22, 289–299.

Lauter, E. A., and R. Knuth, 1967, Precipitation of high energy particles into the upper atmosphere at medium latitudes after magnetic storms, J. Atmos. Terr. Phys., 29, 411–417.

59

Ionospheric Conditions following the Proton Flare Event of 7 July 1966 as measured at Ground-Based Stations:
II. F-Region Effects

H. Lange and J. Taubenheim

Heinrich-Hertz-Institut, Berlin-Adlershof, German Democratic Republic

Abstract

The F-region response to the 7 July 1966 proton flare event, over the European and Asian regions, is characterized by a two-phase ionospheric storm, starting with a positive phase in high and medium latitudes, followed by a two-step decrease of $foF2$, beginning earlier than the main phase of the geomagnetic storm. At $60°$ geomagnetic latitude, the maximum positive phase is reached at a time 33.9 hours after the proton flare. The characteristic features of the $foF2$ time variation during the disturbance show a significant propagation from higher towards lower geomagnetic latitudes, and from eastern towards western geographic longitudes.

On the basis of ionogram characteristics of 27 vertical soundings stations in Europe and Western Asia (between $30°$ and $65°$ geomagnetic latitude and between $80°$ and $150°$ geomagnetic longitude), the behaviour of the ionospheric F region after the 7 July 1966 proton flare has been studied synoptically. Of all the sounding parameters (critical frequencies, minimum virtual heights, and M-factors of the F1 and F2 layers), the most typical and interesting variations during the period following the flare are to be seen in the critical frequencies $foF2$. For the present preliminary study, the deviations of $foF2$ from its monthly median value have been analysed for hourly values only.

In Fig. 1, the variations of $\Delta foF2$/Median ($foF2$), of seven selected stations, are presented for the period 6–11 July 1966. For nearly the whole area considered, the proton flare itself occurred during the night. Thus, no significant F-region effects have been detected at the time of the flare and immediately afterwards, even at high latitudes. A slight positive deviation around the time of the flare, observed at a few stations, commenced several hours before the beginning of the flare, so that it must be regarded as an accidental coincidence not related to the flare. The only exception is for the

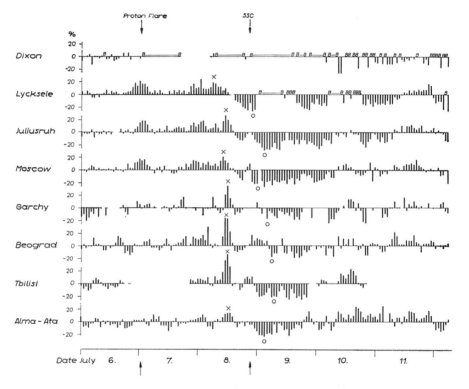

Fig. 1   Hourly deviations of $foF2$ from its hourly median, as a percentage of the median value, for 7 selected stations during the period 6–11 July 1966.

station Dixon (geographic coordinates $\phi = 73.5°$, $\lambda = 80.4°$), where the flare occurred during daylight. At Dixon, total absorption (symbol B) is recorded already at the next full hour following the flare, thus probably indicating an injection of high-energy particles immediately after the flare.

About 30 hours after the proton flare, a two-phase ionospheric F-region disturbance began on all observing stations. The variations of $\Delta foF2$ during this disturbance (cf. Fig. 1) show a number of characteristic features, which are very similar on all sites between Kiruna and Ashkhabad (i.e. between

65.3° and 30.6° geomagnetic latitude). Only at high latitudes are the $foF2$ data interrupted during daylight hours by high absorption, which may be interpreted as polar cap absorption. The disturbance begins with a positive phase (marked in Fig. 1 by crosses above the curves) at both medium and high latitudes. The typical form of this positive phase, together with its latitude shift described below, suggests that it really belongs to the following ionospheric storm, though this positive phase occurs several hours before the geomagnetic sudden storm commencement (ssc) effect. The positive phase is followed by characteristic negative deviations of $foF2$, lasting for one day or more. The first minimum of the $foF2$ depression is marked in Fig. 1 by open circles (∘) below the curves. Attention may be paid to the fact, that at most stations the critical frequencies $foF2$ fall below the median value earlier than the onset of the main phase of the geomagnetic storm (decrease of the H component), and at high latitudes even earlier than the ssc. An interesting feature, to be observed at nearly all stations except in high latitudes, is a significant short-time "recovery effect" prior to the definite beginning of the negative phase, thus giving a characteristic two-step decay of the critical frequencies between the positive and negative phases of the disturbance. This recovery effect occurs approximately at the time of the geomagnetic ssc.

A very similar recovery effect occurred also in the ionospheric disturbance following the September proton flare, being well correlated on all European stations, but at a time when the geomagnetic storm main phase was already in progress. Thus the coincidence of the recovery effect with the ssc in the July event must be regarded as accidental. Probably the recovery effect is related to time of day rather than to storm-time, since both during the July and during the September events the recovery effect took place in the evening hours, about one or two hours after ground sunset.

As it is difficult to define a commencement time of the disturbance variation from the data, only the times of extreme $foF2$ deviations have been analysed. Both the time of maximum positive phase (marked by crosses) and the time of the first minimum of the negative phase (open circles) clearly show a time shift proceeding from higher towards lower geomagnetic latitudes (see Fig. 2). Further, a time shift with geographic longitude seems to be present, proceeding from the east towards the west. A linear double-regression analysis for 24 stations used in this investigation yields the following regression formula for the time T of the maximum positive phase (in hours UT on 8 July):

$$T = 10.2 + (0.156 \pm 0.052)(60° - \Phi) + (0.030 \pm 0.021)\lambda,$$

where Φ means geomagnetic latitude (in degrees), λ means geographic longitude (in degrees). The confidence limits of the regression coefficients, indicated in this formula, correspond to the 5 per cent error probability level. Therefore, both the geomagnetic latitude shift and the geographic longitude shift must be regarded as statistically significant.

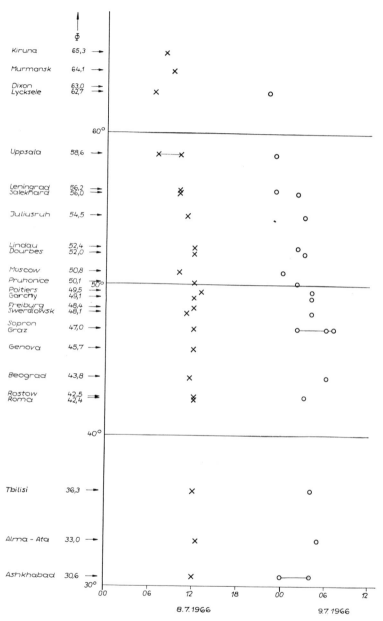

Fig. 2   Times of maximum positive phase (×) and of first minimum of the negative phase (o), as a function of geomagnetic latitude Φ.

Inspection of Fig. 2 shows, however, that linear regression is only approximately fulfilled. In fact, the southward propagation seems to be faster in lower than in higher geomagnetic latitudes. The equatorward velocity, given by the regression coefficient, corresponds to about 700 km h^{-1} along the magnetic meridian. This is not seriously different from the average value of 480 km h^{-1} found for the southward velocity of 15 ionospheric storms during the IGY (Lange 1959). The much higher equatorward velocity, reported by Wright (1961), might be caused by a use of lower latitude stations.

References

LANGE, H., 1959, Über Korpuskularstörungen der F2-Schicht und die Südwärtsbewegung des Störungseinsatzes auf der Nordhalbkugel der Erde, *Gerlands Beitr. Geophys.*, **68**, 230–245.

WRIGHT, M. D., 1961, Possible identification of atmospheric waves associated with ionospheric storms, *Nature, Lond.*, **190**, 898–899.

60

Ionospheric Disturbances after the Proton Flare of 7 July 1966

N. P. Benkova and R. A. Zevakina
IZMIRAN, Moscow, USSR

Abstract

Ionospheric effects caused by the enhancement of solar radiation, high-energy protons and low-energy solar plasma radiated during the proton flare have been considered using the vertical sounding and riometer data of the Soviet stations in Arctic, Antarctic, and at middle latitudes.

I Flare Wave Radiation

The flare of 7 July 1966 was accompanied by an increase of ionization both in the low ionosphere layers (E and D layers) and in the F2 layer. Sudden ionospheric disturbance (SID) was observed on 7 July 1966 at a number of ionospheric vertical sounding stations, as well as by riometers at frequencies of 9, 13, and 25 MHz at the Loparskaya station.

The times of both occurrence and maximum of SID's proved to be close to the corresponding times of the chromospheric flare (Fig. 1). The magnitude of abnormal absorption, according to the riometer data, varied inversely proportionally to the square of the working frequency. This shows that the absorption of radio waves passing through the ionosphere occurred mainly at heights above 60 km, and that X-rays with wavelength $\lambda \lesssim 1$ Å did not play an essential role in the formation of abnormal absorption during the flare.

In accordance with f_{min} data, the duration of disturbance was about 165 minutes. At Loparskaya 60–70 minutes later, i.e. before the end of SID, an anomalous ionization occurred, which was caused by the intrusion of solar cosmic rays.

The proton flare effect in the F region was most clearly seen in Irkutsk (Fig. 1). The maximum effect in $foF2$ is an increase of 18 per cent at this station. The increase of electron concentration occurred simultaneously with the commencement of optical flare in $H\alpha$ and ceased immediately after its termination.

The proton flare effect in the E region was well seen at Salekhard station (Fig. 1). At other stations it was not seen owing to absorption or to shielding of the E layer by the sporadic layer. The increase in critical frequency of the E layer was about 20 per cent. The effect within the E region commenced somewhat earlier than the $H\alpha$ flare and terminated a little later.

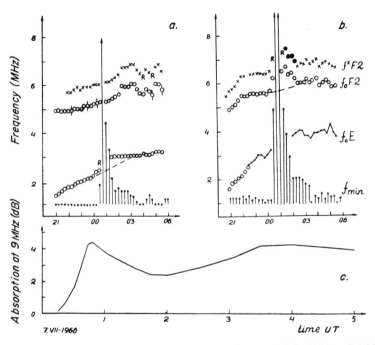

Fig. 1   SID and effect in E and F2 layers during the flare on 7 July 1966. *a*, Salekhard; *b*, Irkutsk (Zui); *c*. Loparskaya (Murmansk).

As seen from changes of $N(h)$ profiles at Moscow (Fig. 2), obvious increase of electron concentration occurred at all heights, but most significantly above 240 km. At the time of maximum effect the increase in electron concentration at heights of 280–300 km was of the order of 40–45 per cent.

The above information shows that the event of 7 July 1966 had a wide spectrum of active ionizing radiation, i.e. hard X-rays, responsible for the increase of ionization in the D region, soft X-rays (shorter than 100 Å), responsible for the ionization of the E region, and ionizing radiation with

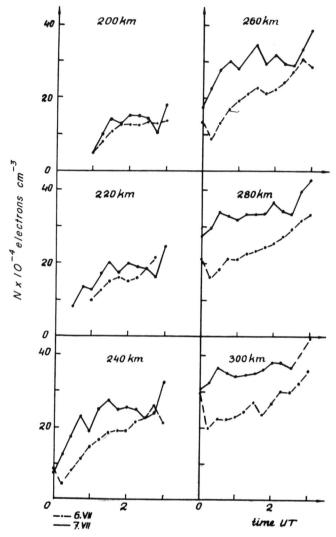

Fig. 2   *N* enhancement at various heights during the flare on 7 July 1966.

λ less than 1000 Å, which caused the effects in the F region. Apparently soft X-ray generation during the flare commenced somewhat earlier than hard X-ray generation.

2   Effects of High-Energy Solar Protons

For the investigation of polar-cap absorption (PCA) on 7 July 1966 the data of nine riometers at a frequency of 32 MHz were taken (Table 1). Five-element Yagi-type antennae were used, directed towards the celestial pole.

Table I Coordinates of Absorption Observing Stations

| Station | Geographical Coordinates | | Corrected Geomagnetic Coordinates | | | | Information on Riometers* | | |
	Lat.	Long.	Lat.	Additional Lat.	Long.		Frequency (MHz)	Antenna Direction	
1. Arctica-13 (Drifting)	84°	135°	76.9°	13.9°	180°		32	Zenith	
2. Heiss Island	80°37'	58°03'	73.8°	16.2°	144.2°		32	Celestial pole	
3. Cape Zhelania	76°57'	68°35'	70.3°	19.7°	141.1°		32	Celestial pole	
4. Dixon	73°30'	80°24'	67.2°	22.8°	154.1°		32	Celestial pole	
5. Amderma	69°46'	61°41'	63.9°	26.1°	137.5°		32	Celestial pole	
6. Norilsk	69°26'	88°15'	63.4°	26.6°	159.5°		32	Celestial pole	
7. Loparskaya	68°15'	33°05'	64.7°	25.3°	114.8°		9–13–25	Celestial pole	
8. Salekhard	66°32'	66°32'	61.0°	29.0°	140.3°		32	Celestial pole	
9. Leningrad (Voyeikovo)	59°57'	30°42'	55.8°	35.0°	108.0°		32	Zenith	

* Antenna: 5-element Yagi type.

The station Arctica-13 only had the antenna directed towards the zenith. Absorption was estimated for the first minute of each hour.

Progressive results are presented in Fig. 3. PCA commencement was fogged by SID effect and by solar radio-noise storm; therefore it could not be precisely determined. It may be considered that PCA started after approximately 60–70 minutes of the beginning of solar flare; 5–6 hours later the absorption in the polar cap reached the maximum level of about 2 dB and stayed at this level for about 10 hours. Then the intensity of PCA gradually decreased, and by the end of 8 July the event was over (if the lower boundary of abnormal absorption is considered to be at 0.5 dB level). The lowest latitude station which observed PCA was Norilsk ($\Phi' = 63.4°$), this boundary going gradually up, and at about 04 UT on 8 July PCA was already absent even at Dixon Island. This is possibly evidence of some decrease of hardness of the stream particles responsible for PCA. At about 05 UT on 8 July the main phase of magnetic storm occurred, which proved the approach of low-energy solar plasma to the earth. It caused the appearance of auroral absorption within the auroral zone. Formation of the equatorial current ring during this period possibly caused the lowering of the PCA southern boundary, but it is difficult to distinguish the two effects, which overlapped.

As a result of observations at Dixon Island (at frequencies of 22.3 and 48.3 MHz) and at Loparskaya station (at frequencies of 9 and 13 MHz) the frequency dependence of the absorption during the PCA period of 7–8 July 1966 was determined. During SID the value of the n index of the frequency dependence of the absorption

$$\frac{A_1}{A_2} = \left(\frac{f_2}{f_1}\right)^n$$

was close to 2. From the moment of PCA occurrence the n values gradually decreased and by 04 UT on 7 July 1966 they reached the values of 1.55–1.60 at both the observational points. Such frequency dependence shows that most of the extra ionization took place around heights 50–60 km. Before the magnetic disturbances, during PCA occurrence, no marked variations were found in the F region (in the Arctic and Antarctic).

3   Effects of Low-Energy Solar Plasma

Low-energy solar plasma caused the most significant variations in the F region. In this connection at a number of stations (Table 2) deviations of $foF2$, $hpF2$ and $h'F$ are considered for 6–11 July 1966 as well as $N(h)$ profiles for some periods. Deviations of the above parameters have been counted from the median on magnetically and ionospherically quiet days (2, 3, 13, 14, 15, 18, 19 July), and deviations of $N(h)$ profiles from 6 July.

F-region disturbance commenced 21.5 hours later than the flare (7 July, 22 h) with the positive phase ($\Delta foF2 > 20\%$). According to its intensity the

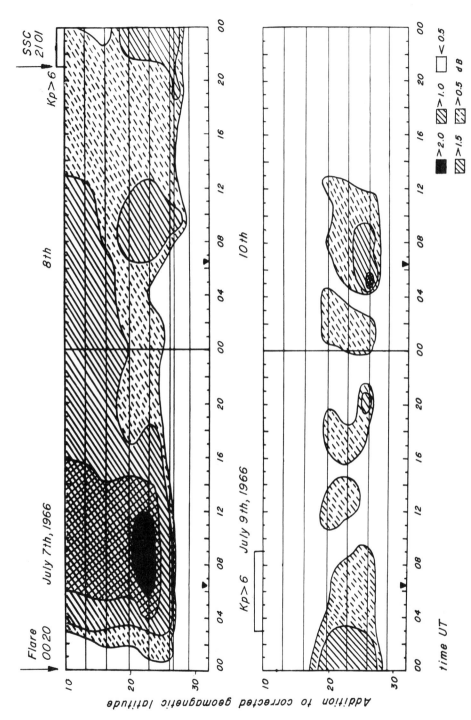

Fig. 3   Development of polar-cap and auroral-zone absorption on 7–10 July 1966 in the northern hemisphere. Solid arrowhead: noon at Dixon.

Table 2   List of Stations used for the Analysis of F-Region Disturbances

Station	Coordinates			
	Geographic		Corrected Geomagnetic	
	ϕ	λ	Φ'	Λ'^{+}
1. Arctica-13 (Drifting)*	83°49′N	134°58′E	76.5°	184.9°
2. Heiss Island*	80°37′N	58°03′E	73.8°	144.2°
3. Dixon	73°30′N	80°24′E	67.2°	154.1°
4. Salekhard	66°32′N	66°32′E	61.0°	140.3°
5. Leningrad (Voyeikovo)	59°57′N	30°42′E	55.8°	108.0°
6. Sverdlovsk (Verkneye Dubrava)	56°44′N	61°04′E	52.3°	133.0°
7. Moscow* (Krasnaya Pakhra)	55°28′N	37°19′E	51.0°	111.7°
8. Kalinigrad	54°42′N	20°37′E	50.9°	98.1°
9. Irkutsk (Zui)	52°28′N	104°02′E	48.2°	175.3°
10. Kiev	50°27′N	30°30′E	46.1°	104.9°
11. Tbilisi	41°43′N	44°48′E	36.7°	116.2°
12. Mirny*	66°33′S	93°01′E	−76.8°	127.7°
13. Vostok*	78°27′S	106°52′E	−84.3°	58.6°

* Stations on which $N(h)$ profiles are computed.

magnetic storm is treated as a moderate one, with a gradual commencement at 01 h on 8 July. However, weak variations of the geomagnetic field commenced simultaneously with the ionospheric disturbance. The delay of the ionospheric–magnetic disturbance for 21.5 hours, according to approximate estimates, corresponds to a velocity of the corpuscular stream of the order of 2000 km s^{-1}. The positive phase of the ionospheric disturbance continued for about 16 hours. The most intensive increase of $foF2$ (up to 60%) was observed within the near-polar region of the southern hemisphere (Vostok station, Fig. 4). During this period the magnetic activity was not large ($Kp \leqslant 4$). The height of maximum electron concentration, as judged from $hpF2$, did not show significant variation within $\pm$ 60 km (from the median).

With the occurrence of the negative phase of ionospheric disturbance (8 July, 15 h) $hpF2$ increased above 100 km and remained higher than the median values until the end of the ionospheric disturbance (until 11 July, 12 h, at high latitudes, and until 10 July, 05 h, at middle latitudes).

It is of interest to note that at the time of sudden commencement (ssc) of the active period of magnetic activity there was observed simultaneously at all stations considered an increase in $foF2$ of more than 20 per cent compared with the values before ssc, and a decrease in $hpF2$ at 60–80 km. Taking into consideration the change of $N(h)$-profile parameters, one can see that during this period a lowering of heights corresponding to concentrations 0.9, 0.7 ... 0.2 of N_{max} occurred (Fig. 5). $T(h_{0.9} - h_{0.5})$, which determines the thickness of the ionosphere, did not suffer significant variations. This shows that during the ssc period the F region was displaced towards lower heights, nearer to the earth. The heights $h_m, h_{0.9} \ldots h_{0.2}$ were lowered (up to 25%) for a period of 5 hours; then h_m increased considerably, but $h_{0.5} \ldots h_{0.2}$ remained low, i.e. an essential expansion of the F region occurred, which

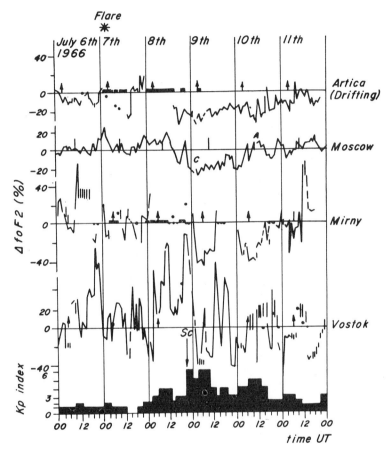

Fig. 4   Development of ionospheric disturbances after the flare on 7–11 July 1966.

lasted until the end of the disturbance. The T-parameter increased to 80 per cent and above during this period (Fig. 5).

F-region expansion is apparently connected with the ionosphere temperature rise, due to the intrusion of charged particles into the upper atmosphere and to the dissipation of magnetohydrodynamic waves. During the positive phase the F-region geometry changes less, which shows that within this

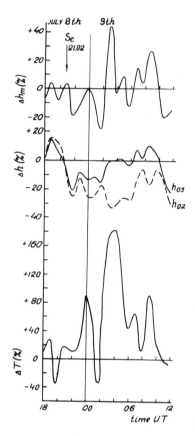

Fig. 5   Changes Δh_m, Δh_{05}, Δh_{02}, ΔT during and after ssc on 8–9 July 1966.

period the ionizing agent causes mainly ionization increase, but not iono-sphere temperature rise. During the negative phase the low-energy solar plasma causes mainly ionospheric heating, due to which the ionization and recombination processes are, apparently, changing greatly.

The F-region variations considered are typical for any disturbance. This indicates that low-energy solar plasma injected during proton flares is not essentially different from the plasma of other corpuscular streams, but only that it propagates with higher velocity.

Acknowledgments

The report is compiled on the basis of work by E. A. Benediktov (Scientific Research Institute on Radio-physics), V. M. Driatsky, A. S. Besprozvannaya, O. N. Struina (Arctic and Antarctic Institute), Z. Rapoport (PGI), R. A. Zevakina, L. A. Judovich, E. V. Lavrova, E. E. Goncharova, I. N. Odintzova (IZMIRAN).

C

Summary on Energetic Particles observed during the July 1966 Proton Flare Event

S. M. Krimigis

Department of Physics and Astronomy, University of Iowa, Iowa City, Iowa, USA

Abstract

A survey of the salient points which have emerged from observations on energetic particles during the July 1966 proton flare event. These are: (a) relativistic electrons of energy 3–12 MeV were observed for the first time; (b) the ratio of protons to α particles at energy above 0.5 MeV/nucleon varies with time during the event; (c) low-energy protons and electrons ($E > 0.5$ MeV) are confined within a tube of force of the interplanetary magnetic field; (d) a bidirectional anisotropy in the stream of protons is associated with the Forbush decrease.

The papers presented so far in this conference on the energetic particles have described the behavior of particles of several species, namely, protons, electrons, and alpha particles of various energies. The question then is, "what have we learned from these several observations from the different experimental groups, and what are the most important observations we have made so far for this event?"

In my estimation, the most important observation which has been presented so far is the identification of relativistic electrons in the energy range of 3 to 12 MeV reported by Cline and McDonald (1968). As we well know, it has been shown or inferred over the past several years that Type IV radio emission is associated with the acceleration of relativistic electrons in the solar magnetic fields. However, such electrons have never been observed, and this is the first time, to my knowledge, that such observations have been made. The authors observed that the number of electrons was fairly small,

457

which seems to imply that most of these electrons were actually trapped in the vicinity of the sun. We also found that lower-energy electrons ($E_e \gtrsim 40$ keV) were also present as reported by Kahler and Lin (1968), but such electrons of course have been observed before associated with solar flares and solar particle events (Van Allen and Krimigis 1965, Anderson and Lin 1966). Just so that we will not think that we have made some progress in this respect, Cline and McDonald have also found that in the event of 28 August 1966 there were no electrons present, although there were some in the event of 14 September 1966 and again no electrons were present in the 28 January 1967 event. Therefore, we certainly cannot draw a general conclusion by saying that every flare is associated with relativistic electrons. The only thing that we can say is that the relativistic electrons responsible for the Type IV radio emission have now been observed, but that these electrons are not always capable of escaping from the sun in sufficient numbers to be observable. Perhaps propagation characteristics and the location of the flare may help in explaining the presence or absence of these electrons in a given event. This is a new area which needs much more detailed study at the present time.

In addition to the observation of relativistic electrons, Cline and McDonald have shown the intensity–time profile for protons of energy greater than 15 MeV and they have observed that the decay of the intensity is not strictly exponential. I would like to emphasize this point because in the past a large number of solar proton events has been observed and measured by the use of ion chambers, and as we all know, the ion chamber is an integrating device; it does not count individual particles, it only measures the amount of ionization. Such measurements could have been easily interpreted if one makes the assumption that solar particles have the same spectrum throughout an event, in which case the ionization would be proportional to the number of incident particles. Unfortunately, this is certainly not the case. We know that the energy spectrum does change during the course of a solar flare event, and therefore the decay curves that have been derived from ionization chamber measurements are not representative of the intensity–time profiles of all the particles involved. They are only representative of a composite effect, incorporating the decay of the particle intensity as well as the change in the energy spectrum. It is unfortunate that several calculations have been based on an exponential decay, which in most cases is not observed.

Observations presented at this conference have shown that the intensity–time profile for low-energy protons ($0.31 \leqslant E_p \leqslant 10$ MeV) and alpha particles ($2.1 \leqslant E_\alpha \leqslant 17$ MeV) is quite complex (see, e.g., Armstrong, Krimigis, and Van Allen 1968). The rise-time is quite slow compared with that of protons whose energy is $E_p \gtrsim 20$ MeV or so. Their intensity–time profile exhibits several relative maxima and minima and the decay is quite a bit slower compared with energetic particles; in this particular case these low-energy particles were present for at least ten days after the event.

One of the important features of the intensity–time profile that have been shown by Armstrong *et al.* (1968) is that solar protons whose energy is less than 0.82 MeV are unable to enter the geomagnetic field close to the equator. This is a rather significant observation because it shows that the radiation belts cannot be directly populated via the infusion of particles of comparable energy from solar-proton events. However, we have to distinguish between solar protons incident on the geomagnetic field at the equator and those appearing at high latitudes because, as we will later see in the paper by Krimigis, Van Allen, and Armstrong (1968), there is evidence that following the sudden commencement, solar protons at high latitudes are indeed indistinguishable from trapped particles.

In addition, Armstrong *et al.* (1968) have shown for the first time the ratio of protons to alpha particles with energies $E_{p,\alpha} > 0.5$ MeV/nucleon as a function of time during the event. It is observed that the ratio has a high value of about 70 at about 0900 UT on 7 July and the value drops to as low as 30 and varies as a function of time for the next several days. It is, of course, remarkable that there is such a variation; the authors have concluded from the variation of the ratio with time that an appreciable fraction of the alpha particles observed required up to one day longer to reach the vicinity of the spacecraft than protons of the same velocity. It is possible that such a variation is strictly attributable to the differences in magnetic rigidity between protons and alpha particles and it reflects the difference in propagation characteristics. Such differences should be studied more thoroughly in the future in order to investigate the propagation mechanism at these low energies.

It is noted that a comparison of the j_α/j_p ratio with previous measurements, for example those made at energies $E_{p,\alpha} > 95$ MeV/nucleon by Ney and Stein (1962), shows that the ratio at these higher energies is also about 40. It is remarkable that these ratios are similar and if one is allowed to compare two different events one may then draw the conclusion that the ratio of protons to alpha particles whose energies are greater than 0.5 MeV/nucleon is the same as that for particles with energies greater than 95 MeV/nucleon, and one would thus infer that the acceleration mechanism at the sun is equally efficient in producing particles of 1 MeV/nucleon and 100 MeV/nucleon.

Kahler and Lin (1968) have presented evidence for the confinement of low-energy protons and electrons in tubes of force of the interplanetary magnetic field. This they did by the use of simultaneous observations from satellites IMP-3 and Explorer 33, which were both located outside the shock front. The simultaneous observations have shown that the onset of increases and decreases in the intensity at the position of IMP-3 preceded the onset of similar structure at the position of Explorer 33. From this they were able to infer that low-energy protons ($E_p > 0.5$ MeV) and low-energy electrons ($E_e > 45$ keV) were confined in a tube of force of the interplanetary magnetic field and that the delay appears to be due to co-rotation of the interplanetary magnetic field past the IMP-3 spacecraft first, and subsequently past Explorer 33. Their observations are complementary to those of O'Gallagher and Simpson (1966) and of Krimigis and Van Allen (1967). However, their points of simultaneous observations were much closer together and they were thus able to establish the diffusion coefficient perpendicular to the lines of force for these particles. They found that $D_{\perp}/D_{\parallel} \simeq 0.01$, that is, the diffusion coefficient perpendicular to the lines of force of the interplanetary field is two orders of magnitude smaller than the diffusion coefficient parallel to the lines of force.

Rao, McCracken, and Bukata (1968) presented some data in which they showed that, although prior to the event solar cosmic rays were streaming away from the sun, during the onset of the Forbush decrease on 9 July, there occurred what they described as a bidirectional anisotropy, that is, protons were arriving at the spacecraft primarily from directions perpendicular to the sun–spacecraft line, rather than from the solar direction. They have observed this effect in the past for several solar proton events (McCracken, Rao, and Bukata 1967) and they consider it a typical occurrence during the onset of a Forbush decrease. In addition, Rao *et al.* observed that, at a later time on 9 July, the anisotropy returned to the so-called "equilibrium anisotropy," which means that the particles were moving away from the sun, and of course, this is due to the connective removal of cosmic rays from the solar system, which was also shown by the observations of Armstrong *et al.* (1968). The mechanism that Rao *et al.* advanced to explain the equilibrium anisotropy is that cosmic radiation is essentially uniformly distributed throughout the solar system and it is swept radially outward by the solar wind. They conclude from this that the velocity of the solar wind during the period 9 to 11 July was of the order of $1100 \, \text{km s}^{-1}$. We have to remark, however, that such velocity seems to be substantially higher than the observations of the solar wind velocity made on Explorer 33 by Lazarus and Binsack (1968).

In conclusion, then, we might say that the most important results that we have learned from the presentations on energetic particles were the following:

a. Relativistic electrons in the energy range of 3 to 12 MeV were observed for the first time.

b. The ratio of protons to alpha particles at energy $E_p > 0.5$ MeV/nucleon was observed for the first time, and was shown to vary as a function of time for the duration of the event.

c. Kahler and Lin have shown from their simultaneous observations with IMP-3 and Explorer 33 that low-energy protons ($E_p > 0.5$ MeV) and electrons ($E_e > 45$ keV) are confined within a tube of force of the interplanetary magnetic field. From this observation, they were able to infer that the value of the ratio $D_{\perp}/D_{\parallel}$ is of the order 10^{-2}.

d. The observations of Rao *et al.* (1968) reconfirm the picture of the bidirectional anisotropy associated with the onset of the Forbush decrease, which they have observed in several other solar proton events.

References

ANDERSON, K. A., and R. P. LIN, 1966, Observations on the propagation of solar-flare electrons in interplanetary space, *Phys. Rev. Lett.*, **16**, 1121–1124.

ARMSTRONG, T. P., S. M. KRIMIGIS, and J. A. VAN ALLEN, 1968, Observations of the solar particle event of 7 July 1966 with University of Iowa detectors, *Ann. IQSY*, this volume, Paper 43.

CLINE, T. L., and F. B. MCDONALD, 1968, Relativistic solar electrons detected during the 7 July 1966 proton flare event, *Ann. IQSY*, this volume, Paper 41.

KAHLER, S. W., and R. P. LIN, 1968, Spatial gradients of energetic protons and electrons observed after the 7 July 1966 solar flare, *Ann. IQSY*, this volume, Paper 42.

KRIMIGIS, S. M., and J. A. VAN ALLEN, 1967, Observations of the February 5–12, 1965, solar particle event with Mariner 4 and Injun 4, *J. Geophys. Res.*, **72**, 4471–4486.

KRIMIGIS, S. M., J. A. VAN ALLEN, and T. P. ARMSTRONG, 1968, Solar particle observations inside the magnetosphere during the 7 July 1966 proton flare event, *Ann. IQSY*, this volume, Paper 54.

LAZARUS, A. J., and J. H. BINSACK, 1968, Observations of the interplanetary plasma subsequent to the 7 July 1966 proton flare, *Ann. IQSY*, this volume, Paper 51.

MCCRACKEN, K. G., U. R. RAO, and R. P. BUKATA, 1967, Cosmic-ray propagation processes. 1. A study of the cosmic ray flare effect, *J. Geophys. Res.*, **72**, 4293–4324.

NEY, E. P., and W. A. STEIN, 1962, Solar protons, alpha-particles, and heavy nuclei in November 1960, *J. Geophys. Res.*, **67**, 2087–2105.

O'GALLAGHER, J. J., and J. A. SIMPSON, 1966, Anisotropic propagation of solar protons deduced from simultaneous observations by earth satellites and the Mariner 4 space probe, *Phys. Rev. Lett.*, **16**, 1212–1217.

RAO, U. R., K. G. MCCRACKEN, and R. P. BUKATA, 1968, Pioneer 6 observations of the solar flare particle event of 7 July 1966, *Ann. IQSY*, this volume, Paper 44.

VAN ALLEN, J. A., and S. M. KRIMIGIS, 1965, Impulsive emission of ~ 40 keV electrons from the sun, *J. Geophys. Res.*, **70**, 5737–5751.

D

Summary on Low-Energy Particle Events in the Ionosphere associated with the July 1966 Proton Flare Event

W. Dieminger

Max-Planck-Institut, 3411 Lindau, Federal Republic of Germany

Abstract

During the proton flare event of July 1966, low-energy particles were observed directly and by their effects on the magnetosphere, on cosmic-ray intensities, on the ionosphere, and on geomagnetic activity. None of the effects observed differed significantly from those observed for normal geomagnetic storms, but it would be premature to make deductions from one solar event of this nature.

This paper is a summary of some highlights of the papers on low-energy particle events in the ionosphere which were presented at the IQSY Symposium and which are published in this volume.

For the sake of clarity we may distinguish between observations by which low-energy particles have been traced directly and others by which their effects in the earth's atmosphere have been established. Low-energy particles in that context mean electrons in the 1–100 keV range and protons in the 10–1000 keV range.

As far as I can see only two papers deal with direct measurements. The results of the simultaneous observations on Explorer 33 and Pioneer 6 are not unambiguous because there were no continuous observations of Pioneer 6 and in addition we had a multitude of flares, and it is not too easy to distinguish between the individual effects.

The paper of Krimigis *et al.* (Paper 54)[1] contains a very important contribution since it answers a crucial question. Simultaneous observations on

---

[1] Paper numbers refer to articles in this volume.

board Explorer 33, which was definitely outside the magnetosphere, and on board Injun 4, which was inside, showed that solar protons in the 0.5–5 MeV range had full and essentially immediate access to the polar caps of the earth. This is to my mind in favour of the so-called open model of the magnetosphere.

A compression of the magnetosphere about one day after the flare has been reported by Lazarus and Binsack (Paper 51) and a very substantial contraction of the plasmasphere by Taylor, Brinton, and Pharo (Paper 53). Similarly a contraction of the plasmasphere from about 5.5 earth radii to 3.5 radii on 8 July between 02 and 14 h UT has been deduced from whistler observation by Corcuff (Paper 52). These contractions, to my mind, are a common feature of geomagnetic storms and are not peculiar to flare effects.

As to cosmic rays Carmichael (Paper 50) shows in his report that, apart from a slight increase at the time of flare, the intensity starts to decrease on 8 July at 23 h UT at Alert and at 24 h UT at McMurdo. The intensity remains low for at least 5 days. This corresponds well with the observations at Lindau where the intensity of both neutrons and mesons decreased distinctly on 8 July between 22 and 24 h UT. This is to be considered a classical Forbush decrease which is not typical for a proton flare.

The remaining papers deal with geomagnetic and ionospheric observations. A very thorough study by Best, Fanselau, Grafe, Lehmann, and Wagner (Paper 56) at Potsdam demonstrates that the period during which the proton flare occurred was geomagnetically quiet. The day of the flare may be called even very quiet until 22 h UT when Kp rose from zero to $2-$. This was very fortunate because under more disturbed conditions the flare effect could have been obscured. As a matter of fact no sudden geomagnetic effect was discovered which could be ascribed to solar protons of high energy although the average intensity of the Sq system on 7 July was greater than on the days before and after the flare day. This may be ascribed to a general increase of the ultra-violet radiation around 7 July. As a matter of fact the critical frequency of the E layer also was about 2 per cent higher on 7 July than on 5 July and 9 July at our station Tsumeb in South-west Africa. So we are quite safe in saying that there was no effect in the dynamo region of the upper atmosphere at middle latitudes produced by fast particles. The disturbance lasting from 8 to 10 July has to be ascribed to low-energy particles, and was in no way different from the well-known features of magnetic storms of low to medium intensity. From the time of the sudden storm commencement (ssc) as observed in middle latitudes a velocity of 1000 km s^{-1} may be derived for the particles assuming that the particles left the sun at the time of the flare.

The Dst variation shows a slow onset of the disturbance which is characteristic for storms of low intensity. The Dp current system derived for the northern hemisphere beyond 50° does not show any unusual features for the main phase of the storm.

At higher latitudes the disturbance started as early as 7 July at 22 h UT. It is worth while to mention that Matveeva and Troitskaya (Paper 55) found that pearl-like pulsations occurred at approximately the same time according to the observations of Soviet stations covering a wide range of geomagnetic latitudes. These pearls are ascribed to protons preceding the slower particles which are supposed to create the main storm. It should be checked if this is a characteristic feature of other proton flares.

The ionospheric effects have been described in four papers, by Herzberg and Nelms (Paper 57), Benkova and Zevakina (Paper 60), Knuth and Lauter (Paper 58), and Lange and Taubenheim (Paper 59). They may be summarized as follows:

From topside soundings on board Alouette 1 and 2 it was found that during the main phase of the ionospheric storm the maximum electron density of the F2 layer at high latitudes was sometimes smaller than that of the F1 layer so that the latter could be seen from above. On one occasion even the E region was visible from above which proves that the E region was the one with the highest electron density. Such conditions are typical for ionospheric storms and cannot be considered a peculiarity of a proton flare.

Now we shall discuss the results of ground-based observations. Nothing peculiar happened on 7 July. The polar-cap absorption which starts at Dixon approximately at the time of the flare is a common feature of many ordinary flare effects. The ionospheric storm does not start before 8 July at approximately 9 h UT at subauroral stations and not before 12 h UT at middle latitudes. It shows a positive phase exhibiting an increase of the F2 critical frequency and a two-step transition to the negative phase approximately at the time of the geomagnetic ssc. The maximum negative deviation of the F2 critical frequency occurs in the morning hours of 9 July. No distinct storm effects have been observed at the subequatorial station Tsumeb at 19°S.

This overall picture has been confirmed by the observations of Soviet stations described by Benkova and Zevakina (Paper 60). During the positive phase a lowering of the height of the F2 region is observed whereas during the negative phase an expansion occurs which is ascribed to heating of the ionosphere by low-energy particles. The ionosphere over Vostok in the antarctic polar night behaves so erratically all the time that I do not dare to discuss it in detail.

Both positive and negative phases started earlier at higher latitudes. This progression of the storm from polar to middle latitudes is a common feature of many ionospheric storms. The apparent velocity was about 700 km h^{-1} for the storm under consideration which agrees fairly well with the average velocity of 480 km h^{-1} deduced from 15 ionospheric storms during the IGY. There is also a progression from eastern to western geographic longitudes. The reason is apparently that the storm does not start until after local sunrise.

Finally the effects in the lower ionosphere will be discussed. The increase of daytime absorption by about 6 dB on 1 MHz during the period 7 to 12

July may be attributed to a general increase of XUV radiation which occurred in connection with the active region to which the proton flare belonged. This has already been mentioned. During night-time the absorption was quite normal in middle latitudes demonstrating that the polar-cap absorption was restricted to really high-latitude stations. The absorption effects of the ionospheric storm at middle latitudes were not too strong but quite distinct. In Central Europe they started on 9 July shortly after sunrise and lasted until noon. They coincided well with the maximum negative deviation of the horizontal component of the geomagnetic field. They are superimposed by two sudden ionospheric disturbances (SID) produced independently by XUV. Subsequently the after-effects described for the first time by Lauter and his co-workers (Knuth and Lauter, Paper 58) appeared after sunset particularly on low frequencies.

All these absorption effects are well-known features of normal geomagnetic and ionospheric storms. The daytime absorption has to be ascribed to direct effects of, or to bremsstrahlung produced by, auroral electrons and protons, the after-effects to dumping of high-energy particles stored in the radiation belts during the main phase of the storm. The fact that the after-effect lasted only one night may be considered another indication that the storm was only a minor one.

Summing up one may say that the effects of low-energy particles did not differ significantly from what has been known for normal storms. It seems premature, however, to draw too many conclusions from only one effect. We are very fortunate indeed that two other effects occurred soon after, which, it is hoped, will give additional information.

IV

GENERAL SUMMARY AND CONCLUSIONS

E

General Summary on the Results of the First Proton Flare Project Period, July 1966

P. Simon* and Z. Švestka†

* Meudon Observatory, France
† Astronomical Institute of the Czechoslovak Academy of Sciences, Ondřejov, Czechoslovakia

Abstract

A survey of all the material presented in the whole Proton Flare volume, picking out the salient points from each contribution, relating these, and indicating possible explanations of the phenomena observed.

I Introduction

In this summary we do not intend to repeat all the results obtained by the various authors who took part in the study of the proton flare event of 7 July, since this can be found in the partial summaries which close the individual sections and in the individual contributions. Our intention has been to pick out the most interesting results which either confirm preliminary conclusions made before by other authors, or to bring new ideas which are to be verified later on and to try to get a general complex picture of the results of the whole Proton Flare Project study.

Of course, one has to realize that we cannot draw many definite conclusions from observations of one single event or build theories on the basis of such a limited assembly of data, and this has not been the task of the Proton Flare Project (PFP). The main purpose of this series of contributions is to bring together as many observed data on one selected proton event as possible covering all the various fields of the related research and, to our mind, this task has been fulfilled much better than we ever expected at the start of the project.

The main purpose of our summary is to give to the reader an orientation in the widely dispersed set of data obtained and to call his attention to the most interesting results achieved, which he can find then in full detail in the individual original contributions.

2 Complex of Activity

Warwick (1965) and Dodson-Prince and Hedeman (1968) have found that proton-flare-active regions show a tendency to grouping in heliographic longitudes. This can also be seen in Fig. 1, which shows that since 1963 essentially all proton-active regions have formed within a solar sector of slightly more than 100° in longitude and avoided the remaining parts of the sun.

For the maximum phase of solar activity, Švestka (1968b) has shown that this grouping in heliographic longitudes is due to the occurrence of proton-flare regions in complexes of activity which stay on the solar disk for many months and form several adjacent proton-active regions during their existence. As an example, we can see in Fig. 1 the last major complex of activity of the last cycle in 1963, which produced five proton-active regions during its development.

After 1963, during the minimum phase of the solar cycle, such complexes never fully developed and only a clustering of individual proton-flare regions in some preferred longitudes can be observed. In fact, the first proton-active complex of the new cycle was that in the year 1966 (marked with an arrow in Fig. 1) which produced all the proton flares observed during the PFP period including the 7 July flare studied in this series of contributions.

About 40° to the east of a decaying active region which produced a proton flare on 24 March 1966, a new region No. 8459 was born in May, at a latitude of about 20° north, which remained fairly inactive during its first four transits over the solar disk. In the last days of June, however, another region, No. 8362, was born to the north-east of the preceding one and it developed very fast as described in the next sections. This region produced the proton flare of 7 July. Due to the differential rotation, these two regions coincided in longitude in early August and since that time the region No. 8459 also became active and produced two proton flares on 28 August and 2 September. As one can see from Fig. 1, all this happened within the 100° range of longitudes exhibited by proton flares since 1963.

Bumba and Howard (1967, private communication) have studied the background magnetic field pattern in relation to the development of these proton regions and in spite of the fact that their investigation has not yet been finished and that their results will only be published in conjunction with the second, August–September, period of the PFP study, their description of the general situation can be mentioned here:

During the first half of 1966 the background field pattern was weak. There were no large features in this pattern and because the active regions were concentrated almost entirely into two zones of longitude, so also were the

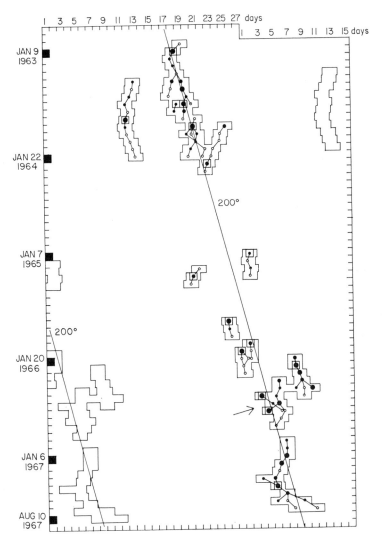

Fig. 1   The distribution of proton-active regions on the sun during 1963–1967. The Bartels 27-day period is plotted on the horizontal axis and subsequent solar rotations on the vertical axis. Active regions which produced proton flares are marked by a square. Each such region was followed from its birth to its decay and this development is drawn in the graph by means of connected solid and open circles. Solid circles represent active regions with developed sunspot groups and open circles are used if only a plage is remaining. An arrow points to the complex of activity which produced all the proton flares observed during the PFP period. The straight line, which corresponds to the solar longitude of 200°, shows that this complex still formed in the same area of the solar surface as did the last major activity complex of the preceding solar cycle which was formed in 1963. It is evident that all proton flare regions of 1963–1967 occurred within a limited range of longitudes, while the remaining part of the sun remained completely inactive as far as proton flare production was concerned.

weak fields of the background pattern. The level of activity was not great enough to sustain a strong background field pattern which could lead to the formation of a unipolar magnetic region.

The proton region No. 8362 was formed in a large weak following-polarity feature at a relatively high latitude, and several small active regions to the west of this feature seemed to provide it with following-polarity flux. The preceding portion of this feature extended across the equator into the southern hemisphere.

In the rotation following the proton flare there was a large leading-polarity feature in the location of the flare region, while the following polarity shifted to the south. In the next rotation the other proton region, No. 8459, intensified in old following-polarity fields which seemed to be made up principally of fields from the first proton region, but located south-east of it.

Bumba and Howard notice that both proton-flare regions developed in old following-polarity fields although, in general, active regions form in old leading-polarity fields (Bumba and Howard 1965).

3 Birth of the Active Region

We have seen from the preceding section that the occurrence of a proton-flare-active region at the place where the region No. 8362 appeared was not astonishing since it was an area on the sun where similar very active regions had formed several times before.

As has been pointed out by Fortini and Torelli (Paper 4)[1], this new active region was born on the eastern periphery of an old large expanding region which covered almost 30° in longitude. This is in agreement with the general conclusion made earlier by Bumba and Howard (1965) that new active regions form inside or very close to old expanding magnetic fields.

The development of this new active region in the first days of its life also closely resembled the scheme described by Bumba and Howard. The developing calcium plage expanded along the borders of three supergranular cells (Paper 4) and the first spots also formed along supergranular boundaries (McIntosh, Paper 5). Therefore, the first phase of development, between 28 June when the region was born and 3 July when a much faster development began, seemed to be quite normal, similar to the birth and initial development of any other non-proton region so far studied.

During these days only two facts might be worth mentioning (Paper 5): (1) for a few hours the separation of newly formed sunspot pairs increased at a rapid rate of about 500 m s^{-1}, which is twice as high a value as the rate of expansion of the calcium plage reported for other regions by Bumba and Howard (1965), and (2) contrary to the normal occurrence, in each pair the leader spots were farther from the equator than the followers. It is difficult to

---

[1] Paper numbers refer to articles in this volume.

say, however, whether these abnormalities might be characteristic and significant for the subsequent fast development of the proton-flare-active region.

4 Development of the Active Region from 3 to 6 July

The fairly slow and usual increase of the active region changed on 3 July after the appearance of a second component of the region 2° east of the older plage (Papers 4 and 5). From that time the active region began to develop at a very fast rate, which seems to be one of the characteristic features of a proton-flare-region development.

On 3 and 4 July the calcium plage brightened and the Hα plage took a compact form (Popovici and Dimitriu, Paper 3). Nevertheless, the fast rate of the sunspot group development was most conspicuous and Fortini and Torelli (Paper 4) emphasize that on 5 July the developed group was unusually large as compared with the extension of the calcium plage.

The respective positions of sunspots in the group were quite remarkable. After their appearance, the sunspots constituted two ranges of inverse polarity, with the neutral line roughly parallel to the equator, which is an orientation somewhat uncommon in well-developed regions although one cannot consider it as a unique feature of proton flare regions. During the night (UT) of 4–5 July a delta configuration was built up, characterized by spots of inverse polarity within the same penumbra (Papers 5 and B, Summary of 1–35). Finally, during the following night the typical proton-flare-active A configuration (Avignon *et al.* 1963) was definitely built up. Both the delta and the A configurations are typical for active regions capable of producing proton flares, and they manifest the existence of steep gradients of magnetic fields in the region. Their occurrence gave rise to a PFP alert which was announced on 5 July from Meudon co-ordinating centre.

The total magnetic energy of the active region was increasing from 1 to 2×10^{32} ergs on 4.3 July up to 20×10^{32} ergs on 6.4 July, which was the last magnetic field measurement carried out before the proton flare appearance (Severny, Paper 1). Maps of the longitudinal magnetic field constructed for these days show three strong magnetic "hills" of each polarity on either side of the neutral line, the southern polarity being somewhat stronger. The gradients of the longitudinal magnetic field along the lines joining the opposite magnetic hills also increased strongly from 4 to 6 July, from about 0.1 gauss km^{-1} to the peak value of about 1 gauss km^{-1} on 6.2 July, on an average. This again was typical magnetic behaviour of a region preparing to produce proton flares (Howard and Severny 1963). On the maps of transverse magnetic field the directions formed something like a cross in the middle of the maps. The variation of the field with depth in the solar atmosphere showed that the magnetic field of the active region was concentrated at deep layers of the atmosphere (Paper 1).

The fast increase of the sunspot group was also reflected in the intensity of the slowly varying component of the radio emission associated with the proton-flare region (Tanaka et al., Paper 9, Krüger, Paper 10). It began to increase strongly on 3 July and until 4.5 July the flux density decreased with increasing frequency between 4 and 9.4 GHz. Simultaneously with the formation of the delta configuration, however, the flux at 9.4 GHz increased substantially so that the spectrum became relatively flat in the 4 – 9.4 GHz frequency interval during the following days. This change of the spectral distribution seems to be associated with some important change of the magnetic structure of the active region (Banin et al., Summary Paper B), perhaps seen as the delta configuration in the sunspot groups, leading to a rapid increase of electron density (Paper 10). According to Tanaka and Kakinuma (1964) this is a generally observed spectral characteristic of proton-flare-active regions, but some exceptions to this rule are possible as Krüger (Paper 10) has shown.

At about the same time, on 5 July, the X-ray flux also began to rise in a significant way, most strongly in the 0–8 Å band (Friedman and Kreplin, Paper 11) so that the X-ray spectrum also became much harder (Michard and Ribes 1968). A summation curve of all sudden ionospheric disturbance (SID) effects produced by the proton-flare region (Křivský, Paper 18) also showed a remarkable change of its slope in the morning hours, UT, of 6 July.

Until midday on 5 July the flare activity was fairly low and only occasional radio bursts with small intensity were observed (Bruzek, Paper 12, Yudin and Kai, Paper 17). Later on, in the second half of 5 July and on 6 July the flare and burst activity increased substantially, but only as far as the number of events was concerned. No important flare or radio burst was produced by the region before the proton-flare occurrence which in fact was the first major event in this active region.

Thus we can conclude that during this phase of development several characteristic features of a typical proton-flare region appeared in the region No. 8362, particularly,

Fast rate of development of the sunspot group.
Formation of a delta configuration with spots of opposite polarity within the same penumbra between 4 and 5 July.
Formation of an A configuration with two rows of sunspots of opposite polarity between 5 and 6 July.
Increase of longitudinal field gradients from 0.1 gauss km^{-1} on 4 July to about 1 gauss km^{-1} on 6 July.
Increase of total magnetic energy at a factor exceeding 10 from 4 to 6 July.
Strong increase of the slowly varying component of the radio emission starting on 3 July.
An outstanding increase of the radio flux at 3 cm wavelength from 5 July,

shifting the maximum of the radio microwave spectrum to higher frequencies.

Significant increase of the X-ray flux after 5 July and hardening of the X-ray spectrum.

5 The Last Twelve Hours before the Proton Flare Occurrence

The last twelve hours on 6 July preceding the proton flare (which appeared at 0026 UT on 7 July) are quite interesting from several points of view. The sunspot group is now formed by two parallel rows of spots of opposite magnetic polarity embedded in a common penumbra. From midday on 6 July the Hα plage began to exhibit two bright ribbons which had a symmetrical disposition with respect to the axis of the group and just covered the penumbra of the two ranges of spots (Popovici and Dimitriu, Paper 3). Thus in fact, at this time the Hα plage already possessed a shape very similar to the shape of the proton flare itself. This indicates that from that time the very strong magnetic field configuration fully dominated the behaviour of all the phenomena in the active region; this was also manifested by the fact that essentially all larger flares in the region developed the same shape of parallel ribbons at least in a rudimentary form (Bruzek, Paper 12).

In the photosphere, during these last hours before the proton flare, the penumbra between the large umbrae in the central part of the group developed exceptionally dark and thick filaments running parallel to the rows of umbrae while before that the north–south orientation prevailed (McIntosh, Paper 5). This unusually dark character of the penumbra, which was particularly impressive in the last ten hours before the proton flare, disappeared shortly after its appearance (McIntosh and Sawyer, Paper 23).

Dodson (Paper 21) studied the behaviour of the active region during these hours from Hα and K-line λ-sweep records. She found that the most obvious characteristic of the region at that time was the presence of a great quantity of absorbing material over both the plage and the surrounding region extending quite far from the plage. Many years ago, d'Azambuja (1930) described the phenomenon of a "circumfacule" in the K_3 line and Dodson suggests that the large amorphous absorption ring observed around the region might be an Hα-aspect of this phenomenon. Since there are no other observations for comparison, one cannot say whether this heavy absorption can be considered as a characteristic feature of the proton-flare region, but in any case it seems to be worthy of consideration.

Dodson also found opposite Doppler shifts in the north-west and south-east parts of the region surroundings, which could be interpreted, apart from other possibilities, as a motion of the gases toward the centre of activity parallel to the surface of the sun. After 20 h UT descending absorbing material came closer and closer to the large spot of northern polarity.

Another interesting feature (Paper 21) was a system of numerous little, parallel, arc-like dark structures observed in both the centre and the wings of the Hα line. These arcs rose in the Hα plage region and also beyond it, and the plage was divided by them into numerous segments. Banin (private communication) alternatively suggests that it was the Hα-plage which was split distinctly into fine, arc-like, bright filaments so that the dark structures Dodson describes were simply the openings between the bright filaments. Such bright parallel threads travelling from one of the plage ribbons to another could be seen in the plage even immediately before the proton-flare onset. One can suspect that these arc-like structures may be a characteristic feature of the pre-flare situation since anything like that has been very rarely observed.

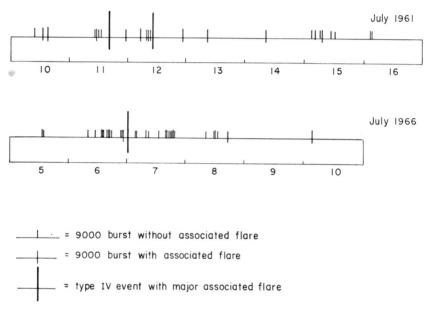

Fig. 2   Occurrence of high-frequency radio bursts.

As mentioned above, no important flare appeared before the proton flare occurrence. Nevertheless the duration of minor flares and the number of small radio bursts increased substantially on the afternoon of 6 July. Of particular interest is the very high number of microwave bursts at around 10,000 MHz, partly associated with subflares, which had no counterpart at lower frequencies, below 8000 MHz (Yudin and Kai, Paper 17, Dodson, Paper 21, and Banin *et al.*, Paper B). It is noteworthy that the production of these high-frequency bursts was not in the least disturbed by the occurrence of the proton flare itself (Fig. 2), (A. D. Fokker, private communication). A somewhat similar burst activity was observed in the proton-flare-active region which passed the central meridian on 13.8 July 1961, but we hardly know any other previous centres of activity that produced so persistently bursts that were so systematically restricted to very high frequencies.

Another fact which might be worth mentioning is that many of the 6 July flares had approximately the same basic configuration as the proton flare itself (Bruzek, Paper 12). For instance the flare at 2220–2255 UT had at its maximum the same shape as the proton flare 4 minutes after its onset. The proton flare, however, was very much brighter and strongly expanded. Obviously, the place of origin and initial shape of both flares were the same regardless of their final size and importance. The occurrence of such pseudo proton flares a few hours before the real proton flare formation does not seem to be an exceptional phenomenon. Obviously, at this stage of development of the active region, the magnetic field is so strong that it fully shapes all flares that occur in it, in a form similar to the much stronger proton flare event, which then appears when a satisfactory amount of energy is released.

On 6 July the X-ray flux was already greatly increased, by a factor of about 15 in the 0–8 Å band. Apart from this, however, the X-ray records on this date are conspicuous by considerable fluctuations even during the period of one telemetry pass (approximately 10 minutes). These fluctuations disappeared entirely after the proton flare appearance and were only renewed at midday on 7 July (Friedman and Kreplin, Paper 11). In this aspect the X-ray emission differs from the flare and radio-burst production, which does not seem to be influenced by the occurrence of the proton flare.

Thus we can conclude that during the last day or half-day preceding the proton flare the following phenomena, uncommon in other active regions, were observed (apart from those existing already before and summarized in the preceding paragraph):

A two-ribbon shape of the Hα plage, covering the penumbra of the two rows of the A configuration of sunspots.

A darkening of penumbral filaments in the central part of the group rearranged parallel to the rows of umbrae.

Heavy absorption over both the plage and its surroundings.

Existence of arc-like structures dividing the plage into numerous segments.

Suspected motion of the gases towards the centre of activity parallel to the solar surface.

Increased duration of minor flares.

High production of small radio bursts systematically restricted to very high frequencies.

Considerable fast fluctuations of the X-ray flux, only partly associated with the flare activity.

Generally, Banin *et al.* (Summary Paper B) suggest that we can distinguish two phases in the development of the active region: The first phase leads to the formation of the appropriate structure necessary for the production of a proton flare; this phase seems to be finished during the night 5–6 July. The second phase, on 6 July, is then the elaboration of the proton flare itself.

6   The Proton Flare of 7 July

The proton flare which appeared in the active region at 0026 UT on 7 July had all the characteristic features of proton flares so far known (McCabe and Caldwell, Paper 24):

It kept the form of two parallel bright ribbons stretched along the spot rows.

Its emission covered umbrae of the large spots.

It was associated with a strong Type IV radio burst.

The flare was classified as of importance 2B and occurred when the active region was about 50° west from the central meridian, which is a very favourable position for ejected particles to reach the earth (Fritzová and Švestka 1966, Lin and Anderson 1967). It was evidently associated with a magnetohydrodynamic wave, since two filaments east of the region abruptly disappeared during the rise of the flare and also sympathetic flares were observed to the west and north of the region during the same time (S. Smith, private communication). No flare nimbus or loop prominences could, however, be detected in association with the proton flare (Paper 24).

Severny (Paper 1) superposed the area occupied by the proton flare on the combined magnetic maps containing the longitudinal and transverse field, as measured closely after the flare decay. From this graph, one can clearly see that the two bright ribbons of the proton flare appeared simultaneously in regions of opposite polarity. One of the flare areas was just to the north of the neutral line and in contact with it, and the other ribbon was about 8" to the south from the neutral line. Both ribbons were parallel to the neutral line. This distribution of the flaring areas is in full agreement with the recent results obtained by Moreton and Severny (1968) for the very active group of 17–26 September 1963, and by Martres, Michard, and Soru-Iscovici (1966) for less important flares.

When compared with the maps of the transverse field, the flare seems to appear in the region of crossing or bifurcation of directions of the transverse field, which again confirms earlier results (Moreton and Severny 1968, Severny 1964). And finally Severny shows that both areas of the flare were just above places with the strongest electric currents, which is another fact already found by Moreton and Severny for the proton-flare-active region of September 1963. Severny suggests that this observation gives support to Alfvén and Carlquist's (1967) theory of flares as interruptions in electric current filaments.

The associated Type IV burst which started at 0018 UT on centimetre wavelengths (Enome, Paper 27) was quite strong on the microwave frequencies and moderately strong in the decimetre wavelength range (Kai, Paper 28). There are some discrepancies, however, where the metre wavelengths are concerned. According to Stewart (Paper 25) the dynamic spectrum at Culgoora covering the frequency range 10 to 200 MHz did not show any Type IV burst, but only an intense Type II burst from 0038 to 0047 UT followed by a weak continuum. On the other hand, however, Warwick (Paper 26) reports a strong Type IV burst starting before 0053 and lasting for more than 70 minutes, in the frequency range 20–41 MHz. Single-frequency measurements at Mitaka and Hiraiso close to 200 MHz also give a definite radio burst lasting for about 90 minutes (Paper 27). The discrepancy between the Culgoora and the Boulder observations can be related to the low sensitivity of the Culgoora equipment.

A strong enhancement of the X-ray emission was recorded with three satellites: NRL-SOLRAD 8, Explorer 33, and OGO-3. The last satellite measured very high energy X-rays above 80 keV and found a relatively short-lived enhancement which started at 0027 UT, reached a maximum (which exceeded more than 30 times the background level) at 0037 and declined within the following 10 or 20 minutes (Cline *et al.*, Paper 29).

Křivský (private communication) emphasizes that before the creation of the two bright flare ribbons, the flare passed through the Y-type development phase (Křivský 1965) when the emission ribbons were separating, and this phase, which started at 0030, was just completed at 0037 when hard X-rays reached their maximum flux. Exactly the same effect has already been observed before for other proton flares (Křivský, in Švestka 1966).

However, McCabe and Caldwell (Paper 24) report 0046 for this "characteristic appearance of the horizontal Y-shape". According to Fig. 2 of Cline *et al.* (Paper 29), the strongest part of the 80-keV X-ray burst occurs really between 0033 and 0042 with its maximum close to 0037. On the isophotal contour maps of the flare of McCabe and Caldwell the most striking event is the brightening over umbra Z starting between 0029 and 0032 (their Fig. 3*c* and *d*): however, it is difficult to be sure of such an event with the perspective effect on the solar sphere.

The shape of the X-ray curve shows an astonishing similarity to the microwave burst published by Enome (Paper 27); one also can find a similarity with the burst at 9400 MHz but this similarity becomes less as one approaches lower frequencies and it hardly exists below 3750 MHz.

The X-ray enhancement in the 2–12 Å range recorded with Explorer 33 (Van Allen, Paper 30) had a much longer duration. It started at 0023, reached maximum flux of 28 times the pre-flare value at 0042 and declined for more than three hours. Any pronounced similarity with the radio burst is missing for this X-ray energy range. One can see from this that, although the very hard X-rays seem to be intimately connected with the production of microwave bursts, this association loses its intimate nature for soft X-rays. In their study of nearly 70 X-ray bursts Winckler and his co-workers (Arnoldy *et al.*

1968) report this better correlation with the 3-cm or 10-cm emission of the rise time, decay time and total duration for the 10–50 keV X-rays than for the extremely soft X-rays or for the extremely energetic quanta. They suggest that both types of emission, particularly in the first part of the events, come from a common source. They build up a model, but the main conclusion is the difficulty of obtaining a single model applicable to all events.

Records of SOLRAD-8 satellite carried out in 8–20, 0–8 and < 3 Å bands are incomplete during the flare life-time (Friedman and Kreplin, Paper 31). They confirm, however, that the decline of the X-ray flux in these energy ranges was fairly slow and took more than five hours in the 0–8 Å range.

SID data, too, indicate that the X-ray enhancement started at about 0026 UT (Donnelly, Paper 32). From sudden frequency deviation (SFD) records Donnelly finds the maximum of the 5–10 Å X-ray flux at 0041 in good agreement with Van Allen's measurement (Paper 30) and the maximum shifts to an earlier time with increasing frequency. A very good resemblance of Van Allen's soft X-ray curve is found for the curve of the ionospheric, D-layer, absorption of cosmic radio noise at 22 MHz (Paper 30).

Geomagnetic pulsations of Pi 2 type with a variable period from 40 to 100 seconds and maximum amplitude at 0027 UT are reported by Pintér (Paper 33) during the rise of the geomagnetic crochet associated with the proton flare.

7 Situation in the Active Region after the Proton Flare

The first post-flare measurement of the magnetic field in the active region was carried out five hours after the onset of the proton flare (Severny, Paper 1). At that time, the total magnetic flux decreased to about the initial value measured on 4.3 July, i.e. was at least 10 times lower than on 6.4 July, twelve hours before the flare. The same decrease of about one order of magnitude was found for the gradients of the longitudinal magnetic field. Unfortunately, due to the gaps in observations between 6.4 and 7.2 July, one cannot say whether this decrease of the magnetic flux and of the gradients preceded or followed the proton flare appearance.

Severny also reports a very interesting change in the directions of the transverse magnetic field. While the directions had formed roughly something like a cross in the middle of the active region about 15 hours before the flare appearance, on the morning of 7 July Severny found instead a stream of purely horizontal directions, in E–W orientation, as if the proton flare had forced the directions to be parallel to its bright ribbons and to the neutral line $H_\parallel = 0$. Thus we find a rotation by 90° of vector fields in the central part of the region during the night when the proton flare appeared, a phenomenon which Severny (1964) had already observed and described earlier for other solar flares. The fact that all six maps of the transverse field obtained on 7 July are similar, including those for the lowest level ($\lambda = 4808$ Å), leads to the conclusion that there were no appreciable changes in the vector field of

$H_\perp$ during the morning hours of 7 July, so that all observed changes must be attributed to the night of 6–7 July when the proton flare formed.

In this connection one is inclined to suspect that the change in orientation of penumbral filaments finally arranged parallel to the row of sunspots for the last ten hours before the flare (McIntosh, Paper 5, see Sec. 5), might indicate a similar phenomenon. If this were the case, it would mean that the rotation by 90° of vector fields occurred between 15 and 10 hours before the flare and not directly in the course of the flare process. Of course, one has to add that, in fact, there is no observational proof that the penumbral filaments follow the transverse field lines.

From isogauss maps of the total vector of the magnetic field **H** Severny (Paper 1) also confirms the process observed recently by Gopasyuk (1967) that there appears a fission of large magnetic tubes of force into small pieces after the active region passed its maximum development, which seems to have happened close to the time of the proton flare occurrence or during the day before it.

The area of the sunspot group continued to increase for at least two days following the proton flare (McIntosh and Sawyer, Paper 23); this seems to be in contradiction with some previous observations of Howard (1963) and Antalová (1965) who have found that the sunspot area generally decreases after cosmic-ray and ribbon-like flares. It has to be emphasized, however, that the observed increase in area was due to the development of new spots which came into existence on 6 or 7 July and were not affected by the flare. On the contrary, that part of the sunspot group which had been covered by the flare began to decay within half a day of the time of the flare, and this decline was probably related to the proton flare occurrence (Papers 23 and Summary B).

The proton flare was followed by a long-enduring importance-1 flare activity lasting until about 13 h UT on 7 July (Bruzek, Paper 12). After that, however, there followed a period of almost 11 hours without any importance 1 flare. A similar inactive period of about 15 hours also followed the second large flare in the region on 9 July. Bruzek concludes from this that important flares may be followed, after a slow and intermittent decrease of activity, by a relatively quiet period, which in fact has already been observed with a number of other important flares. A possible interpretation would be that after large flares a period of recovery is required until another important flare can be produced. The previously mentioned increased number of radio bursts, mostly limited to very high microwave frequencies, continued during 7 July and declined only in the evening hours of that day. On the other hand, as we have already mentioned, the striking variability of the X-ray flux observed on 6 July completely disappeared after the proton flare appearance and appeared again only after 12 h on 7 July. One can see from this that the post-flare activity showed quite different trends in the optical, radio, and X-ray spectral regions.

On 7 July at 12 h UT the photospheric and chromospheric magnetic field in the active region was measured by Brückner and Waldmeier (Paper 2). Apart from results which are in general agreement with Severny's conclusions mentioned above, they found a tremendous difference between the photospheric and chromospheric field strengths. The Hα fields reach only 80 gauss while the photospheric fields go up to 2000 gauss. This would indicate a very high concentration of the magnetic field in the photospheric levels, but one cannot escape the feeling that emission and absorption features in the Hα line might influence the results of measurement in a significant way.

8   The Flare of 9 July

On the days following the proton flare two other flares of importance 2B formed in the active region, one on 8 July and the second on 9 July. The flare of 9 July is of particular interest from several points of view (Bruzek, Paper 12):

It was the second largest disk flare of the active region.
All large spots but the second leader were covered by the flare within a few minutes.
The flare was clearly split into two strands parallel to the axis of the sunspot group.
It developed a pronounced loop prominence system.
It was associated with a radio burst which may be classified as a weak Type IV event (Yudin and Kai, Paper 17).

Nevertheless, no protons were recorded from this flare, even when its position on the disk was favourable for particles to reach the space probes and the vicinity of the earth.

Therefore, it is of interest to compare the two importance 2B flares on 7 July and 9 July and try to find the essential differences which might have caused the different behaviour of these flares as far as the emission of high-energy protons was concerned. According to Bruzek (Paper 12) the following differences were of particular interest:

The 7 July flare was much brighter.
The 7 July flare expanded much more and this expansion proceeded for a longer period.
The 7 July flare covered almost completely all large spots in the group while in
The 9 July event the large north-polarity spot remained outside the flaring area.

The Type IV burst on 9 July was much less intense (Paper 17). However, we must avoid a definite conclusion: the 9 July flare occurred near the limb of the disk, at 75°W. This kind of observation is very interesting for many purposes like loop observation but very difficult to compare with a flare observed in the central part of the disk: Unfortunately for a spot so near the limb it has been impossible so far to obtain good measurements of the magnetic field.

It is well known that loop prominence systems are closely associated with proton flares (Bruzek 1964). It is of interest that in this case loop prominences did not accompany the proton flare itself, but another large flare produced by the same region two days later. This seems to confirm Švestka's (1968a) conclusion that it is more likely that loop prominence systems are associated with proton-flare-active regions than directly with proton flares themselves. One can reasonably suppose that a system of slowly expanding loop prominences suggests that some material was ejected from the flare and found its way into the corona, later to condense and return to the surface in the descending knots of the prominences (Newkirk *et al.*, Paper 8). Obviously, however, according to the 9 July event, this does not mean that, at the same time, a sufficient number of high-energy particles succeeded in penetrating through the corona into interplanetary space. On the other hand, the 7 July event shows that particles can be expelled into space even without some of the ejected material remaining captured in the low corona. Quite often, of course, some of the particles leave the sun and others are captured in the magnetic loops and then both proton flares and loop prominence systems are observed simultaneously as Bruzek (1964) has found in a number of cases.

9   The Limb Event of 11 July

The great eruptive prominence which formed in the active region on 11 July was an outstanding phenomenon and the complicated motions observed during its development indicate the existence of a fairly complex magnetic field structure above the active region (Valníček *et al.*, Paper 16). The measured velocities in the prominence exceeded 300 km s^{-1}. One can suspect that there was another important flare associated with this event but this flare, if existing, was already hidden behind the solar limb. Valníček and his co-authors come to the conclusion that we met here with a twisted prominence which started parallel to the plane of the disk and after completing a twist returned to the chromosphere in a direction nearly perpendicular to the initial direction.

Spectral observations (Gurtovenko *et al.*, Paper 14) indicate that the originally chaotic motions of the prominence became more stable in the later phase of its development and the line profiles took shape similar to that of the loops on 9 July. Nevertheless, direct Hα photographs do not indicate any presence of a loop prominence system at that time.

Křivský and Nestorov (Paper 19) suggest that this prominence could be associated with another proton flare in the region, but there are no direct indications supporting this suggestion. No protons were recorded (which, of course, could be due to the flare position behind the limb) and the radio burst certainly cannot be classified as of Type IV (which again can be due to the directional sensitivity of metre waves and to the location of a part of the source of microwaves behind the limb). No direct X-ray measurements are at our disposal, apart from one telemetry pass which shows that from 1010 to 1025 UT, i.e. about one hour after the onset of the event, all 8–20, 0–8, and 0–3 Å channels on the SOLRAD satellite were saturated (Compilations of Solar–Geophysical Data, Boulder, September 1966). From the SID effects one can find the main maximum of the X-ray emission at about 0945. The atypical shape of the SEA (sudden enhancement of atmospherics) effect confirms that a part of the emitting region was hidden behind the limb (Paper 19).

10 Coronal Measurements

Density of the corona above the active region increased dramatically between 27 June and 10 July, when the active region passed the eastern and western limb of the sun, as one can see both from measurements of the white-light corona (Newkirk *et al.*, Paper 8, Dollfus 1968) and from measurements of coronal line intensities (Leroy, Paper 6, Gnevyshev, Paper 7). Both Gnevyshev and Newkirk *et al.* confirm that the maximum of coronal intensity did not coincide exactly with the position of the proton flare, but was shifted a few degrees to the north.

The deduced coronal electron density on 10 July, i.e. three days after the proton event, was only slightly larger than over other active regions within the heights above 0.3 solar radii, but it significantly exceeded the density in other active regions in the low coronal layers (Paper 8). This observation of a unique, low-elevation coronal condensation, also found for the limb-passage on 5 September, shortly after the two other PFP proton flare occurrences, suggests that proton flares eject material into the corona. Newkirk *et al.* think that the expanding series of loop prominences and the expanding condensation represent different aspects of the same phenomenon brought on by the emergence of a magnetic dome from the lower atmosphere.

11 Later Development of the Active Region

The active region that produced the proton flare of 7 July continued through at least two subsequent rotations (Dodson and Hedeman, Paper 34). In the first of these, in late July, spot area and radio emission were greatly diminished but the calcium plage had increased in area by 50 per cent.

Flares continued to occur in the region, and the major flare of 28 July is of special interest. Its importance was 2B or greater and, again, like the major flares of 7–9 July, it consisted primarily of two bright ribbons. The difference was that in this case the Hα flare emission was far from all spots. Nevertheless, the flare was associated with an enhancement of radio emission for more than two hours, most intense at lower frequencies, and it also produced a strong X-ray emission, of about one half of the intensity of the X-ray enhancement associated with the 7 July proton flare event. Thus even in late July the region was still capable of producing a major flare. Such two-ribbon flares outside sunspots and sometimes in fairly inconspicuous active regions are not extraordinarily infrequent. It might be of interest to check whether perhaps other such events also occur in decaying proton-flare regions.

In the August rotation, as Dodson and Hedeman point out, the post-proton-flare region of July through differential rotation became co-longitudinal at 182° with a previously following region in latitude 22°N. This had been the region which later on produced major proton flares on 28 August and 2 September, during the second active PFP period (cf. Sec. 2). In consequence of it, coronal measurements (Newkirk *et al.*, Paper 8) showed enhancement at about the same longitude but migrating south from 10 July until the limb passage of 19 September. The passage on 10 July, however, showed a higher electron density in the low corona than any of the limb passages that followed.

Mogilevsky *et al.* (Paper 35) investigated the magnetic field decay of the active region after the proton flare appearance. While before the 7 July flare an approximate equality of magnetic fluxes had been conserved in the sunspot group, after the proton flare a sudden growth of the southern-polarity magnetic flux and considerable decrease of the northern-polarity flux was observed. After that the active region was on the opposite, invisible, side of the solar disk, but one may assume that this run of development continued, since in the next rotation in late July the group looked like a relatively stable unipolar spot of southern polarity, with the magnetic class αp. It may be of interest to note that the area of the remaining spot was near to the area of a supergranule at this time. Magnetographic measurements (Paper 34) showed that the extensive and relatively bright plage associated with the sunspot group was bipolar. On the third rotation in late August only a small α-spot without penumbra was remaining of the active region, and the calcium plage, though greatly fragmented and reduced in intensity, was still a detectable feature.

At this time, however, the activity was already shifted to the second proton-flare region, located at lower latitude. As mentioned in Sec. 2, both these regions appeared in one complex of activity, which dominated solar activity during the entire second half of 1966 (Paper 34). Already in the late July rotation the activity of the region No. 8362 was observed in its tail part situated close to this neighbouring active region which developed fully only during the next rotation in August. Mogilevsky *et al.* suggest that this subsequent rapid development of this neighbouring group, which was a fairly inactive small group during the three previous rotations, might have been stimulated by the magnetic field of the decaying high-latitude group which produced the proton flare on 7 July, an opinion which has already been expressed by Bumba and Howard (Sec. 2).

12   GeV Protons and Relativistic Electrons

A very small ground solar-proton event was detected by the high-latitude network of high counting-rate neutron monitors close to 0100 UT on 7 July (Carmichael, Paper 36, Ahluwalia *et al.*, Paper 37, Fréon *et al.*, Paper 40). Since the increase did not exceed 3 per cent (it was the smallest ground-level event (GLE) ever distinguished), it is fairly difficult to determine its exact onset time from individual records, but the average gives 0059 ± 15, i.e. 33 minutes after the start of the proton flare and the associated Type IV burst. The fact that the GLE could be clearly distinguished in neutron monitor records at Leeds and Kiel indicates that 33 minutes after the Type IV onset protons of energy as high as 2.3 GeV penetrated to the earth. The GLE reached its maximum between 0145 and 0150 and ended at about 06 h on 7 July.

At about the same time, at 0100, the satellite IMP-3, for the first time in the history of interplanetary space research, recorded relativistic solar electrons with energies between 3 and 12 MeV (Cline and McDonald, Paper 41). These energies are nearly two orders of magnitude higher than any previously studied in space. The observed flux of relativistic electrons decayed at about 0500. Since the direct field-line propagation time for electrons of these energies would be about 8.3 minutes, the delay of 34 minutes after the Type IV onset means either that considerable storage of particles must have taken place near the sun or that they were produced only in a later phase of the flare.

The first explanation seems plausible, because the existence of storage of protons has been proved in many other cases and even relativistic protons show similarly delayed behaviour (Bryant *et al.* 1965). Nevertheless, the fact that electrons of much smaller energy, above 45 keV, were recorded simultaneously with the relativistic electrons aboard IMP-3 and Explorer 33 (Armstrong *et al.*, Paper 43, Kahler and Lin, Paper 42) seems to be in favour of the second alternative, i.e. a delayed ejection of the relativistic electrons from the flare region. These low-energy electrons were first recorded at 0058 ± 02, in spite of our expectation that they would be delayed with respect to the MeV electrons as is observed with protons of different energies.

The maximum flux of very high energy solar X-rays was observed at about 0037–0038 (Cline *et al.*, Paper 29, see Sec. 6) and this time coincides with a sharp maximum of the microwave component of the Type IV burst (Enome, Paper 27, Kai, Paper 28). At about the same time the shape of the flare changed (McCabe and Caldwell, Paper 24) and the Y-phase of the flare dissolved (Křivský, private communication). Therefore, one can suspect that while the low-energy electrons were ejected from the flare region after the onset of the Type IV burst, the relativistic electrons were only produced in this crucial phase of the flare development. If this explanation were accepted, the delay time of the first arriving $\geqslant 45$ keV electrons would be about 12 minutes longer than that of the relativistic electrons, which seems to be more plausible. Of course, some storage, delaying the relativistic electrons for about 13 minutes, must still have taken place near the sun.

Without any detailed comparison with other proton events it is difficult to form any conclusion why this proton flare of 7 July was a source of GeV protons and relativistic electrons which must be considered as exceptional proton-flare behaviour. No relativistic electrons, for example, were present during the proton events of 28 August 1966 and of 28 January 1967 (Krimigis, Summary Paper C).

13   Protons within the Energy Range 1 to 10^2 MeV

While Armstrong *et al.* (Paper 43) suspect that > 55 MeV penetrating protons might have accompanied the $\geqslant 45$ keV electrons from the onset of the particle event (and certainly high-energy protons were present at that time as the GLE showed), the first direct record of proton flux was recorded only at 0110 by the SPARMO balloon launched in Northern Scandinavia at about 20 h on 6 July (Heristchi *et al.*, Paper 38). The total counting rates of protons with energies above 100 MeV reached a maximum at 0206, when the integral proton flux was 2.6 protons cm^{-2} s^{-1} sr^{-1}. At that time the spectrum was fairly hard; when assuming the power-law form of the differential energy spectrum, Heristchi *et al.* found the spectral exponent γ close to 2.0. From calculations of the differential proton flux, Heristchi *et al.* found that the maximum of the 200-MeV proton flux occurred at about 0230, of 150-MeV protons at about 0400 and of 100-MeV protons at about 0500. This shift of maxima towards earlier times with increasing energy, as well as faster decrease for higher energetic protons are a good manifestation of the well-known increase of the delay time with decreasing energy of the arriving protons. At 0500 the value of the exponent γ was increased to 3.5 and afterwards it varied between 3.5 and 4.0 (Paper 38, Ageshin *et al.*, Paper 39).

Kahler and Lin (Paper 42) report a detection of 3–33 MeV protons by OGO-3 after 0135 and the maximum flux of 32-MeV (OGO-3) and > 20-MeV protons (IMP-3) between 06 h and 07 h UT. On the other hand, Cline and McDonald (Paper 41) could not identify 15–75 MeV protons aboard IMP-3 before 0200, and protons with energies lower than 4 MeV did not arrive before 0300, as recorded by Explorer 33 (Krimigis *et al.*, Paper 54). Since OGO-3 made a pass through the radiation belts close to the beginning of the particle event, its records seem to be open to some doubt during the starting period.

The low-energy protons (below 10 MeV) did not reach their maximum before the late morning hours on 8 July. The proton spectrum from 0.31 to 10 MeV was initially very hard, it was becoming softer as the lower energy protons arrived for the first two days and changed less markedly thereafter (Armstrong *et al.*, Paper 43).

Simultaneous observations at Explorer 33, IMP-3 and OGO-3 (Kahler and Lin, Paper 42) as well as significant fluctuations of the intensity of protons arriving at Explorer 33 on time scales as short as the 82-second resolution of the data (Armstrong *et al.*, Paper 43) can be attributed to a filamentary spatial structure of proton and electron intensities as observed earlier by Fan *et al.* (1966) and Bartley *et al.* (1966). A comparison of the local magnetic field vector with the parameters of the anisotropy of 0.31–10 MeV protons shows that the anisotropy of solar protons is intimately related to the local magnetic field (Paper 43). The large spatial gradients found in fluxes of 0.5–20 MeV protons and $\geqslant 45$ keV electrons (Paper 42) are most probably due to the non-uniform filling of the field lines at the sun with particles or to the mixing of interplanetary magnetic flux tubes with different particle densities, or possibly to both these effects. The intensity variations of the proton flux were found to be larger for low-energy protons than for protons with higher energies. Kahler and Lin conclude that these observed spatial gradients indicate that propagation across the field lines is very limited, particularly for low-energy protons, and they found that the diffusion co-efficient perpendicular to the lines of force of the interplanetary magnetic field was two orders of magnitude smaller than the diffusion coefficient parallel to the lines of force (Krimigis, Summary Paper C).

14 Alpha Particles

The flux of alpha particles could be separately identified in the records of Explorer 33, within the energy range 2.1–17 MeV and the abundance ratio of protons to alpha particles, p/α, has been measured for the first time in the energy range 0.5–4 MeV/nucleon (Armstrong *et al.*, Paper 43).

The p/α ratio was initially large and decreased during the first day of the event, indicating that an appreciable fraction of the alpha particles observed required up to one day longer to reach the vicinity of the earth than protons of the same velocity. From 8 July onwards the p/α ratio was found to range from 28 to 55. Armstrong *et al.* have concluded that the intensities of low-energy protons within energies from 0.3 to 10 MeV and of alpha particles from 2.1 to 17 MeV are modulated in a very similar way in the propagation from the sun to the earth. There appear, however, significant time variations in the spectrum of protons and in the relative abundance of protons to alpha particles.

15 The Polar-Cap Absorption

The first onset of PCA was noticed at 0120 UT at Shepherd Bay, 10° from the North Pole. Auroral zone stations observed the polar-cap absorption

(PCA) onset after 0200 and the lowest latitudes of appreciable PCA were Healy, Alaska, 63.7°, where PCA started at about 0400 (Hakura, Paper 45) and Norilsk, 63.4° (Benkova and Zevakina, Paper 60). In the polar region the PCA reached a maximum of 2.5 dB on 30 MHz at about 1300 on 7 July, then decayed to 0.3 dB during the next 36 hours and stayed near this level for several days (Hakura, Paper 45, Masley and Goedeke, Paper 46). In relation to this fairly small PCA event the preceding occurrence of a GLE seems a little surprising.

Hakura distinguishes three phases of development of the PCA event: (1) a slightly enhanced ionization near the geomagnetic pole, starting at 0120, which he ascribes to electrons; (2) a remarkable development of the PCA thereafter in the polar caps above 65°, which he ascribes to protons; (3) an extension of the enhanced radiation to lower latitude zones, which only occurred after the arrival of alpha particles from the sun.

On the other hand, Masley and Goedeke believe that protons played the predominant part in the absorption from its very onset. Since the energy range of solar protons effective for PCA is below 100 MeV, the decision between these two points of view depends on whether the OGO-3 record of the 33-MeV proton arrival at 0135 (Paper 42) can be relied upon. If the protons of energies below 100 MeV only appeared after 02 h UT, as IMP-3 indicates (Paper 41), Hakura's explanation would be the correct one.

16   Time Sequence of the High Energy Particle Event

We can thus summarize the time development of the high-energy particle event as follows:

7 July

0026	Proton flare: Type IV burst onset: 1–6 keV X-ray burst
0029⎫ 0032⎭	Brightening over umbra Z: 80 keV X-ray burst
0037⎫ 0038⎭	Change of shape of flare: maxima of hard X-ray emission: microwave Type IV burst: relativistic electrons and protons produced?
0058	Onset of $\geqslant 45$ keV electron flux near the earth
0045⎫ 0115⎭	GLE onset: arrival of GeV protons
∼0100	Arrival of relativistic electrons
0110	Onset of > 100 MeV proton flux
0120	PCA onset: start of the first phase: produced by electrons?
0135	Somewhat doubtful onset of 33 MeV protons
∼0150	GLE maximum (0130–0230): onset of 80 MeV proton flux
0200	Onset of 15–75 MeV proton flux
∼0200	Start of second phase of PCA, at auroral zone stations, clearly caused by < 100 MeV protons
∼0206	Maximum integrated flux of > 100 MeV protons

~0220   Maximum flux of relativistic electrons
~0230   Maximum flux of 200 MeV protons
~0300   Onset of <4 MeV proton flux
~0400   Maximum flux of 150 MeV protons
~0400   Last PCA onset (at 63.7° latitude)
~0500   Maximum flux of 100 MeV protons
~0500   Decay of relativistic electrons
~0600   End of GLE
$\gtrsim$0630   Maximum flux of 32 MeV protons
$\gtrsim$0700   Maximum flux of 17 MeV protons
   1300   PCA maximum
            8 July
~1000   Maximum flux of <10 MeV protons (This maximum might have been caused—and seemingly shifted to a later hour—by an additional influx of protons stored behind the sector boundary)

17 Passage across the Sector Boundary on 8 July

During the period investigated the interplanetary magnetic field was measured by Explorers 28 and 33 (Ness and Taylor, Paper 48). At 16 h on 4 July these satellites passed a sector boundary and entered a sector in which the magnetic field lines were directed out of the sun. They remained inside this sector for about 4 days. Thus the proton flare occurred at a time when the interplanetary field of 4γ at 1 AU was directed along the general Archimedean spiral in a sense away from the sun and all the events on 7 July described in the previous section happened inside the sector of the orientation described.

At 05 h on 8 July, however, magnetic records of Explorers 28 and 33 showed that the earth passed another boundary and then entered an oppositely directed sector. This passage across the sector boundary during the particle event in progress seems to have quite significant consequences in the recorded particle flux.

At about 06 h on 8 July, IMP-3, Explorer 33, and OGO-3 recorded a sharp rise of the $\geqslant$45keV electron flux and a few hours earlier a smooth rise of <20-MeV proton flux (Kahler and Lin, Paper 42). The highly increased electron flux decayed again after 11 h while the high flux of low-energy protons continued for several more hours. This sudden secondary increase was obviously an increase in the flux of the low-energy particle component and not an increase in the energetic penetrating radiation. Kahler and Lin compared the records aboard IMP-3 and Explorer 33 and found that variations in the count rate of the IMP-3 counters were followed 50 ± 10 minutes later by similar variations of the Explorer 33 counters. That means that we meet here with the co-rotation effect and the observed flux variations must have been due primarily to a spatial gradient in the particle density across the interplanetary magnetic field lines. Therefore, one may consider that the sudden increase in the flux of low-energy electrons and protons reflected an accumulation of these particles within and behind the sector boundary which the earth crossed at 05 h on 8 July.

This increase of low-energy particles started 30 hours after the proton flare occurrence and 15 hours before the sudden commencement (ssc) which can be attributed to an interplanetary shock wave coming from the proton flare. Nevertheless, there appeared several effects which resembled, in a less impressive measure and without any ssc, the behaviour which was later on observed after the shock wave arrived at the earth:

a. Particularly at stations in higher geomagnetic latitudes considerable geomagnetic disturbances started at about 06 h on 8 July (e.g. College station) and these disturbances continued until the ssc onset at 2102 on the same day (Best *et al.*, Paper 56, Benkova and Zevakina, Paper 60).

b. In the time interval from 06 h to 09 h on 8 July the *K* index increased to 4+.

c. About 30 hours after the particles flare, a two-phase ionospheric F-region disturbance started at all observing stations (Lange and Taubenheim, Paper 59). The disturbance began with a positive phase in high and medium latitudes which reached its maximum after 10 h on 8 July.

d. Apart from a regular Forbush decrease which started at about midnight on 8–9 July, there was a transient decrease recorded by some of the neutron monitors starting about 0800 on 8 July (Carmichael, Paper 50).

e. About two days after the flare, a marked compression of the plasmasphere was observed by OGO-3 (Taylor *et al.*, Paper 53); but the OGO-3 orbital period was nearly 48 hours. Corcuff (Paper 52), using whistler observations, specifies more precisely that such an event occurred between 02 h and 14 h on 8 July and that the boundary of the plasmapause moved from 5.5 to 3.5 earth radii. This last value has been confirmed by the OGO-3 report of 9 July (the exact time of this observation has not been reported but it seems to be close to 15 h).

All these measurements indicate that the passage of the sector boundary across the earth carried an increased number of < 20 MeV protons to the earth's vicinity and produced effects similar to those evoked by the magnetic cloud behind the shock wave coming from the proton flare.

18   The Sudden Storm Commencement

A shock wave coming from the flare caused a sudden storm commencement at the earth at 2102 on 8 July, i.e. 44 h 36 min after the proton flare onset. The ssc was accurately independent of longitude and the magnitude of the maximum increase in the horizontal component was between 17 and 48 γ at the various stations (Van Allen and Ness, Paper 49, Best *et al.*, Paper 56).

It is well known that protons of energy a few MeV may be trapped and stored in the sudden commencement plasma cloud and then observed at the earth with a fairly sharp onset at the time of the ssc (Bryant *et al.* 1962). No such increase, however, was recorded after the ssc on 8 July, nor was there any discontinuity in riometer records around the time of the ssc (Hakura, Paper 45). On the contrary, about two hours after the ssc all the particle fluxes dropped (Kahler and Lin, Paper 42, Krimigis *et al.*, Paper 54).

This intensity drop was also recorded by Explorer 33 in interplanetary space at 187,000 km in the antisolar direction from the earth at 2106 (Van Allen and Ness, Paper 49). The counting rate of ~ 0.5 MeV solar protons dropped to about 37 per cent. Simultaneous magnetic field measurements show at the same time an abrupt increase of the magnetic field strength from 12 to 21γ with a rise time from 5 to 10 seconds. The direction of the field was observed to be nearly that of the classical Archimedean spiral, but the field vector was directed below the plane of the ecliptic by 10–20°.

The apparent travel time of the shock wave between the earth and Explorer 33 is 3.5 ± 0.15 minutes and the corresponding velocity of propagation is 890 ± 40 km s^{-1}. This is in good agreement with the mean propagation velocity of 950 km s^{-1} corresponding to the time lapse of 44 h 36 min between the flare onset and the start of the sudden commencement at the earth.

From the rise time of the magnetic field strength as recorded with Explorer 33, Van Allen and Ness find the apparent thickness of the transition region at the shock front to be 1×10^4 km or less. The drop in flux of particles behind the shock wave can be explained either as a discontinuous drop of 37 per cent in integral intensity after sweeping in front of the shock, the low-energy particles flowing along the sector boundary of the interplanetary magnetic field, or as a decrease of the particle energy behind the shock by about 0.16 MeV, due to energetic losses of particles reflected from the inner side of the shock boundary.

At 2106 the shock wave was also observed at IMP-3, which was much nearer to the earth than Explorer 33. Ness and Taylor (Paper 48) conclude from this that the propagation velocities through the magnetosphere and magnetosheath are significantly different from the interplanetary value. They also conclude that the interplanetary velocity of the shock when it passed these satellites was at least 200 km s^{-1} less than the average velocity of the shock during its propagation from the sun to the earth.

In the Pioneer 6 records (Paper 48) a shock occurred at 1822 on 10 July, when the field magnitude increased from 9 to 22γ. If this shock was also associated with the 7 July flare, this observation would imply that the shock propagated more rapidly out along the spiral magnetic field than transverse to it. Such a supposition, however, is in contradiction to the Forbush decrease already observed on 9 July aboard Pioneer 6 (see Sec. 19). Therefore we take it as plausible that this shock was produced by the second largest flare in the active region on 9 July at 0230 (cf. Sec. 8). For the space probe, the flare was nearer the centre of the solar disk. Since the delay time between the flare start and the magnetic field strength increase on Pioneer 6 amounts to 40 hours and this "sudden commencement" is a second event (Caroubalos 1964, Obayashi 1962) this explanation does not seem unreasonable, and does not disagree with the reported observations by Lazarus and Binsack (Paper 51).

19 The Forbush Decrease

The Forbush decrease started at the two north- and south-pointing stations, Alert and McMurdo, on 8 July between 23 h and 24 h UT (Carmichael, Paper 50). The intensity decreased about 3 per cent. At other stations the decrease, up to 5 per cent, started later and, as already mentioned in Sec. 17, at some stations there was a transient decrease starting at about 06 h on 8 July and followed by a main decrease at 08 h on 9 July.

The first phase (0800 on 8 July) can be associated with the small decrease described as "prebaisse" by Legrand (1960). On this first occasion it was obviously related to the earth's crossing of the interplanetary magnetic field boundary: it would be interesting to confirm such an interpretation from other reported "prebaisses". Taking the position of the flare into account, the Forbush decrease was fairly strong, since a Forbush effect deeper than 5 per cent has never been recorded for flares situated farther than 50°W from the central solar meridian (Haurwitz *et al.* 1965, Švestka 1967).

Aboard Pioneer 6, from which only data after 08 h on 9 July are complete, the Forbush decrease was characterized by bi-directional fluxes of particles typical of the minimum intensity phase of a Forbush decrease (Rao *et al.*, Paper 44). The minimum phase occurred between 12 h and 16 h on 9 July, which can be compared with the minimum intensity at the earth at about 15 h on the same day. Rao *et al.* conclude from this that the Forbush decrease at Pioneer 6 occurred simultaneously with or earlier than at the earth and this implies that the shock wave expanded radially outwards over at least 45° of solar longitude. This observation seems to exclude the possibility mentioned in the previous section that the shock recorded aboard Pioneer 6 on 10 July might be associated with the 7 July proton event.

According to Rao *et al.* the proton flare effects as reflected in particle anisotropies were completely typical: The period in question exhibited field-aligned anisotropies before the appearance of the proton flare, bi-directional anisotropies during the minimum of the Forbush decrease and convective removal anisotropies thereafter.

20 Conditions in the Magnetosphere

Apart from the compression of the magnetosphere and of the plasmasphere about one day after the flare, mentioned in Sec. 17 (Lazarus and Binsack,

Paper 51 and Corcuff, Paper 52), a very substantial contraction of the plasma-sphere after the ssc has been found by OGO-3 (Taylor *et al.*, Paper 53). The magnetosphere was disturbed during the period following the proton flare and on 9 July the plasmapause was observed to be unusually low, at $L = 3.3$. This observation occurred approximately 6 hours after the highest magnetic activity was recorded (this happened between 03 h and 09 h on 9 July). On 11 July the plasmapause partially recovered, to $L = 4.7$. Finally, on 13 July it reached the value of 6.3, close to the average for quiet periods. Taylor *et al.* emphasize that their observation verifies the existence of expansions and contractions of the envelope of light ions surrounding the earth which cor-relate with changes in geomagnetic activity. The authors also mention Frank's (1967) observation of a strong enhancement of 31–49 keV protons which appears to coincide exactly with the location of the plasmapause observed from the same satellite. They suggest that the bunching of these particles into ring currents results in magnetic field depressions and conse-quent plasmasphere compressions.

Krimigis *et al.* (Paper 54) measured absolute intensities of ~ 0.5 MeV protons in identical energy channels with Explorer 33 outside, and Injun 4 inside, the magnetosphere. They found the same intensities moment by moment in interplanetary space and over the polar caps of the earth during the entire 4-day period of simultaneous observations. Therefore, Krimigis *et al.* conclude that, on the whole, low-energy solar protons have full access to the earth's polar caps from the interplanetary medium, which seems to favour strongly the open model of the magnetosphere suggested by Dungey (1961) and Levy *et al.* (1964). On the contrary, these observations are in drastic disagreement with the magnetospheric tail model of Michel and Dessler (1965).

On 13 July Explorer 33 recorded magnetospherically trapped protons (Armstrong *et al.*, Paper 43) and their spectrum was found to be very much softer than that of the solar protons. This places limitations on the possibility of direct injection of energetic solar protons as an important source of outer zone trapped protons (see also Krimigis, Summary Paper C).

21   The Geomagnetic and Ionospheric Storms

The period during which the proton flare occurred was geomagnetically quiet (Best *et al.*, Paper 56). As Dieminger (Summary Paper D) points out, this was very fortunate because under more disturbed conditions the flare effect could have been obscured. No effect was produced in the dynamo region of the upper atmosphere at middle latitudes by fast particles, and both the disturbances which occurred on 8 July morning (discussed in Sec. 17) and after the ssc on 8–10 July have to be ascribed to low-energy particles.

The only effect which perhaps might be a characteristic feature of proton events was an occurrence of pearl-like pulsations observed with a wide range of geomagnetic latitudes about one day after the proton flare (Matveeva and Troitskaya, Paper 55). These pearls could be ascribed to protons of higher energy which are missing in non-proton flares.

The geomagnetic storm which followed the ssc can be described simply as a typical magnetic storm of low to medium intensity (Papers 56, 60, D).

From topside soundings aboard Alouette 1 and 2 (Herzberg and Nelms, Paper 57) it was found that from 9 to 12 July, i.e. during the progress of the magnetic storm, the F2 layer and exceptionally even the E layer could be seen from above, which is a proof of a decrease of the electron density in the F2 layer. This again represents typical conditions for ionospheric storms (Summary Paper D).

Another unusual condition of the ionosphere detected in topside sounding records is the presence of sharp, narrow vertical bands or spikes at low frequencies, which cross the reflection trace. Herzberg and Nelms emphasize that this is an effect which was observed after the 7 July flare for the first time and they are inclined to think that it occurs only in connection with a proton flare event. This effect seems to be well correlated with abrupt changes in the intensity of the > 35 keV electrons trapped in the outer radiation belt.

As already mentioned in Sec. 17, the ionospheric storm in the F region had already started before the ssc, at about 09 h on 8 July (Lange and Taubenheim, Paper 59), possibly as one of the consequences of the earth crossing the sector boundary. The originally positive phase changed to the negative phase approximately at the time of the ssc.

In the lower ionosphere (Knuth and Lauter, Paper 58) the first onset of high absorption only occurred in the early hours of 9 July, after the plasma cloud of the flare had reached the earth. Knuth and Lauter conclude that the ionospheric storm was a small but well detectable event with fairly regular behaviour.

Summing up one can say that apart from the peculiar low-frequency spikes recorded by Alouette 2 the effects of low-energy particles did not differ significantly from what has been known for normal storms and no conspicuous special property which might be characteristic for storms following proton flares could be detected (Dieminger, Summary Paper D). The pre-storm disturbances most probably caused by low-energy protons trapped behind the sector boundary (Sec. 17) cannot occur with a non-proton flare but one cannot consider them as characteristic, since this effect occurred only accidentally when the earth just crossed the sector boundary when the proton flux was in progress.

22 Conclusion

The effect of the co-operation during the PFP is evident: the wealth of the information is only restricted by unsolved technical difficulties and by the scattering of the instruments around the world and on the space probes.

We must point out that the most promising results come from high-quality records: the patterns of the weak magnetic field, the magnetic structure of the active centre, the white light observations of the photosphere and of the corona, the interferometric and/or spectrometric records in radio-astronomy, the spectra and the polarization of the active prominences, the λ-sweep records, the very sophisticated process of the flare observation in the centre of and outside the Hα line, the X-ray records, and any space records. Unfortunately observations of such high quality exist just in one or two places in the world and the places are different for each of them: it is impossible to have simultaneously such complementary records of one event or of one active centre. This fact is obvious for the umbra structures described by McIntosh (Paper 5) and the magnetic field distributions described by Severny (Paper 1): a new difficulty in this example is the difference of resolving power between the two records.

An active centre is really a complex situation: its magnetic field determines its structure, but the accurate description of this magnetic field is a very difficult enterprise. So we have had to build up the picture of the active centre from many different records: Hα, calcium line, white-light pictures, interferometric radio measurements, etc. According to the material available, one's "feeling" of the active centre and of its evolution will vary appreciably: very few people are fortunate enough to be able to use all these types of observations simultaneously.

The record of the flare itself is a very difficult problem. We need simultaneous observation with high resolution of white-light records, of umbra structure covering the period from a few hours before the flare to a few hours after the flare and, on the same scale, a cinematographic patrol of the magnetic field components, of the Hα observations, and of λ-sweep records. It would be useful also to have spectrographic observations (unfortunately no spectrographic observations have been reported), X-ray records within a small energy band, interferometric and spectrometric radio observations particularly at intermediate frequencies.

And for good interpretation of the event, it would be useful to have this flare in the central part of the disk but with simultaneous observation from a space probe in such a position that to it the flare appears as a limb flare: the white-light corona, the loop (if any), the prominence structure (and something of the magnetic structure) would be reported by this space observatory. At the present time, the lack of information is due to the discrepancy between the resolving powers of the different kinds of observations and to the gaps between successive observations, particularly during the last hours preceding the flare.

For the terrestrial environment, this July event gave a good opportunity to study a very complicated situation: shock wave, interplanetary magnetic field boundary, relativistic and low-energy electrons and protons. Apparently in the near future it will be possible to explain any ground-based observation directly in terms of space observation. The most surprising report is the approximately simultaneous arrival of the < 45 keV electrons, relativistic electrons and protons. Another point is the relatively weak PCA: the polar ionosphere is a bad indicator for a flux of high-energy particles and is more affected by less energetic particles. Very promising results can also arise from space probes at long distances from the earth: the differences between records from these remote positions are very useful to describe the interplanetary processes: direction, speed of the shock wave, extension of the plasma clouds, etc.

We have been very fortunate with this 7 July event: it would have been difficult to have more material and the time of the flare was quite well related to existing ground-based observatories. In spite of some disagreement between the reporters, it is roughly a typical proton event, clearly isolated, in a good position on the disk, in the centre of the week and with forecasts issued on time.

What can we expect from further co-operation? New information will come from new instruments such as the Australian solar radio spectroheliographs or from new space probes, though time must be allowed for testing these new instruments. The declining phase of the solar cycle could supply a further isolated proton event.

It would only remain that this should again occur during the organized period of co-operation.

References

(Apart from contributions published in this volume.)

ALFVÉN, H., and P. CARLQUIST, 1967, Currents in the solar atmosphere and a theory of solar flares, *Solar Phys.*, **1**, 220–228.

ANTALOVÁ, A., 1965, Interdependence of sunspot proper motions and chromospheric flares, *Bull. Astr. Insts Czech.*, **16**, 32–38.

ARNOLDY, R. L., S. R. KANE, and J. R. WINCKLER, 1968, The observation of 10–50 keV solar flare X-rays by the OGO satellites and their correlation with solar radio and energetic particle emission, *Proc. IAU Symposium No. 35, Structure and Development of Solar Active Regions*, Ed. K. O. Kiepenheuer (Reidel Publ. Co., Dordrecht, Holland), pp. 490–512.

AVIGNON, Y., M. J. MARTRES, and M. PICK, 1963, Identification d'une classe d'éruptions chromosphériques responsables des absorptions ionosphériques polaires, *C.R. Acad. Sci., Paris*, **256** 2112–2114.

D'AZAMBUJA, L., 1930, Recherche sur la structure de la chromosphère solaire, *Annls Obs. Paris*, **8**, 1–120.

BARTLEY, W. C., R. P. BUKATA, K. G. McCRACKEN, and U. R. RAO, 1966, Anisotropic cosmic radiation fluxes of solar origin, *J. Geophys. Res.*, **71**, 3297–3304.

BRUZEK, A., 1964, On the association between loop prominences and flares, *Astrophys. J.*, **140**, 746–759.

BRYANT, D. A., T. L. CLINE, U. D. DESAI, and F. B. McDONALD, 1962, Explorer 12 observations of solar cosmic rays and energetic storm particles after the solar flare of September 28, 1961, *J. Geophys. Res.*, **67**, 4983–5000.

—— 1965, Studies of solar protons with Explorer XII and XIV, *Astrophys. J.*, **141**, 478–499.

BUMBA, V., and R. HOWARD, 1965, A study of the development of active regions of the sun, *Astrophys. J.*, **141**, 1492–1501.

CAROUBALOS, C., 1964, Contribution à l'étude de l'activité solaire en relation avec les effects géophysiques, *Annls Astrophys.*, **27**, 333–388.

DODSON, H. W., and E. R. HEDEMAN, 1968, Some patterns in the development of centers of solar activity, 1962–66, *Proc. IAU Symposium No. 35, Structure and Development of Solar Active Regions*, Ed. K. O. Kiepenheuer (Reidel Publ. Co., Dordrecht, Holland), 56–63.

DOLLFUS, A., 1968, Observation des jets et concentrations de la couronne au-dessus des régions actives, *Proc. IAU Symposium No. 35, Structure and Development of Solar Active Regions*, Ed. K. O. Kiepenheuer (Reidel Publ. Co., Dordrecht, Holland), pp. 359–378.

DUNGEY, J. W., 1961, Interplanetary magnetic field and the auroral zones, *Phys. Rev. Lett.*, **6**, 47–48.

FAN, C. Y., J. E. LAMPORT, J. A. SIMPSON, and D. R. SMITH, 1966, Anisotropy and fluctuations of solar proton fluxes of energies 0.6–100 MeV measured on the Pioneer 6 sphere probe, *J. Geophys. Res.*, **71**, 3289–3296.

FRANK, L. A., 1967, On the extraterrestrial ring current during geomagnetic storms, *University of Iowa Report No. 67–9* (University of Iowa, Iowa).

FRITZOVÁ, L., and Z. ŠVESTKA, 1966, Type IV bursts: II. In association with PCA events, *Bull. Astr. Insts Czech.*, **17**, 249.

GOPASYUK, S., 1967, Temporal variation of the magnetic field in active solar regions, *Izv. Krȳm. Astrofiz. Obs.*, **36**, 56.

HAURWITZ, M. W., S. YOSHIDA, and S.-I. AKASOFU, 1965, Interplanetary magnetic field asymmetries and their effects on polar cap absorption events and Forbush decreases, *J. Geophys. Res.*, **70**, 2977–2988.

HOWARD, R., 1963, On the relation of major solar flares with changes in sunspot areas, *Astrophys. J.*, **138**, 1312–1313.

HOWARD, R., and A. B. SEVERNY, 1963, Solar magnetic fields and the great flare of July 16, 1959, *Astrophys. J.*, **137**, 1242–1250.

KŘIVSKÝ, L., 1965, Flight time of solar cosmic and proton radiation to the earth, *Bull. Astr. Insts Czech.*, **16**, 27–32.

LEGRAND, J. P., 1960, Les prébaisses de rayons cosmiques en périodes de maximum de l'activité solaire (avril 1957–décembre 1958), *Annls Géophys.*, **16**, 140–142.

LEVY, R. H., H. E. PETSCHEK, and G. L. SISCOE, 1964, Aerodynamic aspects of the magnetospheric flow, *Amer. Inst. Aeronaut. Astronaut. J.*, **2**, 2065.

LIN, R. P., and K. A. ANDERSON, 1967, Electrons > 40 keV and protons > 500 keV of solar origin, *Solar Phys.*, **1**, 446–464.

MARTRES, M. J., R. MICHARD, and I. SORU-ISCOVICI, 1966, Etude morphologique de la structure magnétique des régions actives en relation avec les phénomènes chromo-sphériques et les éruptions solaires. I. Classification magnétique et éruptivité, *Annls Astrophys.*, **29**, 245–253.

MICHARD, R., and E. RIBES, 1968, La composante lentement variable des rayons X solaires en relation avec la structure des centres d'activité, *Proc. IAU Symposium No. 35, Structure and Development of Solar Active Regions*, Ed. K. O. Keipenheuer (Reidel Publ. Co., Dordrecht, Holland), pp. 420–430.

MICHEL, F. C., and A. J. DESSLER, 1965, Physical significance of inhomogeneities in polar cap absorption events, *J. Geophys. Res.*, **70**, 4305–4311.

MORETON, G., and A. B. SEVERNY, 1968, Magnetic fields and flares in the region with CMP 20 September 1963, *Solar Phys.*, **3**, 282–297.

OBAYASHI, T., 1962, Propagation of solar particles through interplanetary magnetic fields, *J. Phys. Soc. Japan*, **17**, Suppl. A II, 572.

SEVERNY, A. B., 1964, Observations of transverse and longitudinal magnetic fields connected with solar flares, *Izv. Krȳm. Astrofiz. Obs.*, **31**, 159–199.

ŠVESTKA, Z., 1966, Optical observations of solar flares, *Space Sci. Rev.*, **5**, 388–418.

—— 1967, Type IV bursts: III. In association with Forbush effects, *Bull. Astr. Insts Czech.*, **18**, 55–61.

—— 1968a, Loop-prominence systems and proton-flare active regions, *Proc. IAU Symposium No. 35, Structure and Development of Solar Active Regions*, Ed. K. O. Keipenheuer (Reidel Publ. Co., Dordrecht, Holland), 287–292.

—— 1968b, On long term forecasts of proton flares, *Solar Phys.*, **4**, 18–29.

—— 1968c, Effects associated with the sector boundary crossing on July 8, 1966, *Solar Phys.*, **4**, in press.

TANAKA, H., and T. KAKINUMA, 1964, The relation between the spectrum of slowly varying component of solar radio emission and solar proton event, *Rep. Ionosph. Space Res. Japan*, **18**, 32–44.

WARWICK, C., 1965, Longitude distribution of proton flares, *Astrophys. J.*, **141**, 500–504.

Author Index

NOTE: References are to *Paper* numbers.

Subject Index

Because the whole volume is concerned with the Proton Flare event of **7 July 1966**, all entries are to be considered as associated with this flare or with the general project unless otherwise stated.

Main references to the subject of individual papers are in **bold type**.